MATH SENSE®

2 FOCUS ON PROBLEM SOLVING

Math for the High School Equivalency Tests

Cathy Fillmore Hoyt

Math Sense 2 Book Two: Focus on Problem Solving
ISBN 978-1-56420-692-3

New Readers Press
ProLiteracy's Publishing Division
104 Marcellus Street, Syracuse, New York 13204
www.newreaderspress.com

Printed in the United States of America
10 9 8 7 6 5 4 3 2

Proceeds from the sale of New Readers Press materials support professional development, training, and technical assistance programs of ProLiteracy that benefit local literacy programs in the U.S. and around the globe.

Editorial Director: Terrie Lipke
Technology Specialist: Maryellen Casey

CONTENTS

INTRODUCTION 5

SKILL PREVIEW 6

UNIT 1: NUMBERS AND PROPERTIES .. 14

The Number Line 16

Comparing and Ordering Integers 18

Problem Solver: Kinds of Numbers 20

Problem Solver: Prime Numbers and Prime Factoring 22

Tools: Properties of Numbers 24

Adding and Subtracting Signed Numbers 26

Problem Solver: Absolute Value 28

Multiplying and Dividing Signed Numbers 30

Powers and Roots 32

Order of Operations 34

Tools: Using a Calculator 36

Unit 1 Review 38

UNIT 2: THE BASICS OF ALGEBRA 40

Expressions and Variables 42

Evaluating Expressions 44

Simplifying Expressions 46

Tools: The Rules of Exponents 48

Negative Exponents 50

Tools: Scientific Notation 52

Simplifying Radicals 54

Mixed Review 56

Problem Solver: Reading and Writing Equations ... 58

Solving Addition and Subtraction Equations 60

Solving Multiplication and Division Equations 62

Solving Multistep Equations 64

Solving Equations with Separated Terms 66

Solving Equations with Parentheses 68

Tools: Graphing Inequalities 70

Solving Inequalities 72

Test Taker: Try the Answer Choices 74

Unit 2 Review 76

UNIT 3: SOLVING PROBLEMS WITH ALGEBRA 78

Translating Words to Equations 80

Number Puzzles and Age Problems 82

Problem Solver: Solving Equations with Fractions and Decimals 84

Solving Motion Problems 86

Solving Value Problems 88

Solving Work Problems 90

Problem Solver: Using Inequalities to Solve Word Problems 92

Test Taker: Using Formulas 94

Rewriting Formulas 96

Unit 3 Review 98

UNIT 4: GEOMETRY BASICS 100

Points, Lines, and Angles 102

Tools: Using Protractors 104

Working with Angles 106

Quadrilaterals 108

Triangles 110

The Pythagorean Theorem 112

Similar Geometric Figures 114

Problem Solver: Finding Patterns in Algebra and Geometry 116

Mixed Review 118

Perimeter 120

Area of Squares, Rectangles, and Parallelograms 122

Area of Triangles and Trapezoids 124

Circumference and Area of Circles 126

Problem Solver: Area of Complex Figures 128

Volume of Prisms and Cylinders 130

Volume of Pyramids, Cones, and Spheres 132

Surface Area 134

Problem Solver: Choosing Area, Perimeter, Volume, or Surface Area 136

Tools: Using Algebra in Geometry Problems 138

Unit 4 Review 140

UNIT 5: CONNECTING ALGEBRA AND GEOMETRY 142

The Coordinate Plane 144

Problem Solver: Making a Table to Graph an Equation 146

Using Intercepts to Graph a Line 148

Slope: Rise over Run 150

Parallel and Perpendicular Lines 152

Problem Solver: Problem Solving with Slope 154

Writing the Equation of a Line 156

Using Point-Slope Form 158

Distance between Points 160

Problem Solver: Geometric Figures on the Coordinate Plane 162

Unit 5 Review 164

Simulated GED® Math Test 170

Answer Key 180

Glossary 214

TOOL KIT

Calculator Basics 218

Basic Computations 219

Basic Formulas 220

Other Formulas 221

INTRODUCTION

Math skills play an increasingly vital role in today's world. Everyone needs to work confidently with numbers to solve problems on the job and in daily life.

The increasing role of mathematics is reflected on the new GED® Mathematics Test and other high school equivalency tests, such as the HiSET® and TASC. This book is part of a three-book series designed to help you pass these tests and prepare for new opportunities in education and employment.

In *Math Sense 2, Focus on Problem Solving,* you will acquire skills in algebra, geometry, and reasoning that will help you become a better problem solver. Each unit is organized around four key areas that will build your competence and confidence.

- Skills pages present instruction and practice with both computation and word problems.
- Tools pages provide insight on how to use calculators, key ideas, and mathematical properties to solve math problems.
- Problem Solver pages present strategies that will help you find the best way to approach different types of problems.
- Test Taker pages provide math tips and problem-solving approaches that good test takers use to take standardized tests.

KEY FEATURES

SKILL PREVIEW The Skill Preview can help you determine what skills you already have and identify which areas you most need to concentrate on.

UNIT PREVIEW The beginning of each unit features questions and topics to write about or discuss with classmates. Talking about math is key to building your understanding.

CORE CONNECTIONS Throughout each unit, you will work with topics that connect math ideas to real life and to other math concepts. These Core Connections add depth to your learning and correspond to the national Common Core State Standards (CCSS).

SPECIAL PROBLEMS These specially labeled problems require an in-depth exploration of math ideas. You may be asked to explain your reasoning or to find multiple solutions. These problems will prepare you for the short-response items on the GED Math Test.

MIXED REVIEWS AND UNIT REVIEWS Periodic checkups will help you see how well you understand and can apply the material. Unit Reviews also allow you to practice the types of questions that you will see on the GED Math Test, including:

- Multiple-choice questions
- Fill-in-the-blank questions
- Drop-down and matching questions
- Short-response questions

SIMULATED GED MATH TEST At the end of the book is a 30-item simulated GED Math Test that focuses on the topics from this book only. You can use this final assessment to judge how well you have mastered the skills and strategies presented in this book.

If you are taking the TASC or HiSET test, go to newreaderspress.com. On the *Math Sense 2* product page, you can download a free practice test.

GLOSSARY This list of terms defines key math words and ideas.

TOOL KIT These resource pages provide helpful information you can use as you work through the book.

Skill Preview

This survey of math skills will help you and your teacher decide what you need to study to get the most out of this book. It will show you how much you already know and what you need to learn.

Do as much as you can of each section below. If you can't do all of the problems in a section, go ahead to the next section and do all of the problems that you can.

PART 1: NUMBERS AND PROPERTIES

Find the value of each of the following expressions.

1. $-14 - (-3) =$

2. $(4)(-2)(7)(-1) =$

3. $\frac{132}{-11} =$

4. $3^3 =$

5. $\sqrt{144} =$

6. $|-5 - 13| =$

7. $\left|\frac{-48}{-8}\right| + |3 - 11| =$

8. $|-11| - 2(-9 + 4) =$

9. $\frac{(13-9)^2}{2} + \sqrt{81} =$

Solve the following problems.

10. Out of 20 company employees, 5 earn \$20 an hour, and the rest earn \$15 an hour. In an 8-hour workday, how much does the company pay in wages?

11. Write and simplify an expression for the perimeter of the rectangle shown here.

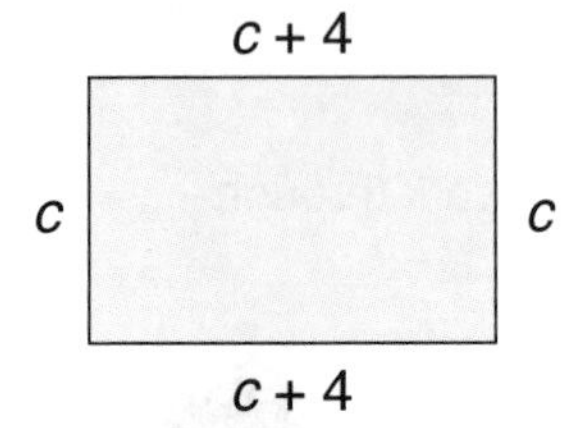

12. Find the value of $3x + 8$ when x equals -5.

13. Simplify the expression $4(2x + 5) - 13x - 6$.

14. Find the value of $6 - (x + 9)$ when x equals 1.

PART 2: THE BASICS OF ALGEBRA

Simplify the following expressions. Use only positive exponents.

15. $(xy^3)^2$

16. $m^4 \times m^{10}$

17. $\frac{n^{10}}{k^{-3}n^6}$

18. $\sqrt{108}$

19. $\sqrt{36x^3y^4}$

20. $\sqrt{\frac{9n^4}{16m^2}}$

Solve the following problems.

21. $7(y - 5) = 21$

22. $11 - 2n = 5$

23. $-4(2x - 3) = -36$

24. $9 = \frac{m}{5} - 3$

25. The rectangle shown here has a perimeter of 72. Find the value of *x*.

2x

x

Solve each inequality and graph the solution on the number line.

26. $3x + 5(x - 2) < 3(x - 5)$

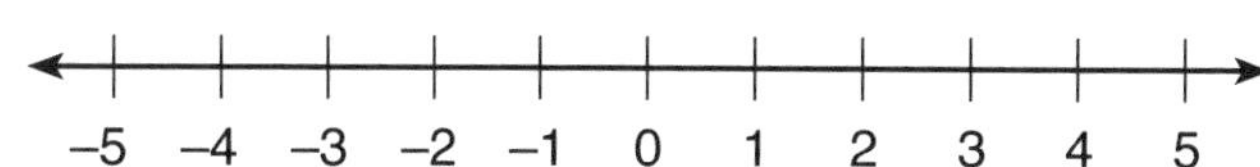

27. $-8n \leq 2n + 20$

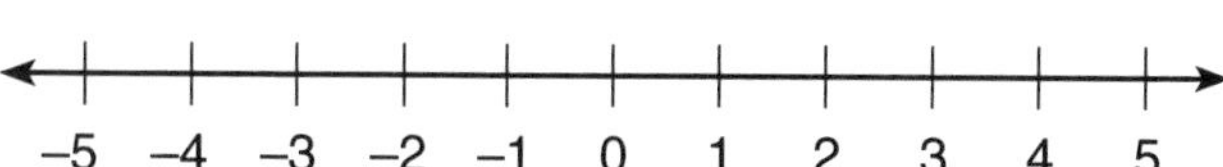

PART 3: SOLVING PROBLEMS WITH ALGEBRA

Solve the following problems.

28. One number is 5 less than twice another number. The sum of the two numbers is 13. What are the numbers?

29. Maia is twice as old as Christian. In six years, the sum of their ages will be 60. How old are they now?

30. At 2:00 p.m., Joon and Grace start driving toward each other from points 174 miles apart. They meet at 4:00 p.m. Joon's speed was 7 miles per hour greater than Grace's speed. Find their speeds.

31. Pierce has 29 quarters and dimes with a total value of $4.25. How many of each coin does he have?

32. A painter can paint a room in 6 hours. His assistant can complete the job in 9 hours. Working together, how long would it take them to paint the room?

33. A rectangle has an area of 115.5 cm^2. If the width of the rectangle is 7.5 centimeters, what is the length?

PART 4: GEOMETRY BASICS

Solve the following problems.

Use the figure below for problems 34 and 35.

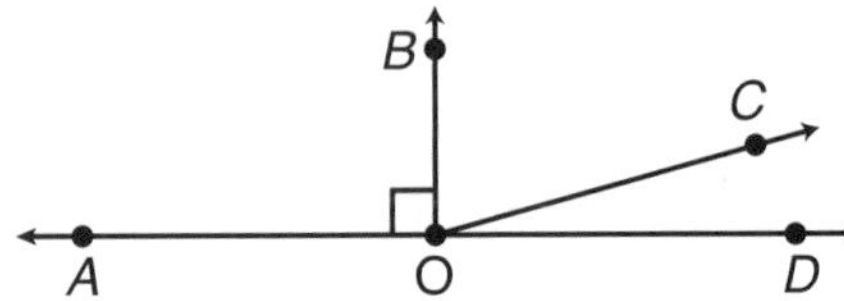

34. $\angle AOD$ is a straight angle. Name an angle that is supplementary to $\angle AOB$.

35. $\angle BOC$ measures 75°. What is the measure of $\angle COD$?

36. Find the measure of DE.

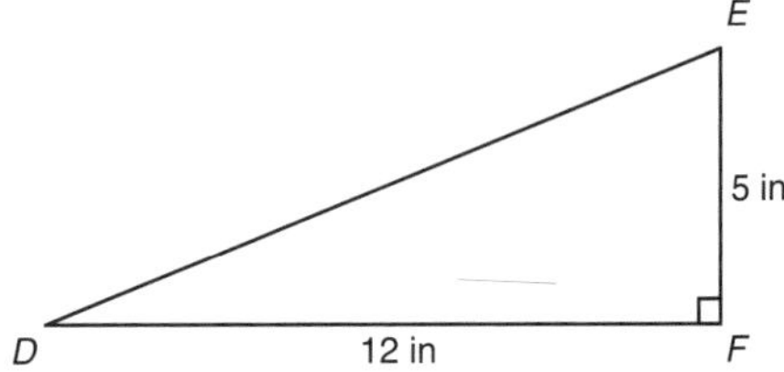

37. A 17-foot ladder leans against a building. The bottom of the ladder is 8 feet from the building. How high up on the wall does the ladder reach?

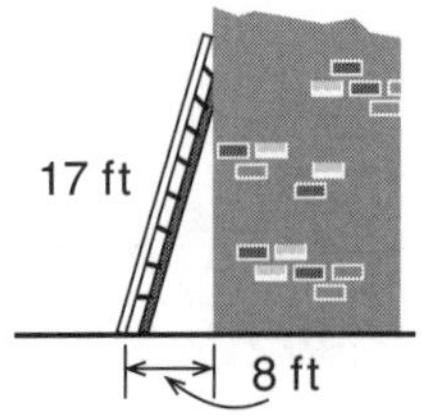

38. A tree casts a 12-foot shadow. A 3-foot stake, perpendicular to the ground, casts a 4-foot shadow at the same time. How many feet tall is the tree?

39. $\triangle JKL$ and $\triangle MKN$ are similar. What is the measure of MN?

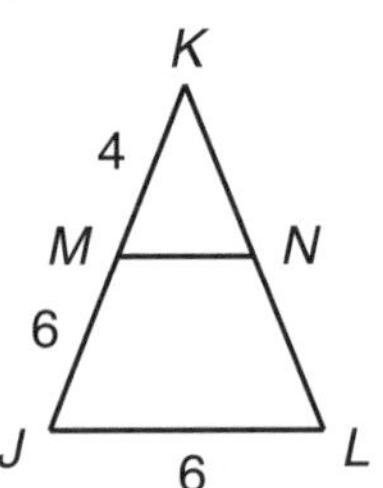

40. A community center is planting a circular garden with a diameter of 10 feet. What is the area of the garden?

41. A cylindrical can has a height of 6 centimeters and a radius of 3 centimeters. What is the volume of the can?

42. A shipping container is a rectangular prism 9 inches wide, 9 inches long, and 2 inches high. How many cubic inches can the container hold?

Use the drawing to answer problems 43 and 44.

The drawing below shows the floor plan of a shop and an adjoining storage room.

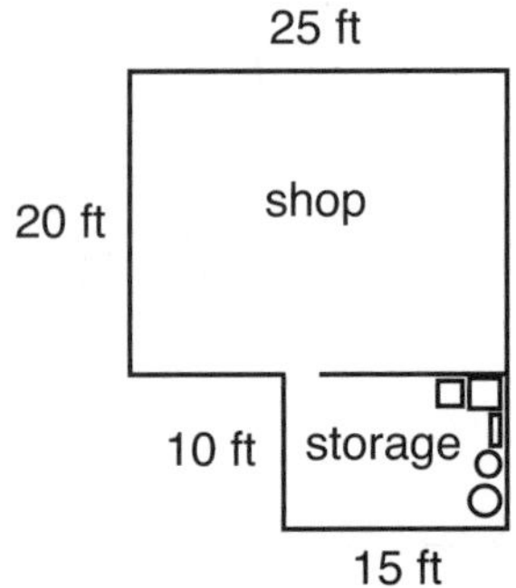

43. What is the perimeter of the space?

44. What is the area of the space?

PART 5: CONNECTING ALGEBRA AND GEOMETRY

Solve the following problems.

Use the figure for problems 45 and 46.

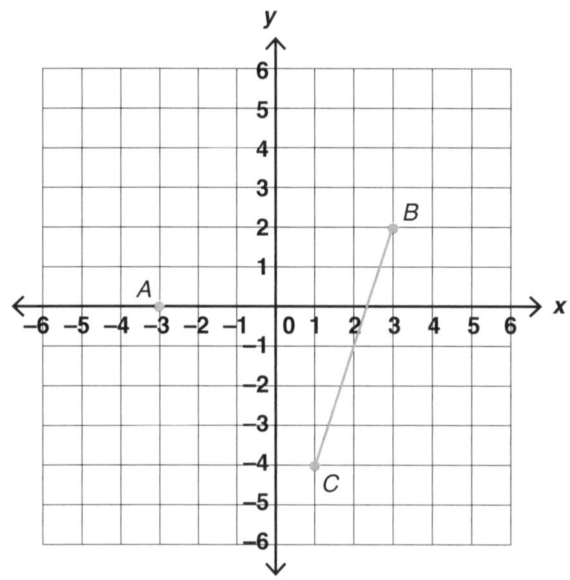

45. What are the coordinates of point *A*?

46. What is the slope of the line passing through points *B* and *C*?

47. What is the slope of the line passing through points (7, –4) and (–5, –1)?

48. Graph the line $x + 2y = -4$ on the coordinate grid.

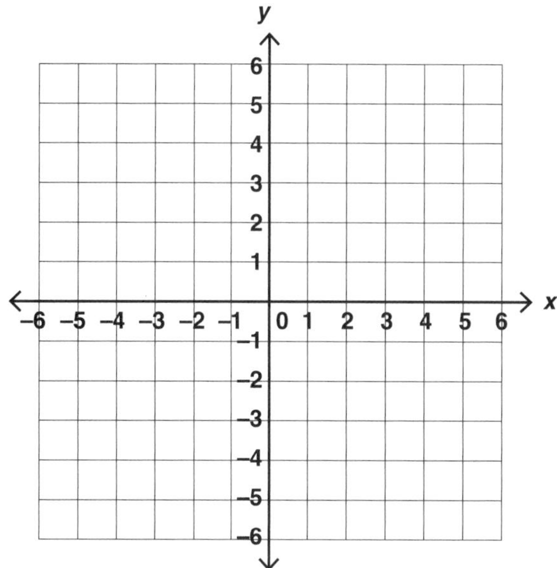

49. What is the equation of the line with a slope of 3 that passes through point (1, 7)? Write the equation in slope-intercept form.

50. What is the equation of the line passing through points (–2, –4) and (6, 0)? Write the equation in slope-intercept form.

Answers start on page 10.

Skill Preview Answer Key

1. -11
2. 56
3. -12
4. 27
5. 12
6. **18**
   $|-5 - 13| = |-18| = 18$
7. **14**
   $\left|\frac{-48}{-8}\right| + |3 - 11| = |6| + |-8| = 6 + 8 = 14$
8. **21**
   $|-11| - 2(-9 + 4)$
   $= |-11| - 2(-5)$
   $= 11 - 2(-5)$
   $= 11 + (-2)(-5)$
   $= 11 + 10$
   $= 21$
9. **17**
   $\frac{(13-9)^2}{2} + \sqrt{81}$
   $= \frac{4^2}{2} + \sqrt{81}$
   $= \frac{16}{2} + 9$
   $= 8 + 9$
   $= 17$
10. **\$2,600**
    5 employees earn \$20 per hour
    20 – 5 = 15 employees earn \$15 per hour
    (5)(\$20)(8) + (15)(\$15)(8)
    = \$800 + \$1,800 = \$2,600
11. **$4c + 8$**
    $c + c + 4 + c + c + 4 = 4c + 8$
12. **-7**
    $3(-5) + 8 = -15 + 8 = -7$
13. **$-5x + 14$**
    $4(2x + 5) - 13x - 6$
    $= 8x + 20 - 13x - 6$
    $= -5x + 14$
14. **-4**
    $6 - (1 + 9) = 6 - 10 = -4$
15. x^2y^6
16. m^{14}
17. n^4k^3
18. **$6\sqrt{3}$**
    $\sqrt{108}$
    $= \sqrt{4 \times 9 \times 3}$
    $= 2 \times 3\sqrt{3}$
    $= 6\sqrt{3}$
19. $6xy^2\sqrt{x}$
20. $\frac{3n^2}{4m}$
21. $7(y - 5) = 21$
    $7y - 35 = 21$
    $7y = 56$
    $\boldsymbol{y = 8}$
22. $11 - 2n = 5$
    $-2n = -6$
    $n = \frac{-6}{-2}$
    $\boldsymbol{n = 3}$
23. $-4(2x - 3) = -36$
    $-8x + 12 = -36$
    $-8x = -48$
    $\boldsymbol{x = 6}$
24. $9 = \frac{m}{5} - 3$
    $12 = \frac{m}{5}$
    $\boldsymbol{m = 60}$
25. $x + 2x + x + 2x = 72$
    $6x = 72$
    $\boldsymbol{x = 12}$
26. $3x + 5(x - 2) < 3(x - 5)$
    $3x + 5x - 10 < 3x - 15$
    $8x - 10 < 3x - 15$
    $5x < -5$
    $\boldsymbol{x < -1}$
    –5 –4 –3 –2 –1 0 1 2 3 4 5
27. $-8n \le 2n + 20$
    $-10n \le 20$
    $\boldsymbol{n \ge -2}$
    –5 –4 –3 –2 –1 0 1 2 3 4 5
28. **6 and 7**
    1st number: x
    2nd number: $2x - 5$
    $x + 2x - 5 = 13$
    $3x - 5 = 13$
    $3x = 18$
    $x = 6$
    $2(6) - 5 = 12 - 5 = 7$

29. Christian: 16, Maia: 32

	Now	In 6 years
Christian	x	$x + 6$
Maia	$2x$	$2x + 6$

$x + 6 + 2x + 6 = 60$
$3x + 12 = 60$
$3x = 48$
$x = 16$
$2(16) = 32$

30. Grace: 40 mph, Joon: 47 mph

	Rate	Time	Distance
Grace	r	2	2r
Joon	$r + 7$	2	$2(r + 7)$

$2r + 2(r + 7) = 174$
$2r + 2r + 14 = 174$
$4r + 14 = 174$
$4r = 160$
$r = 40$
$40 + 7 = 47$

31. 9 quarters, 20 dimes

	Number	Value	Total Value
Quarters	x	0.25	$0.25x$
Dimes	$29 - x$	0.10	$0.10(29 - x)$

$0.25x + 0.10(29 - x) = 4.25$
$0.25x + 2.90 - 0.10x = 4.25$
$0.15x + 2.90 = 4.25$
$0.15x = 1.35$
$x = 9$
$29 - 9 = 20$

32. $3\frac{3}{5}$ hours

	Rate	Time	Work Done
Painter	$\frac{1}{6}$	x	$\frac{x}{6}$
Assistant	$\frac{1}{9}$	x	$\frac{x}{9}$

$\frac{x}{6} + \frac{x}{9} = 1$
$18(\frac{x}{6} + \frac{x}{9}) = 18(1)$
$3x + 2x = 18$
$5x = 18$
$x = \frac{18}{5} = 3\frac{3}{5}$

33. 15.4 cm
$A = lw$
$l = \frac{A}{w}$
$l = \frac{115.5}{7.5} = 15.4$

34. $\angle BOD$ or $\angle DOB$

35. 15°
$90° - 75° = 15°$

36. 13 in
$a^2 + b^2 = c^2$
$5^2 + 12^2 = c^2$
$\sqrt{25 + 144} = c$
$\sqrt{169} = c$
$13 = c$

37. 15 ft
$a^2 + b^2 = c^2$
$8^2 + b^2 = 17^2$
$b = \sqrt{289 - 64}$
$b = \sqrt{225}$
$b = 15$

38. 9 feet
$\frac{\text{stake}}{\text{shadow}} = \frac{\text{tree}}{\text{shadow}}$
$\frac{3}{4} = \frac{x}{12}$
$4x = 36$
$x = 9$

39. 2.4
$\frac{KM}{KJ} = \frac{MN}{JL}$
$\frac{4}{10} = \frac{x}{6}$
$10x = 24$
$x = 2.4$

40. 78.5 sq ft
$A = \pi r^2$
$= 3.14 \times 5^2$
$= 78.5$ sq ft

41. 169.56 cm^3
$V = \pi r^2 h$
$= 3.14 \times 3^2 \times 6$
$= 169.56 \text{ cm}^3$

42. 162 in^3
$V = Bh$
$= 9 \times 9 \times 2$
$= 162 \text{ in}^3$

43. 110 ft
Missing vertical side: 20 + 10 = 30 ft
Missing horizontal side: 25 – 15 = 10 ft
$P = 25 + 30 + 15 + 10 + 10 + 20 = 110$ ft

44. 650 sq ft
Area of shop: 25 × 20 = 500 sq ft
Area of storage: 15 × 10 = 150 sq ft
500 + 150 = 650 sq ft

45. (–3, 0)

46. 3
$m = \frac{-4-2}{1-3} = \frac{-6}{-2} = 3$

47. $-\frac{1}{4}$
$\frac{-1-(-4)}{-5-7} = \frac{-1+4}{-5-7} = \frac{3}{-12} = -\frac{1}{4}$

48.

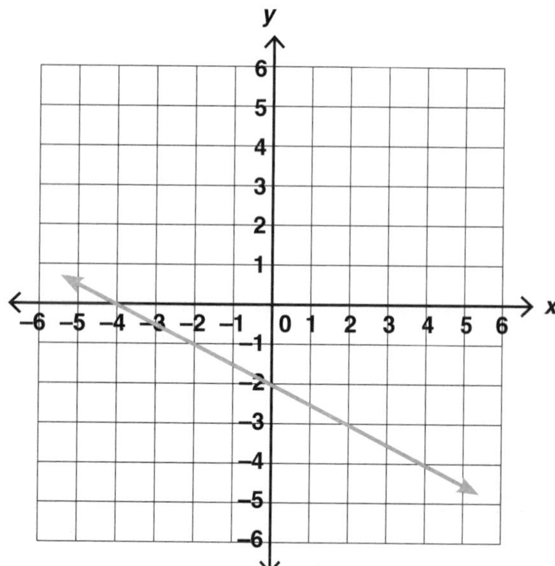

Sample points for $x + 2y = -4$:

x	y
−4	0
0	−2
2	−3

49. $\mathbf{y = 3x + 4}$

$y - y_1 = m(4 - x_1)$
$y - 7 = 3(x - 1)$
$y - 7 = 3x - 3$
$y = 3x + 4$

50. $\mathbf{y = \frac{1}{2}x - 3}$

$m = \frac{-4-0}{-2-6} = \frac{-4}{-8} = \frac{1}{2}$
$y - y_1 = m(x - x_1)$
$y - 0 = \frac{1}{2}(x - 6)$
$y = \frac{1}{2}x - 3$

Skill Preview Diagnostic Chart

On the chart below, circle the numbers of the problems that you answered incorrectly. Notice the skill area for each problem that you missed. As you work through the book, be sure to focus on these skill areas.

Problem Number	Skill Area	Unit
1, 2, 3	Signed Number Operations	1
4, 5	Finding Powers and Roots	1
6, 7	Using Absolute Value	1
8, 9, 10	Order of Operations	1
11, 12, 13, 14	Evaluating and Simplifying Expressions	2
15, 16, 17	Using the Rules of Exponents	2
18, 19, 20	Simplifying Radicals	2
21, 22, 23, 24, 25	Solving Equations	2
26, 27	Graphing and Solving Inequalities	2
28, 29, 30, 31, 32, 33	Solving Algebra Word Problems	3
34, 35	Finding Missing Angle Measures	4
36, 37	Pythagorean Theorem	4
38, 39	Similar Figures	4
40, 41, 42, 43, 44	Finding Perimeter, Area, and Volume	4
45, 48	Plotting Points and Graphing Lines	5
46, 47	Finding Slope	5
49, 50	Writing the Equation of a Line	5

NUMBERS AND PROPERTIES

SKILLS

- Prime factoring
- Operations with signed numbers
- Finding powers and roots
- Using the order of operations

TOOLS AND STRATEGIES

- Finding absolute value
- Using a calculator with powers, roots, and grouping symbols

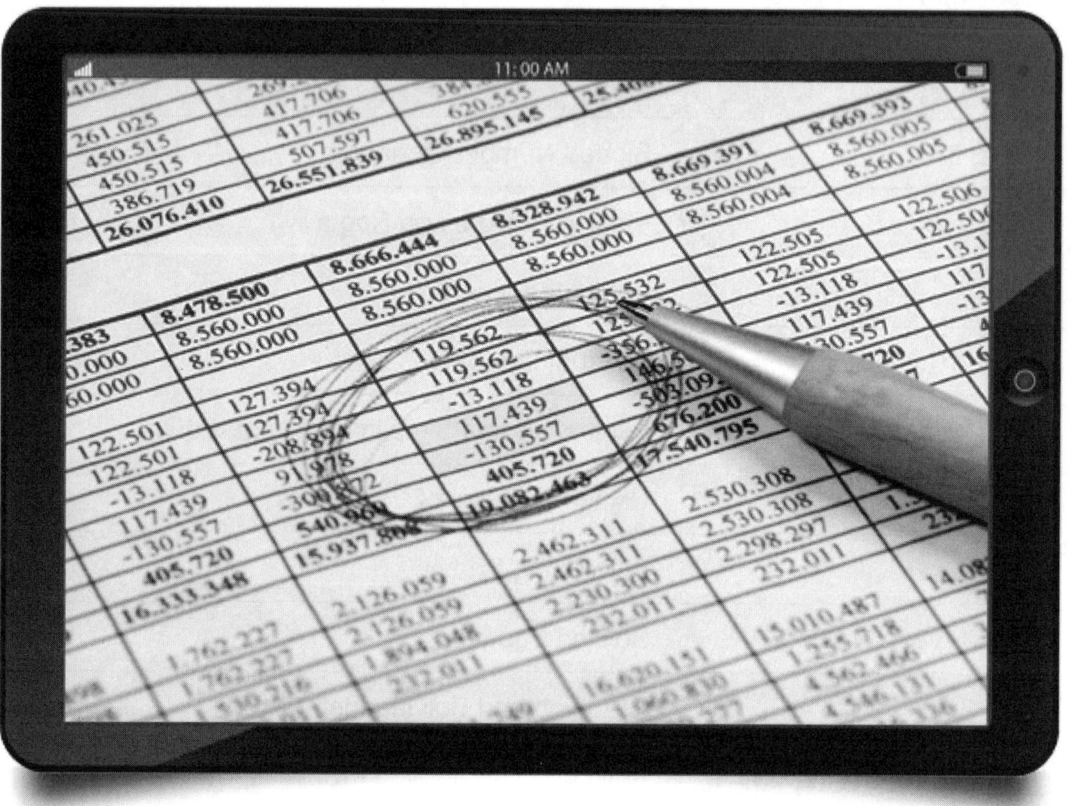

HAVE YOU EVER NOTICED the patterns numbers make? For example, some numbers can be divided exactly by two, while others can't. When you count by fives, the numbers always end with zero or five. In this unit, you'll learn the number patterns that you will need to solve algebra problems.

You've already learned how to work with numbers greater than zero. In this unit, you'll learn how to perform operations with **signed numbers,** which include numbers greater than and less than zero. You'll also learn the basics of a few new operations such as powers and roots.

Everything you will do in algebra is based on certain **properties,** or rules. Properties tell you what you can and can't do as you solve problems. In this unit, you will also learn the properties that make algebra work.

USING NUMBERS AND PROPERTIES

You use the properties of numbers when you:

- Withdraw or deposit money in a bank account
- Find a common denominator
- Play a game with scores below zero
- Check whether a number is divisible by a certain number

Read the following items. Describe some of your experiences in writing or discuss them with a partner.

1. Think of a game where scores can go below zero. If you lose more points than you have, how do you know what your new total is? For example, if you have 300 points and lose 500, how would you calculate your score?

2. What rules of divisibility have you learned? Can you tell whether a number can be divided evenly by two without needing to divide? What about dividing by three or five?

3. What strategy do you use to find the lowest common denominator when you add or subtract fractions with different denominators?

4. How do you figure temperature change? If the temperature starts above zero and drops below zero, how could you tell how much the temperature changed?

MATH TALK

Find the value of the following expression by subtracting, multiplying, dividing, and adding from left to right:

$4 - 2 \times 10 \div 5 + 3$

Now find the value of the expression by performing the operations in a different order. For example, you might multiply, then divide, then subtract, then add.

How many different results can you find by changing the order of the operations?

THE NUMBER LINE

One way to show numbers and their relationship to each other is on a **number line.** The markings on a number line divide the line into equal spaces. The arrows on a number line show that the numbers continue.

The number line to the right shows the **whole numbers** from 0 to 10. The set of whole numbers starts at 0 and includes the numbers you use for counting. On this number line, each mark represents 1.

In this number line, we have zoomed in on the space between 0 and 1 where fractions or decimals would be located. Here, each space represents $\frac{1}{4}$.

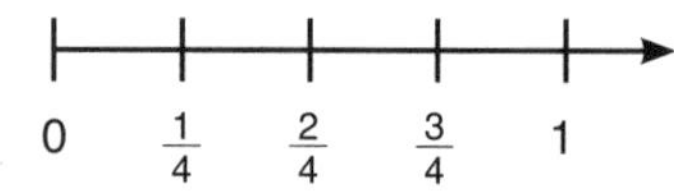

Values increase as you move to the right along the number line. What happens when you move to the left? They decrease.

Algebra includes the use of **signed numbers.** Signed numbers are either **positive** or **negative.** A negative number is written with a – sign.

A negative number has a value less than 0. Negative numbers are written to the left of 0.

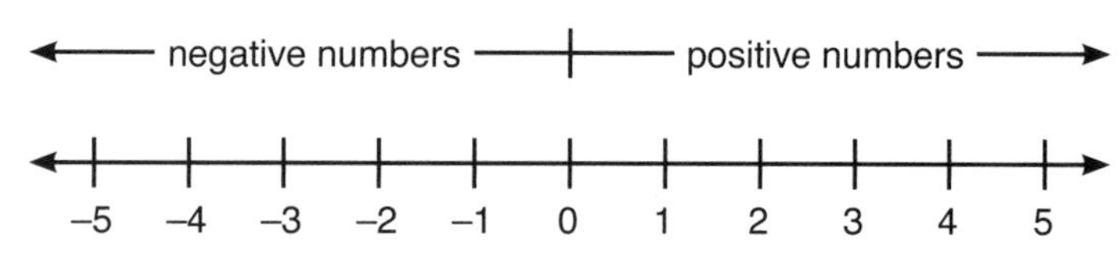

Note: 0 is neither positive nor negative.

Positive numbers, to the right of 0, can be written with or without a + sign. Both +5 and 5 mean "positive 5." A negative number must be written with a – sign.

Sometimes a negative number will have parentheses to help you see that the negative sign is attached to the number. Both –2 and (–2) mean "negative 2."

On each number line, write the missing numbers in the boxes.

1.

2.

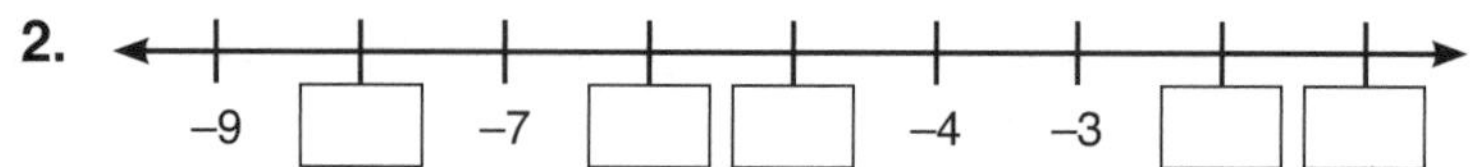

3.

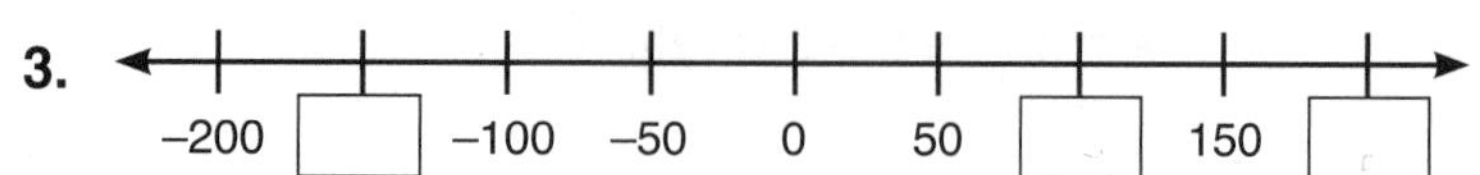

Number lines can also be drawn vertically. On a vertical number line, numbers above 0 are positive, and numbers below 0 are negative.

Write the missing numbers in the boxes.

4.

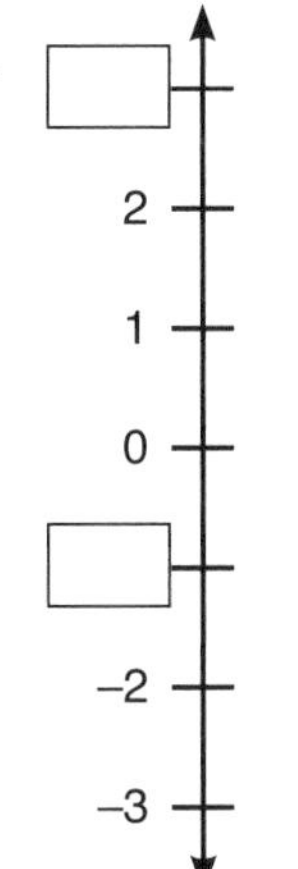

5.

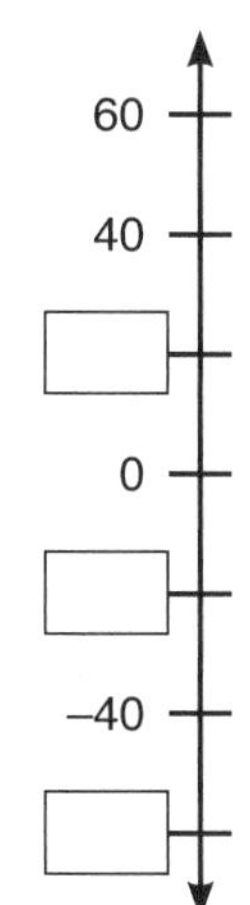

6.

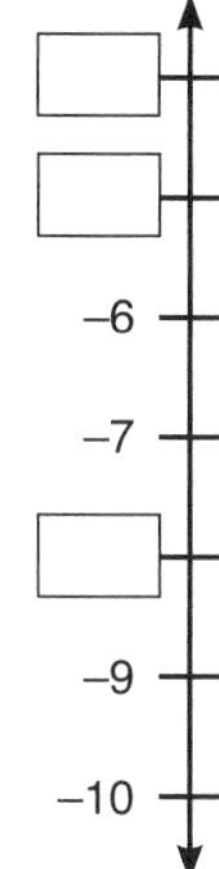

CORE CONNECTIONS: Positive or Negative?

As you have seen, positive and negative numbers are used to show whether a number is greater than or less than zero. You already apply this kind of thinking in your everyday life.

Max has $100 in his checking account. He deposits $350 and writes a check for $400. Will his new balance be positive or negative?

Payment		✓	Deposit		$ + 100.00	
			+350	00	450	00
- 400	00				50	00

He will have enough in the bank to cover the check, so his account balance will be **positive.**

For each situation, describe the outcome.

1. A game show gives 200 points for a correct answer and takes away 100 points for every wrong answer. A contestant answers 1 question right and 3 questions wrong. Does the contestant have a positive or a negative number of points?

2. After reaching 12°F, the temperature drops 15 degrees and then increases by 5 degrees. Will the new temperature be positive or negative?

3. Ned buys 2 baseball cards for $40 each. He sells the first card for $50 and the second for $20. Did Ned make a profit (a positive outcome) or lose money (a negative outcome)?

4. A patient's temperature is 3.6° above normal. After taking medication, his temperature drops 4.2°. Is the patient's temperature above or below normal?

Answers start on page 180.

COMPARING AND ORDERING INTEGERS

An **integer** is any number in the following set: {... , –3, –2,–1, 0, 1, 2, 3, ...}

The dots (...) on each end of the list show that the integers continue forever in both directions.

What numbers are not integers? Fractional quantities such as $\frac{3}{4}$, 0.75, and 30% are not integers because they represent part of a whole.

You can use a number line to decide whether one integer is greater than or less than another.

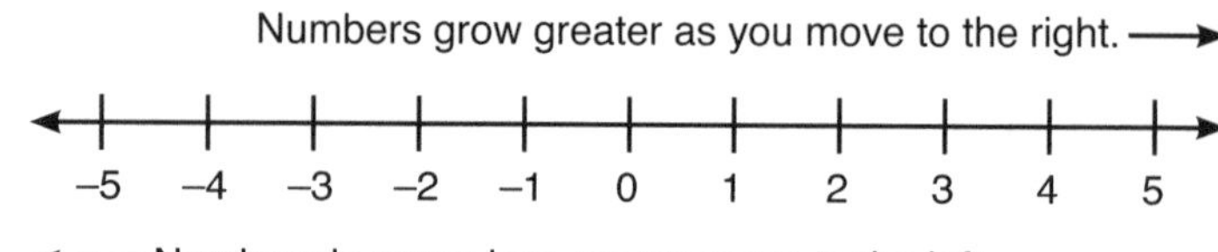

COMPARING INTEGERS

Example Which is greater, –3 or –1?

Find both integers on the number line.

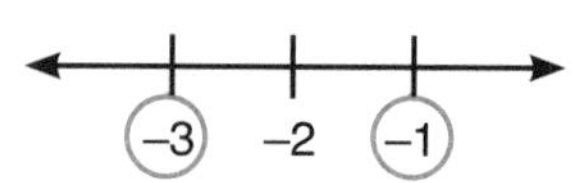

–1 is to the right of –3, so **–1** is greater than –3.

Example Which is less, –2 or 1?

Find both integers on the number line.

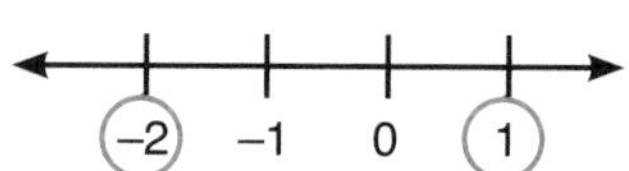

–2 is to the left of 1, so **–2** is less than 1.

Thinking about the number line will help you avoid mistakes. For example, you are used to thinking that 8 is greater than 5, so you might also think that –8 is greater than –5. However, the opposite is true. Because –5 is to the right of –8 on the number line, –5 is greater. If you aren't sure of an answer, try sketching a number line.

To compare the values of numbers, use the symbols shown here.

Symbol	Meaning	Example
=	is equal to	7 = 7
<	is less than	–4 < 6
>	is greater than	5 > 2

 **TIP**

To remember the difference between < and >, think of each symbol as an arrow that points to the smaller number.

2 < 5   5 > 2

ORDERING INTEGERS

Example Write 15, –10, –12, 3, and –3 in order from least to greatest.

Step 1
Think about the negative integers. The negative integers must be less than the positive integers.

From left to right on a number line, –12 would be first, followed by –10, and then –3.

Step 2
There are two positive integers: 3 and 15.

You already know 3 is less than 15.

Step 3
Put it all together.

From least to greatest, the integers are –12, –10, –3, 3, and 15.

Fill in each blank with a symbol (=, <, or >) that makes the statement true.

1. 8 _____ 15   –8 _____ –6   5 _____ –5

2. 9 _____ –3   –1 _____ –1   –11 _____ –12

In the blanks, write the list of integers in order from *least to greatest.*

3. –20, –12, –17, –22

_____ _____ _____ _____

4. 4, 0, –2, –1

_____ _____ _____ _____

In the blanks, write the list of integers in order from *greatest to least.*

5. –6, 2, –8, –2

_____ _____ _____ _____

6. –40, 10, –20, 30

_____ _____ _____ _____

Use this information for problems 7 and 8.

Record Low Temperatures by State

State	Elevation	Temperature
Maine	770 ft	–50°F
Massachusetts	640 ft	–35°F
Michigan	785 ft	–51°F
Montana	5,470 ft	–70°F
Nevada	5,200 ft	–50°F
New Jersey	70 ft	–34°F

7. Of the states on the table, which had the lowest temperature?

8. **Explain** Craig says that the locations with the highest elevations have the lowest temperatures. Do you agree? Explain your thinking.

9. How many integers are greater than –8 *and* less than 0?

10. How many integers are less than 9 *and* greater than 4?

11. How many integers are greater than –1 *and* less than –3?

Answers start on page 180.

KINDS OF NUMBERS

Numbers make patterns, and recognizing these patterns can help you solve math problems. In this lesson, you will explore different ways to classify numbers.

Numbers can be odd or even. An **even number** can be divided exactly by 2. In other words, when you divide an even number by 2, there will not be a remainder.

An **odd number** is not divisible by 2. If you divide an odd number by 2, there will be a remainder. If a number is not even, it must be odd.

Look at the drawing. You can break 6 squares evenly into 2 columns. You can't break 5 evenly, so 5 is odd.

5 6

You can tell whether a larger number is even or odd by looking at the ones place. If the ones place contains 0, 2, 4, 6, or 8, the entire number is even. You know 156 is even because 6 is even. You know 247 is odd because 7 is odd.

The word **divisible** is important in math. A number is divisible by another number if you can divide by that number and have no remainder.

For example, 8 is divisible by 1, 2, 4, and 8. If you divide 8 by any of these numbers, there will be no remainder.

1 × 8 = 8

The numbers 1, 2, 4, and 8 are factors of 8.

Factors are numbers that multiply to make a certain product.

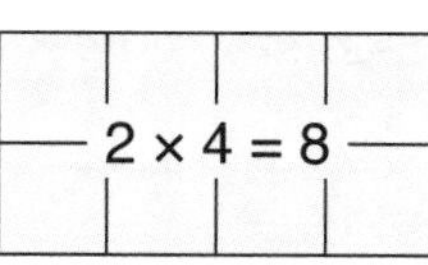

Think of the factors as the rows and columns of a rectangle.

List all factors of each given number. The first one is done for you.

1. 15

   1, 3, 5, 15

2. 18

3. 26

4. 24

5. 30

6. 36

The answer to a multiplication problem is called the **product.** The product is a **multiple** of both factors in the problem.

In the problem 6 × 2 = 12, the factors are 6 and 2. The answer 12 is the product of 6 and 2. You can also say that 12 is a multiple of 2 and a multiple of 6.

To find multiples of a number, try counting by the number. For example, the multiples of 5 are 5, 10, 15, 20, 25, and so on.

Answer as directed.

7. Write the first five multiples of 10.

8. What is the product of 7 and 8?

9. If you list the multiples of 5 and 7, what is the first multiple that will be in both lists?

10. Circle the numbers that are multiples of 6.

    3 6 9 12

    15 18 24 27

    30 33 36 39

CORE CONNECTIONS: Using Divisibility Rules

Divisibility rules are easy ways to tell whether one number is divisible by another. Good test takers memorize the divisibility rules listed in the chart. These rules can help you save time and better understand the numbers you are working with.

Divisibility by:	Rule:
2	If the ones place is even (0, 2, 4, 6, or 8), the number is divisible by 2.
3	Find the sum of the digits. If the sum is a multiple of 3, the number is divisible by 3. *Example:* 5,127 is divisible by 3 because 5 + 1 + 2 + 7 = 15, and 15 is a multiple of 3.
4	If the last two digits are divisible by 4, the whole number is divisible by 4. *Example:* 10,940 is divisible by 4 because 40 is divisible by 4.
5	If the ones place is 0 or 5, the number is divisible by 5.
6	If the number passes the divisibility tests for 2 *and* 3, the number is divisible by 6.
9	Find the sum of the digits. If the sum is a multiple of 9, the number is divisible by 9. *Example:* 6,021 is divisible by 9 because 6 + 0 + 2 + 1 = 9, and 9 is a multiple of 9.
10	If the ones place is 0, the number is divisible by 10.

Use the rules of divisibility to answer questions about the following numbers.

375 1,690 20,720 198 103,080 1,333

1. Which numbers are divisible by 4?

2. Which numbers are divisible by 10?

3. Which numbers are divisible by 6?

4. Which numbers are divisible by 5?

5. **Explain** Max says, "If a number is divisible by 9, it must be divisible by 3." Is Max correct? Explain your thinking.

6. Create a five-digit number that is divisible by 2, 3, 4, and 9. How do you know your number is correct?

Answers start on page 180.

PRIME NUMBERS AND PRIME FACTORING

Any whole number greater than 1 is either a prime number or a composite number. A **prime number** has exactly two factors: itself and 1. A **composite number** has more than two factors.

The first 10 prime numbers are **2, 3, 5, 7, 11, 13, 17, 19, 23, 29.**

Every composite number can be written as a product of prime factors. You can find the prime factors of a number using a factor tree.

In the box below, two factors are written for each composite number. If the factor is a prime number, it is circled and the factoring of composite numbers continues. At the end, all the prime numbers become the prime factorization of the number.

FINDING THE PRIME FACTORS OF A NUMBER

Example Write the prime factorization of 48.

Step 1
Write 48 as the product of any two factors. The factors 6 and 8 are used in this example. Neither are prime numbers, so continue factoring.

48
6 × 8

Step 2
Factor 6 as 2 × 3. Both 2 and 3 are prime. Factor 8 as 2 × 4. Only 2 is prime. Circle the prime factors.

(2) × (3) (2) × 4

Step 3
Factor 4 as 2 × 2. The number 2 is prime, so both are circled.

(2) × (2)

Step 4
All the ending numbers are prime. Write the prime factorization with the factors in order from least to greatest.

2 3 2 2 2

The prime factorization of 48 is **2 × 2 × 2 × 2 × 3.**

Use a factor tree to find the prime factorization of each number. The first tree is started for you.

1. 90

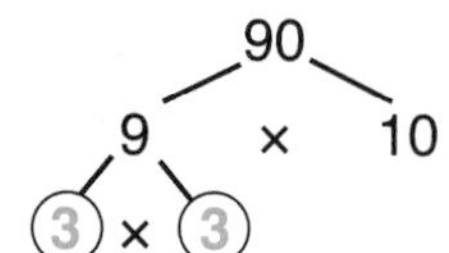

2. 135

3. 162

4. 300

Why learn prime factoring? Prime factoring is useful when working with fractions. It will also improve your ability to factor expressions in algebra.

In this next example, you will use prime factoring to find the greatest common factor for a group of factors.

FINDING THE GREATEST COMMON FACTOR

Example Find the greatest common factor of 60, 132, and 420.

Step 1
Write the prime factorization for each number.

$60 = 2 \times 2 \times 3 \times 5$
$132 = 2 \times 2 \times 3 \times 11$
$420 = 2 \times 2 \times 3 \times 5 \times 7$

Step 2
Find the factors that all the factorizations have in common. Each factorization has two 2s and one 3.

$60 = 2 \times 2 \times 3 \times 5$
$132 = 2 \times 2 \times 3 \times 11$
$420 = 2 \times 2 \times 3 \times 5 \times 7$

Step 3
Multiply to find the greatest common factor.

$2 \times 2 \times 3 = 12$

The greatest common factor of 60, 132, and 420 is **12.** In other words, 12 is the greatest number that you can divide evenly into all three numbers.

Solve.

5. Find the greatest common factor of 18, 54, and 90.

$18 = 2 \times 3 \times 3$

54 =

90 =

6. Find the greatest common factor of 48, 80, and 112.

7. What number does this prime factorization represent?

$2 \times 2 \times 5 \times 5 \times 13$

8. Carla is simplifying the fraction $\frac{178}{1386}$. To simplify a fraction, divide the numerator and the denominator by the same number. What is the greatest number Carla could use that would divide evenly into both numbers?

9. List the prime numbers between 40 and 60. (***Hint:*** Use the rules of divisibility on page 21 to test the numbers.)

10. Explain The first prime number is 2. Tamar says that there will never be another even prime number. Do you agree? Explain your thinking.

Answers start on page 180.

PROPERTIES OF NUMBERS

All actions in algebra are based on certain properties, or rules. These properties give you the freedom to make decisions about the best way to solve problems.

Properties are written using **variables.** You can replace the variables with any kind of number: fractions, decimals, signed numbers, and so on.

Addition and subtraction operations are written using + and –. Multiplication is shown using × or a dot (•) or by writing two letters or numbers next to each other. For example, $a \cdot b$ and ab both mean $a \times b$, or "*a* times *b*."

The **commutative property** works only with addition or multiplication.

You can add or multiply numbers in any order, and the result will be the same.

$a + b = b + a$
$a \cdot b = b \cdot a$

The **associative property** also works with addition or multiplication. It allows you to change how numbers are grouped.

Parentheses are used to show which operation should be done first. However, when the operations are addition only or multiplication only, you can change how the numbers are grouped.

$(a + b) + c = a + (b + c)$
$(a \times b) \times c = a \times (b \times c)$

In the example, notice how these two properties make it easier to multiply numbers.

Example (25 × 12) × (4 × 5)

Remove the parentheses.	25 × 12 × 4 × 5
Change the order.	= 25 × 4 × 12 × 5
Group as you'd like.	= (25 × 4) × (12 × 5)
Multiply.	= 100 × 60
	= 6,000

TIP
Look for ways to group compatible numbers—numbers that are easy to work with. Here, it's easier to multiply 25 by 4 than 25 by 12.

The **distributive property** involves multiplication and addition. Study this example to understand how the property works.

Example At a dollar store, all items are $1.10. Maia buys 7 plastic tablecloths and 3 packs of paper plates. How much money did she spend?

Method 1

Total items: 7 + 3 = 10
Multiply by cost: 10 × $1.10 = $11.00

Method 2

Cost of tablecloths: 7 × $1.10 = $7.70
Cost of plates: 3 × $1.10 = $3.30
Total cost: $7.70 + $3.30 = $11.00

In the example, both methods gave a final answer of \$11. How would you describe the difference between the methods? Method 1 adds first. Method 2 multiplies first. The distributive property describes this relationship between adding and multiplying.

Instead of adding b and c and then multiplying by a, you can distribute a to both b and c and then add.

$a(b + c) = ab + ac$

Note: Writing two variables next to each other indicates multiplication: $a(b + c)$ means $a \times (b + c)$, and $ab + ac$ means $(a \times b) + (a \times c)$.

You can also use the distributive property with subtraction.

$a(b - c) = ab - ac$

Example Carol used to earn \$11 per hour. Now she earns \$16 per hour. How much more does she earn now for a 40-hour work week?

Method 1

40 × (\$16 – \$11)
= 40 × \$5
= \$200

Method 2

(40 × \$16) – (40 × \$11)
= \$640 – \$440
= \$200

Solve as directed.

1. Use the commutative and associative properties to easily find the sum.

   (99 + 98 + 97) + (1+ 2 + 3)

2. Use the distributive property to write another way to solve the expression.

   11(12 + 7)

3. Laurie bought 4 bottles of correction fluid, each containing 0.7 fluid ounces. She also bought 4 refill bottles, each containing 4.5 fluid ounces.

   a. How many fluid ounces of correction fluid did she buy?

   b. Use the distributive property to write two ways of solving the problem.

4. The area of a rectangle is found by multiplying the length by the width.

   In the drawing, the larger rectangle is formed from two smaller rectangles.

   4 in
   2 in
   3 in

   One way to find the area of the larger rectangle is (4 × 3) + (2 × 3). Write another way to find the area.

5. Write the name of the property used in each lettered step.

   5(14 + 8 + 6)

   a. = 5(14 + 6 + 8)

   b. = 5(20 + 8)

   c. = (5 × 20) + (5 × 8)

Answers start on page 181.

ADDING AND SUBTRACTING SIGNED NUMBERS

Adding signed numbers is like walking on a number line. Positive distances are to the right, and negative distances are to the left.

The number line shows what happens when you add +3 and –5. Starting at 0, go 3 steps to the right. To add –5, go 5 steps to the left.

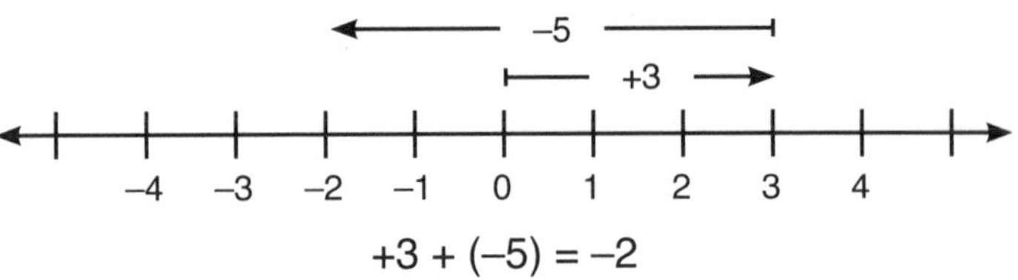

+3 + (–5) = –2

What would happen if you took 1 step forward and then 1 step back? You would be right back where you started. In other words, +1 plus –1 is 0.

(+) + (–) = 0

In the examples below, positive and negative counters are used to model addition.

ADDING SIGNED NUMBERS

Example (+2) + (+3) = +5

(+)(+) + (+)(+)(+) = +5

Example (–4) + (–2) = –6

(–)(–)(–)(–) + (–)(–) = –6

These examples add positive *and* negative numbers.

Example (+5) + (–2) = +3

Draw 5 positive circles and 2 negative circles.
Since +2 plus –2 = 0, there are 3 positives left.

(+)(+)(+)(+)(+) ← 3 positives are left.
(–)(–) ← This equals 0.

Example: (–4) + (+3) = –1

Draw 4 negative circles and 3 positive circles.
Since –3 plus +3 = 0, there is 1 negative left.

(–)(–)(–)(–) ← 1 negative is left.
(+)(+)(+) ← This equals 0.

There are rules for adding signed numbers. Make sure you understand how the rules in the box relate to the examples. Good test takers do more than memorize rules. They try to visualize what the rules are saying.

Rules for Adding Signed Numbers

- If the signs are the same, add the numbers and keep the same sign.
- If the signs are different, subtract the numbers (without their signs). Think about the circles. Keep the sign that would have more circles.

Solve.

1. $(+7) + (+4)$ $\qquad (+8) + (-10)$ $\qquad 15 + (-4)$ $\qquad (-8) + (-6)$

2. $(-11) + 3$ $\qquad (-15) + 20$ $\qquad -10 + (-5)$ $\qquad 3 + (+4)$

3. $(+9) + 12$ $\qquad -4 + (-13)$ $\qquad (-16) + 9$ $\qquad (-12) + (+24)$

Subtraction has special meaning in algebra. To explore that meaning, think about an ordinary subtraction problem: $5 - 3 = 2$. To subtract 3 on a number line, you move 3 spaces to the left.

From your work with addition, you know that moving to the left is how you add a negative number. The number line represents two equal ideas. As you can see, when you subtract, you are really *adding the opposite.*

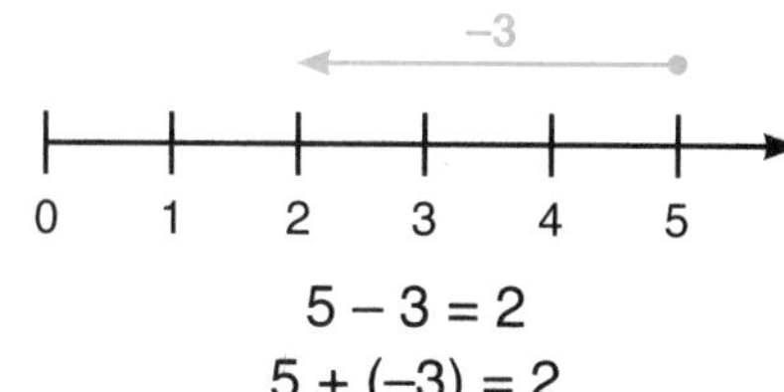

$5 - 3 = 2$
$5 + (-3) = 2$

SUBTRACTING BY ADDING THE OPPOSITE

Example $12 - (-6)$

Step 1
Change the subtraction symbol to addition. Replace the number that was being subtracted to its opposite.

$12 - (-6)$
$= 12 + (+6)$

Step 2
Add the signed numbers.

$= \mathbf{18}$

Example $(-5) + (+6) - (+10) - (-7)$

Step 1
Change any subtracting to adding the opposite.

$(-5) + (+6) - (+10) - (-7)$
$= (-5) + (+6) + (-10) + (+7)$

Step 2
Rearrange the order of the terms. Add the positive and negative numbers separately.

$= (+6) + (+7) + (-5) + (-10)$
$= 13 + (-15)$

Step 3
Find the final sum.

$= \mathbf{-2}$

Solve.

4. $8 - (+2)$ $\qquad (+7) - (-9)$ $\qquad (-6) - (+3)$ $\qquad 14 - (-1)$

5. $(-1) - 6$ $\qquad (+10) - (+9)$ $\qquad -15 - (-5)$ $\qquad 4 - (-4)$

6. $5 - 12 - (-7)$ $\qquad (-1) + (+6) - (-2)$ $\qquad (-3) + (-16) - (+5) - (-10)$

7. $(-9) - 8 + 6 - (+12)$ $\qquad 0 - (-4) + (+11)$ $\qquad (-9) + (+8) - (+9) - (-8)$

Answers start on page 181.

ABSOLUTE VALUE

Consider the following problem.

Example A jogger runs 5 kilometers in a positive direction, turns around, and runs 9 kilometers in the opposite direction. How many kilometers did the jogger run in all?

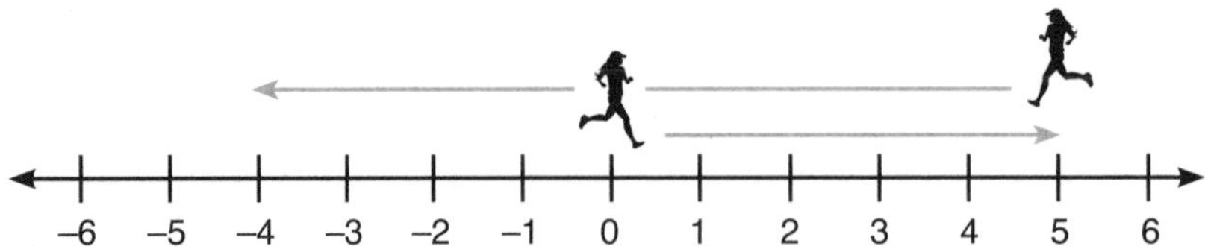

The problem seems to say that you should add +5 and –9, which equals –4. But that answer doesn't make sense. How can anyone run a negative number of kilometers?

If you remove the number line, the problem is easy. The jogger ran 5 kilometers and then 9 kilometers: 9 + 5 = **14 kilometers**

This problem shows the need for absolute value in problem solving. The **absolute value** of a number is its distance from zero. To show the absolute value of a number, write the number inside vertical bars.

The absolute value of 3 is 3. $|3| = 3$
The absolute value of –3 is 3. $|-3| = 3$

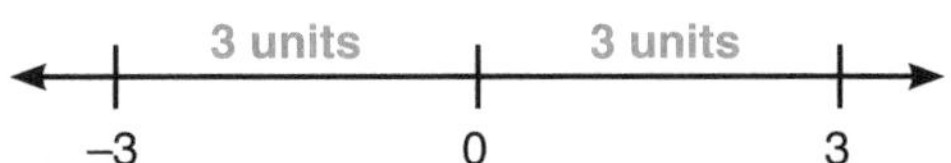

$|3| = |-3|$ because both are the same distance from 0.

You can use absolute value to describe the actions of the jogger mentioned at the start of the lesson. First, the jogger ran $|5|$ kilometers. Then he turned around and ran $|-9|$ kilometers.

$|5| + |-9| = 5 + 9 = 14$ kilometers

Study how absolute value is applied in these examples.

Example Find the value of $|3 - 10|$.

Step 1
Perform the operation inside the absolute value bars. $|3 - 10| = |-7|$

Step 2
Find the absolute value of the number in the bars. $|-7| = 7$

The value of $|3 - 10|$ is **7.**

Example Find the value of $-|-15|$.

Step 1
Perform the operation inside the absolute value bars. $-|-15| = -(15)$

Step 2
Apply the negative sign that was outside the absolute value bars. $-(15) = -15$

The value of $-|-15|$ is **–15.**

Find the value.

1. $|-10|$ $|+6|$ $-|+5|$

2. $-|-14|$ $|9|-|-2|$ $|-8|+|-10|$

3. $|9-5|$ $|1-14|$ $-|6+2|$

Use the number line for problems 4–7.

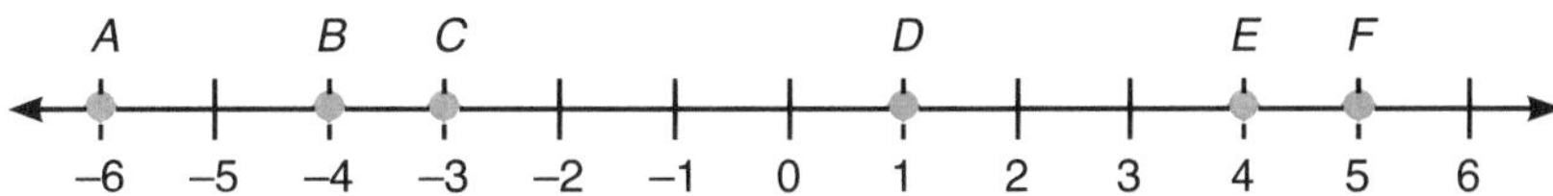

4. What is the absolute value of point *A*?

5. Which two points have the same absolute value?

6. Which has a greater absolute value, point *C* or point *D*?

7. Explain How could you use absolute value to find the distance from point *C* to point *F*?

Fill in each blank with a symbol (=, <, or >) that makes the statement true.

8. $|4|$ _____ $|-2|$ $|-5|$ _____ $|-6|$ $|-1|$ _____ 0

9. $|-10|$ _____ $|+10|$ $|-9|$ _____ $|7|$ 50 _____ $|-100|$

CORE CONNECTIONS: True or False Questions

A statement is true if it is *always* true. If any part of a statement is false or if you can think of even one example that makes the statement false, the entire statement is false.

Write *True* or *False*. If your answer is *False,* explain your thinking.

1. The absolute value of any negative number is greater than zero.
2. The smallest positive number is greater than the absolute value of any negative number.
3. On a number line, numbers with the same absolute value are the same distance from zero.
4. The absolute value of zero must be greater than the absolute value of any negative number.

Answers start on page 181.

MULTIPLYING AND DIVIDING SIGNED NUMBERS

Multiplication is fast addition. In other words, you can multiply when you have to add the same number many times.

5 + 5 is the same as 2 × 5. Both equal 10.
(–5) + (–5) is the same as 2 × (–5). Both equal –10.

Multiplying a negative number by a negative number is hard to visualize. You can apply your reasoning skills to find out how it works.

What number works in the blank? –5 × _____ = 10

If you put a positive number in the blank, the product would have to be –10. A positive number won't work. The missing number must be negative: –5 × **–2** = 10

Use these rules to multiply two signed numbers:

- If the signs are the same, the answer is positive. 3 × 4 = 12 –3 × –4 = 12
- If the signs are different, the answer is negative. –3 × 4 = –12 3 × –4 = –12

As you work the following problems, remember that multiplication can be written in three ways: using a times symbol (×), using a raised dot (•), or writing the numbers next to each other in parentheses.

Multiply.

1.	7 • –6	(–5)(8)	–3 × –9
2.	(12)(–2)	–9 × 3	–24 • –1
3.	2 × –16	(–4)(–5)	24 × –2

You can multiply more than two numbers. Multiply the numbers, then decide whether the answer is positive or negative. If there is an even number of negative numbers, the answer will be positive. If the number of negative numbers is odd, the answer will be negative.

Multiply.

4.	3 • –2 • 3	(–2)(–2)(–2)(–2)	–1 • –4 • –1
5.	5 × (–3) × (–4)	(3)(3)(–3)(1)	(–1)(2)(–2)(–1)(–2)
6.	(8)(–1)$(-\frac{3}{4})$	–7 • –6 • $-\frac{1}{2}$	2 × 5 × (–6.8)

In algebra, division is written using a fraction bar. For example, $15 \div 5$ is written $\frac{15}{5}$.

The same rules for multiplying signed numbers will work for dividing signed numbers.

Use these rules to divide two signed numbers:

- If the signs are the same, the answer is positive. $\frac{12}{3} = 4$ $\frac{-12}{-3} = 4$
- If the signs are different, the answer is negative. $\frac{12}{-3} = -4$ $\frac{-12}{3} = -4$

Divide.

7. $\frac{-6}{-2}$	$14 \div (-14)$	$\frac{35}{7}$	$-102 \div 6$
8. $\frac{0}{-6}$	$\frac{-20}{4}$	$85 \div (-5)$	$(-30) \div (-6)$
9. $27 \div (-9)$	$\frac{121}{-11}$	$\frac{-90}{6}$	$50 \div (-10)$

CORE CONNECTIONS: Fractions and Division

You know how to simplify fractions by dividing both the numerator and denominator by the same number. For example, $\frac{6 \div 2}{8 \div 2} = \frac{3}{4}$. In the same way, you can simplify a division problem.

Example $-2{,}000 \div 16$

This would be a frustrating problem to do without a calculator. But if you write it as a fraction, you can simplify to find an easier problem to solve.

Divide the numerator and denominator by the same number.

$\frac{-2{,}000}{16} \div \frac{2}{2} = \frac{-1{,}000}{8}$ $\frac{-1{,}000}{8} \div \frac{2}{2} = \frac{-500}{4}$ $\frac{-500}{4} \div \frac{2}{2} = \frac{-250}{2}$

This problem is much easier to solve: $-250 \div 2 =$ **–125**

The answer to the original problem $-2{,}000 \div 16$ is also **–125.**

Divide.

1. $210 \div -15$	$-828 \div 12$	$-720 \div -48$
2. $600 \div -24$	$-1{,}080 \div 36$	$9{,}750 \div 150$

Answers start on page 182.

POWERS AND ROOTS

Repeated multiplication of the same number can be shown using a **power.** The expression 5^2 is read "5 to the second power." The number 5 is the **base** and 2 is the **exponent.** To solve a power, multiply the base by itself the number of times shown by the exponent.

$5^2 = 5 \times 5 = 25$ $\quad$ $5^3 = 5 \times 5 \times 5 = 125$

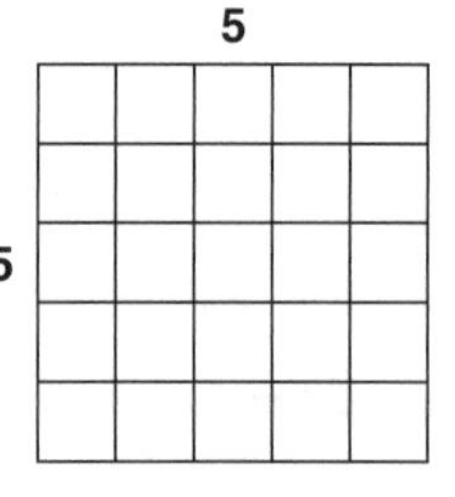

The 5 columns and 5 rows form a square.

A number raised to the second power is often called a **square.** A number raised to the third power is called a **cube.** Can you see why?

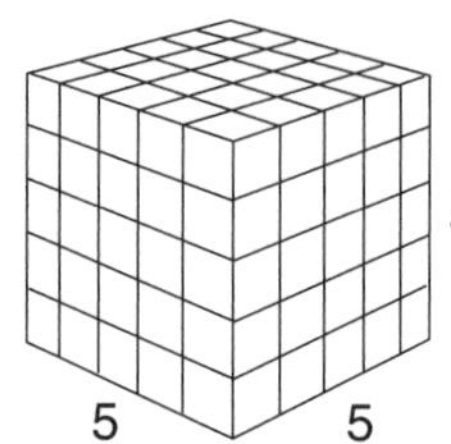

The depth is also 5. Now we have a cube.

SOLVING POWERS

Example 1 5^3

$5 \times 5 \times 5 =$
$25 \times 5 =$ **125**

Example 2 3^4

$3 \times 3 \times 3 \times 3 =$ **81**

Example 3 2^5

$2 \times 2 \times 2 \times 2 \times 2 =$ **32**

You can use a calculator to find the value of a power.

To square 5, press: 5 [x^2] [enter] $\quad$ The display reads: 5^2 $\quad$ 25
To find 6^4, press: 6 [^] 4 [enter] $\quad$ The display reads: 6^4 $\quad$ 1296

Find each value. The first one is started for you.

1. $7^2 = 7 \times 7 =$ _____ $\quad$ $3^3 =$ _____ $\quad$ $2^3 =$ _____
2. $11^2 =$ _____ $\quad$ $1^5 =$ _____ $\quad$ $12^2 =$ _____
3. $5^3 =$ _____ $\quad$ $8^2 =$ _____ $\quad$ $9^3 =$ _____
4. $4^2 =$ _____ $\quad$ $6^3 =$ _____ $\quad$ $10^3 =$ _____

When a whole number is squared, the result is called a **perfect square.** In the problem $5^2 = 25$, the number 25 is a perfect square.

Complete this table of common perfect squares. These will be useful to know throughout your work in algebra and geometry.

$2^2 =$	$5^2 =$	$8^2 =$	$11^2 =$	$14^2 =$
$3^2 =$	$6^2 =$	$9^2 =$	$12^2 =$	$15^2 =$
$4^2 =$	$7^2 =$	$10^2 =$	$13^2 =$	$20^2 =$

SQUARE ROOTS

The opposite of raising a number to the second power is finding the **square root.** The symbol for this operation is called a **radical sign** ($\sqrt{\ }$).

SOLVING SQUARE ROOTS

Example $\sqrt{81} = ?$

Step 1
Ask yourself, "What number multiplied by itself equals 81?" The square root of 81 is 9. $\sqrt{81} = \mathbf{9}$

Check: To check a square root, multiply the answer by itself. $9 \times 9 = 81$, so $\sqrt{81} = \mathbf{9}$

Find the value of each square root. Ask yourself, "What number times itself gives this number?"

5. $\sqrt{100}$ = _____ $\sqrt{121}$ = _____ $\sqrt{49}$ = _____ $\sqrt{64}$ = _____

6. $\sqrt{144}$ = _____ $\sqrt{169}$ = _____ $\sqrt{400}$ = _____ $\sqrt{81}$ = _____

Many numbers do not have a whole number as a square root. To find the square root of a large number, you can use a calculator. Press the square root key and then the number. Press enter to display the square root.

If you use a calculator to find the square root of a number that is not a perfect square, the answer will have a decimal part. If you don't have a calculator, you can estimate the square root of a number by comparing it to the square roots you do know.

Example Find the square root of 110.

You know that 10^2 is 100 and 11^2 is 121. Therefore, you can conclude that $\sqrt{110}$ is between the values of 10 and 11.

Use your knowledge of perfect squares to find the approximate value of each square root.

7. $\sqrt{50}$ is between
A. 5 and 6
B. 6 and 7
C. 7 and 8
D. 9 and 10

8. $\sqrt{125}$ is between
A. 10 and 11
B. 11 and 12
C. 12 and 13
D. 14 and 15

9. $\sqrt{10}$ is between
A. 3 and 4
B. 4 and 5
C. 5 and 6
D. 7 and 8

10. Explain Describe how your knowledge of perfect squares could help you estimate the square root of 90.

Answers start on page 182.

ORDER OF OPERATIONS

The expression $3 + 4 \times 5$ contains two operations: addition and multiplication. Remember that multiplication can be represented by a multiplication dot.

What is the value of the expression?

If you add first, it equals 35.

$$\begin{aligned} &3 + 4 \times 5 \\ &= 7 \times 5 \\ &= 35 \end{aligned}$$

If you multiply first, it equals 23.

$$\begin{aligned} &3 + 4 \times 5 \\ &= 3 + 20 \\ &= 23 \end{aligned}$$

Both 35 and 23 can't be right. To make sure people agree on the value of an expression, mathematicians developed rules called the **order of operations.** The following example demonstrates how to use the order of operations.

USING THE ORDER OF OPERATIONS

Example Find the value of the expression $(3 - 7)^2 + 3(4) - \sqrt{2 \times 32}$.

Step 1
Perform operations in grouping symbols: parentheses, brackets, fraction bars, and radicals.

$$\begin{aligned} &(3 - 7)^2 + 3(4) - \sqrt{2 \times 32} \\ &= (-4)^2 + 3(4) - \sqrt{64} \end{aligned}$$

Step 2
Evaluate powers (exponents) and roots.

$$\begin{aligned} &= (-4)^2 + 3(4) - \sqrt{64} \\ &= 16 + 3(4) - 8 \end{aligned}$$

Step 3
Multiply and divide, working from left to right.

$$\begin{aligned} &= 16 + 3(4) - 8 \\ &= 16 + 12 - 8 \end{aligned}$$

Step 4
Add and subtract, working from left to right.

$$\begin{aligned} &= 16 + 12 - 8 \\ &= 28 - 8 \\ &= 20 \end{aligned}$$

The value of the expression is **20.**

Good test takers use memory tricks to help them remember rules. To remember the order of operations, many students use the sentence "Please Excuse My Dear Aunt Sally," or PEMDAS. The first letter of each word is an order clue.

P represents **P**arentheses and other grouping symbols.
E represents **E**xponents and roots.
M and **D** represent **M**ultiplication and **D**ivision.
A and **S** represent **A**ddition and **S**ubtraction.

The next example uses a fraction bar as a grouping symbol. A fraction bar expresses division. Find the value of the numerator and the denominator separately. Then divide.

WORKING WITH A FRACTION BAR

Example Find the value of the expression $\frac{(6+1)^2-4}{6-1}$.

Step 1
Find the value of the numerator and the denominator separately. Notice how the order of operations is followed in the numerator.

$$\frac{(6+1)^2-4}{6-1} = \frac{(7)^2-4}{6-1} = \frac{49-4}{6-1} = \frac{45}{5}$$

Step 2
Divide.

$$\frac{45}{5} = 9$$

The value of the expression is **9.**

Evaluate each expression.

1. $-4 \times 5 + 3 \times 2$ $\qquad \frac{10+15}{10-5}$ $\qquad 2 \times 4^2 + 12$
2. $9 - 7 + 6 - 5$ $\qquad 3(8 - 4)$ $\qquad 5(2 - 7)^2$
3. $\sqrt{81} - 5$ $\qquad 5 \times 3^2$ $\qquad -6 \times 2 - (5 + 6)$
4. $\frac{24}{6} - \frac{36}{12}$ $\qquad \frac{40-4}{9}$ $\qquad \frac{-60}{20-8}$
5. $(3 + 8)^2$ $\qquad 3(8 + 4) - (15 + 9)$ $\qquad 9(12 - 9)^2$

Choose the expression that shows the result after the *first operation* is completed.

6. $7 \times 6 - 5 \times 4$
   A. $7 - 1 - 4$
   B. $42 - 20$
   C. $7 + 1 - 4$

7. $\frac{20+40}{10} - 5$
   A. $\frac{60}{10} - 5$
   B. $\frac{60}{5}$
   C. $20 + 4 - 5$

8. $2(9 - 6)$
   A. $18 - 6$
   B. $2(15)$
   C. $2(3)$

9. $\frac{21+18}{3}$
   A. $(21)(18)$
   B. $\frac{39}{3}$
   C. $\frac{21-18}{3}$

10. $(8 + 5)(8 - 5)$
   A. $13(3)$
   B. $8 + 40 - 5$
   C. $13 - 13$

11. $15 + \sqrt{36}$
   A. 51
   B. $15 + 36$
   C. $15 + 6$

Read the situation below and write an expression that could be used to solve it.

12. Three families are going to a play. They decide to split the cost of the tickets evenly. The families need to buy 7 tickets for children at \$9 each and 6 tickets for adults at \$12 each. How much does each family owe?

13. **Analyze** Is the order of operations important in solving problem 12? Try performing the operations out of order to see if the answer is affected.

Answers start on page 182.

USING A CALCULATOR

Most tests, including the GED® Math Test, allow you to use a scientific calculator. A calculator is helpful only if you know how to use it. All scientific calculators have the same abilities, but the keys might be in different places. Before you take any test, make sure you practice with the calculator you will be allowed to use.

In this lesson, you will learn how to evaluate powers and roots on a scientific calculator, and how to work with grouping symbols.

EXPONENT KEYS

To square any number, press: [x^2]
To raise a number to any power, press: [^]

Example Find the value of $5^2 - 2^4$.

Press: 5 [x^2] – 2 [^] 4 [enter] The display reads: 5^2-2^4 9

(5 [x^2] = 5^2; 2 [^] 4 = 2^4)

Note: Sometimes you need to press the arrow key (▶) to move the cursor.
For example: $2^4 - 5^2$ = 2 ^ 4 ▶ [(–)] 5 [x^2] [enter] –9

To work with roots, you need the second functions above the exponent keys. To access a second function, press the button marked 2nd in the upper left corner of most calculators.

ROOT KEYS

To find the square root of any number, press: [2nd] [$\sqrt{\ }$]
To find a certain root of a number, press: [2nd] [$\sqrt[x]{\ }$]

Example Find the value of $\sqrt{81}$.

Press: [2nd] [$\sqrt{\ }$] 81 [enter] The display reads: $\sqrt{81}$ 9

Example Find the value of $\sqrt[5]{32}$.

Press: 5 [2nd] [$\sqrt[x]{\ }$] 32 [enter] The display reads: $\sqrt[5]{32}$ 2

Notice that the calculator displays the calculation as you would write it on paper. Always check the display to make sure you have entered the calculation correctly. If you make a mistake, always press clear before starting over.

Scientific calculators are programmed to follow the order of operations. You can enter an expression exactly as it is written to find its value. If grouping symbols are needed, use the parentheses keys. You can also enter an expression as a fraction.

> **GROUPING KEYS**
>
> To write an expression in parentheses, press: [(] [)]

Example Find the value of 6(2 + 7).

Press: 6 [(] 2 + 7 [)] [enter] The display reads: 6(2+7) 54

Use parentheses to enter an expression with a fraction bar. Remember, the fraction bar indicates division.

Example Find the value of $\frac{6-15}{-3}$.

Press: [$\frac{n}{d}$] 6 – 15 ▼ [(–)] 3 ▶ [enter] The display reads: $\frac{6-15}{-3}$ 3

(***Hint:*** You must use the negative symbol key [(–)] to enter a negative number.)

Good test takers practice with the calculator they will use on the test. Use the items below to practice the keystrokes you have learned in this lesson.

Evaluate these expressions using a scientific calculator.

1. $\frac{(7-2)\times 3}{-5}$ $(12+18)(-2)^3$ $\left(-\frac{16}{4}\right)-\frac{18}{-6}$

2. $\frac{3(15-12)}{-1}$ $(-3)-\frac{\sqrt{81}}{5-2}$ $\frac{-10+6^2}{6-4}$

3. $\frac{2-7\times 4}{13}$ $\frac{\sqrt{729}}{(-6)+3}$ $\frac{12\times\sqrt[6]{64}}{5-1}$

4. $(-4)^5+5^4$ $[(-9)-(-12)]^2$ $\frac{\sqrt{576}}{4}+\frac{(-44)-2(-4)}{-9}$

(***Hint:*** Use parentheses for the brackets.)

5. $\frac{9\times 3-15}{-12}-13\times 3$ $9-\left(4-\frac{-3-13}{-12+10}\right)$ $\frac{5^3-3^6}{-\sqrt{4}}$

6. Explain The scientific calculator you will use on the GED® Math Test does not have a way to enter absolute value. Describe how you could use a calculator to find the value of –3 × | 8 – 15 | .

Answers start on page 182.

Unit 1 Review

Solve.

1. 18 + (–12) =   8 – (–10) =   2 + (–3) + 1 =

2. 8 + (–20) – 13 =   13(–6) =   20(–2)(–3) =

3. –5(–1)(2)(–5)(–1) = $\frac{-216}{8}$ = $\frac{50}{-5}$ =

In problems 4–7, select the name of the property that was used.

4. 3 × (–4) × 5 = 3 × 5 × (–4)

- associative
- commutative
- distributive

5. (18 + 43) + (32 + 7) = (18 + 32) + (43 + 7)

- associative
- commutative
- distributive

6. 12(1 – 5) = (12 × 1) – (12 × 5)

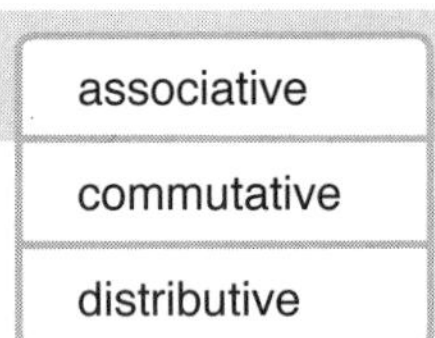

7. 6(2 + 10) = (6 × 2) + (6 × 10)

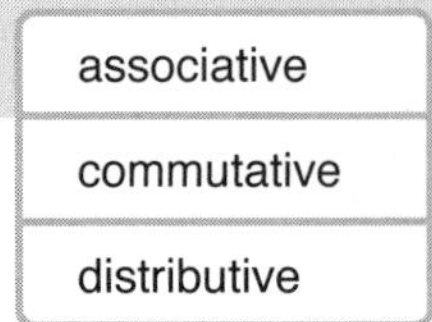

Choose the best answer to each problem.

8. What is the greatest common factor (GCF) of 18 and 30?

   A. 2
   B. 3
   C. 6
   D. 9

9. Which symbol belongs in the blank?

   –11 ______ –6

   A. <
   B. >
   C. ≥
   D. =

10. Which of the following is *not* a prime factor of 150?

   A. 2
   B. 3
   C. 5
   D. 7

11. Which of the following is a common multiple of 12 and 9?

   A. 18
   B. 48
   C. 54
   D. 72

Solve.

12. $8^2 =$ $3^3 =$ $2^4 =$ $(-6)^2 =$

13. $\sqrt{121} =$ $\sqrt{196} =$ $\sqrt{900} =$ $\sqrt{81} =$

Solve as directed.

14. Simplify: $11 - 6 \times 4 + 3$

A. −16

B. −10

C. 23

D. 35

15. Simplify: $\frac{(1-5)^2}{8}$

A. −2

B. $-\frac{1}{2}$

C. $\frac{1}{2}$

D. 2

16. Mitch's bank statement shows the following transactions. What is his current balance?

Balance	$638.00
Debit Card	–$20.38
Deposit	$120.50
Withdrawal	–$280.00

17. Simplify $-2(9 + 2) - 5(4 - 6)$.

18. Overnight, the temperature rose from −9° to 4°. By how many degrees did the temperature change?

degrees

19. Use a factor tree to find the prime factorization of 180.

20. $\sqrt{155}$ is between

A. 11 and 12

B. 12 and 13

C. 13 and 14

D. 14 and 15

21. Simplify $|-7 - 8| + 5^2$.

22. Is the following statement true or false? An even number will never have an odd factor.

Explain your thinking.

Answers start on page 182.

THE BASICS OF ALGEBRA

SKILLS

- Evaluating and simplifying expressions
- Using the rules of exponents
- Simplifying radicals
- Writing and solving equations
- Graphing and solving inequalities

TOOLS AND STRATEGIES

- Using scientific notation
- Reading and writing equations
- Graphing inequalities
- Trying answer choices

WHEN SOLVING A MATH PROBLEM, there needs to be a way to write down the thought process. Algebra is a language that shows mathematical ideas using numbers and symbols.

Algebra uses **expressions** to describe relationships between different quantities. Often, one of those quantities is unknown. Algebra uses **variables** as placeholders for unknown quantities. In this unit, you will learn how to translate words into expressions.

If you know what an expression equals, you can write an **equation.** You can use the rules of algebra to find the missing value in an equation. In this unit, you will learn how to solve equations, or find the value of the variable.

USING THE BASICS OF ALGEBRA

You use the basics of algebra when you:

- Estimate how long it will take to get somewhere
- Compare cell phone plans
- Make a plan to get all the dishes of a meal ready at the same time
- Determine how much the insurance company will pay in an accident
- Create a monthly budget

Read the following items. Describe some of your experiences in writing or discuss them with a partner.

1. Have you ever had to compare two plans, such as cell phone plans or cable television plans? How do you decide which plan is better for your family?

2. How do you estimate how long it will take to drive from one place to another? What factors make a trip go faster or slower?

3. When you or your favorite team is losing a game, how do you figure out how many points you need to catch up?

4. How early do you need to wake up in the morning in order to get to work or school on time? How do you decide when to set your alarm?

MATH TALK

A student is worried about passing his math class. His final grade will equal the average of five test scores. If his average is at least 70, he will pass. The student has already taken four tests, and he wants to know what score he needs on the last test.

Discuss with a partner how you could figure out what score the student needs on the last test.

If his first four scores are 65, 60, 75, and 70, what can he score on his final test and still pass?

If his first four scores are 60, 75, 80, and 75, what can he score on his final test and still pass?

EXPRESSIONS AND VARIABLES

Mathematics is a language for expressing relationships among numbers. Variables are used to hold the place for unknown numbers. A **variable** is a letter that represents a number. Any letter can be used as a variable, although x and n are used most often.

The example below shows a sentence translated from words into mathematical symbols.

Example A number increased by four is nine.

$$x \quad + \quad 4 = 9$$

In algebra, the focus is on three kinds of mathematical statements.

- An **expression** states a relationship among numbers and variables.
- An **equation** tells what an expression equals.
- An **inequality** shows how an expression compares to another number or expression. Inequalities use the phrases *greater than* and *less than.*

Study the next examples carefully to see how to translate words to symbols.

In Words	In Symbols
The product of 3 and a number	$3n$
Eight less than a number	$x - 8$
The difference of 14 and a number	$14 - n$
The quotient of a number divided by 4 is 6.	$\frac{x}{4} = 6$
Two times a number decreased by 7 is 23.	$2n - 7 = 23$
Three times a number is greater than 9.	$3x > 9$
The sum of 5 and a number is less than 12.	$5 + x < 12$

What did you notice? Certain words indicate specific operations.

Addition	Subtraction	Multiplication	Division
sum increased by more than	difference decreased by less than	product times	quotient divided by

Small word changes can make big mathematical changes. For example, "seven less than a number" has a different meaning than "seven is less than a number." The first is written $x - 7$; the second is written $7 < x$.

Choose the correct mathematical statement for each of the following.

1. The product of 6 and a number
   A. $6 + n$
   B. $6n$
   C. $n - 6$
   D. $\frac{6}{n}$

2. Twelve less than a number is 19.
   A. $12n < 19$
   B. $12 + n = 19$
   C. $n - 12 = 19$
   D. $12 - n = 19$

3. One less than two times a number is fifteen.
   A. $2x - 1 = 15$
   B. $2x < 15 - 1$
   C. $1 - 2x = 15$
   D. $1 < 2x + 15$

4. The quotient of a number and 5 is equal to the number decreased by 9.
   A. $5x = x - 9$
   B. $\frac{x}{5} = x - 9$
   C. $\frac{5}{x} = x - 9$
   D. $5 - x < 9$

Write each expression using mathematical symbols.

5. The quotient when 4 times *n* is divided by 4 more than *n*.

6. The sum of the product of 3 and *x* and the number 15.

7. Twenty less a number times 4.

8. The sum of a number and 2 multiplied by 6.

9. The difference of 12 and the product of 5 and a number.

10. The quotient of 30 and the product of 7 and a number.

A building set has four types of blocks, shown in the drawing. A letter is used to represent the number of each type of block in the set. For each operation shown, write two different ways of expressing the operation in words.

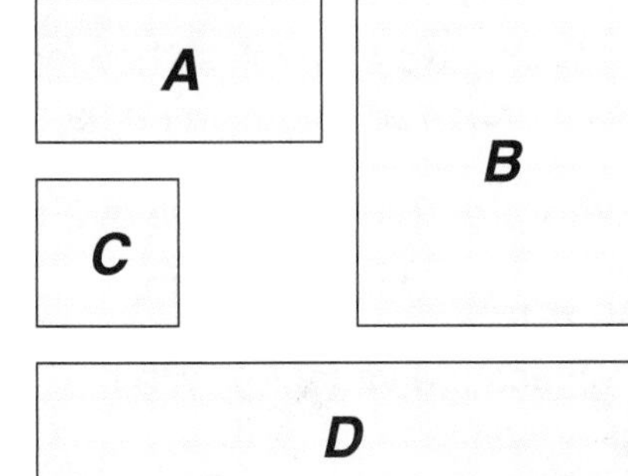

11. $A + C$

12. $D - C$

13. $A \cdot B$

14. $\frac{C}{D}$

15. Explain $A + B + C < D$ Based on this statement, what conclusion can you draw about the number of *D* blocks in the set?

Answers start on page 183.

EVALUATING EXPRESSIONS

An expression is written with numbers, variables, and operation symbols. If you are given the values of the variables, you can evaluate the expression. Evaluating an expression means to find its value.

FINDING THE VALUE OF AN EXPRESSION

Example Find the value of $2x - y$ when $x = 4$ and $y = -3$.

Step 1
Replace the variables with the given values.

$2x - y$
$= 2(4) - (-3)$

Step 2
Use the order of operations.

Multiply.	$2(4) - (-3)$
	$= 8 - (-3)$
Add the opposite.	$= 8 + 3$
	$= 11$

The value is **11.**

When you write a negative number, you are using a **negation** symbol (–). The symbol means "the opposite of." You can already see that –6 is the opposite of 6. In the same way $-x$ is the opposite of x, and $-(n - 3)$ is the opposite of $(n - 3)$. Study how negation symbols are used in the following example.

Example If $x = 5$, which expression has the greater value, $-(x)^2$ or $(-x)^2$?

This expression squares 5 and then negates the result.

$-(x)^2 = -(5)^2$
$= -(25)$
$= -25$

This expression negates 5 and then squares the result.

$(-x)^2 = (-5)^2$
$= 25$

If $x = 5$, then $\mathbf{(-x)^2}$ is greater than $-(x)^2$.

The next two examples show how to evaluate expressions that contain grouping symbols. Remember, absolute value bars and fraction bars are two kinds of grouping symbols.

Example Find the value of $2\,|\,a - b\,|\,- a$ when $a = 5$ and $b = 8$.

Step 1
Replace the variables with the given values.

$2\,|\,a - b\,|\,- a$
$2\,|\,5 - 8\,|\,- 5$

Step 2
Find the absolute value part of the expression.

$2\,|\,5 - 8\,|\,- 5$
$2\,|\,-3\,|\,- 5$
$2(3) - 5$

Step 3
Multiply; then subtract.

$2(3) - 5$
$= 6 - 5$
$= 1$

The value of the expression is **1.**

Example Find the value of $\frac{m-n}{3m+2n}$ when $m = -2$ and $n = 4$.

Step 1
Replace the variables with the given values. $\frac{m-n}{3m+2n} = \frac{-2-4}{3(-2)+2(4)}$

Step 2
Find the values of the numerator and denominator separately. $= \frac{-6}{-6+8}$

Step 3
Simplify the fraction. $= \frac{-6}{2}$

$= -3$

The value of the expression is **–3.**

Evaluate.

1. Find the value of $(a - b)^2 - c$.
   - **a.** when $a = 2$, $b = -1$, and $c = 4$
   - **b.** when $a = -1$, $b = 3$, and $c = -4$

2. Find the value of $4m \cdot \frac{n}{6}$.
   - **a.** when $m = -6$ and $n = 2$
   - **b.** when $m = -3$ and $n = -1$

3. Find the value of $4(5 - x)^3 - 2x$.
   - **a.** when $x = 7$
   - **b.** when $x = 0$

4. Find the value of $a - |b + 2c|$.
   - **a.** when $a = 10$, $b = 1$, and $c = -4$
   - **b.** when $a = 3$, $b = 4$, and $c = -1$

5. Find the value of $x(|x| - (y - x))$. (***Hint:*** Work from the inside out.)
   - **a.** when $x = -2$ and $y = 1$
   - **b.** when $x = 4$ and $y = -5$

6. Find the value of $\frac{m}{2} + \frac{4n}{3}$
   - **a.** when $m = -10$ and $n = 9$
   - **b.** when $m = 8$ and $n = -12$

Solve.

7. Choose different values for x and y from the integers –5, –3, –1, 0, 1, 3, and 5. Which values for x and y will give the expression below the greatest value?

   $-|-2x + y|$

8. **Explain** Will the value of x^3 always be greater than x^2? Explain your reasoning.

Answers start on page 183.

SIMPLIFYING EXPRESSIONS

Compare these two expressions:

Expression 1	**Expression 2**
$4x + 9 + 3x - 1$	$7x + 8$
When $x = 2$, the expression is $4(2) + 9 + 3(2) - 1 =$ $8 + 9 + 6 - 1 = \mathbf{22}$	When $x = 2$, the expression is $7(2) + 8 = \mathbf{22}$

When $x = 2$, these two expressions have the same value. In fact, the expressions are equal for any value of the variable. The two expressions are called **equivalent expressions.** Expression 2 is a **simplified** form of Expression 1.

SIMPLIFYING EXPRESSIONS

Example 1 Simplify $2x + 2 + x - 4$.

Step 1
Group **like terms.** These are terms that have the same variable.
Note: *x* means the same as 1*x*. $2x + 2 + x - 4$

Step 2
Group the numbers. Use the rules for adding signed numbers. $3x + 2 - 4$

Step 3
Write the simplified expression. $\mathbf{3x - 2}$

Example 2 Simplify $-6k + 3 + 2k - 7$.

Step 1
Group the variables. Use the rules for adding signed numbers with the **coefficients** (the numbers multiplying the variable). $-6k + 3 + 2k - 7$

Step 2
Group the numbers. $-4k + 3 - 7$

Step 3
Write the simplified expression. $\mathbf{-4k - 4}$

Simplify each expression.

1. $5x - 2x$
2. $-6k + k$
   (***Hint:*** *k* is the same as 1*k*.)
3. $7t + 5 - 9t$
4. $2a + 9a - 9 + 6$
5. $10 + 7m - m + 3$
6. $12 - 6y - 5 + 18$
7. $k + m - 2k - 9m$
8. $8c + 3d - 2c + 5d$
9. $-2s - 8t + 9t - 6s$

Use the triangle to solve each problem.

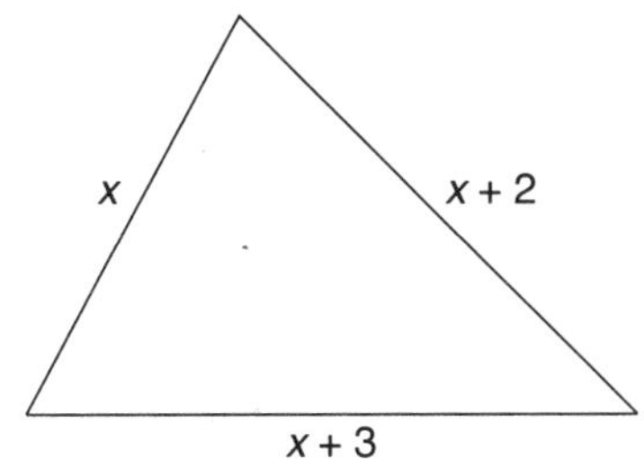

10. Which side is the longest? How could you tell that it's the longest side besides how it looks?

11. Write an expression for the perimeter of the figure. (***Hint:*** Perimeter is the distance around a figure. It is found by adding the sides of a figure.)

12. Simplify the expression.

13. Find the value of the expression when $x = 8$.

14. What is the value of the perimeter when $x = 25$?

Use the rectangle to solve each problem.

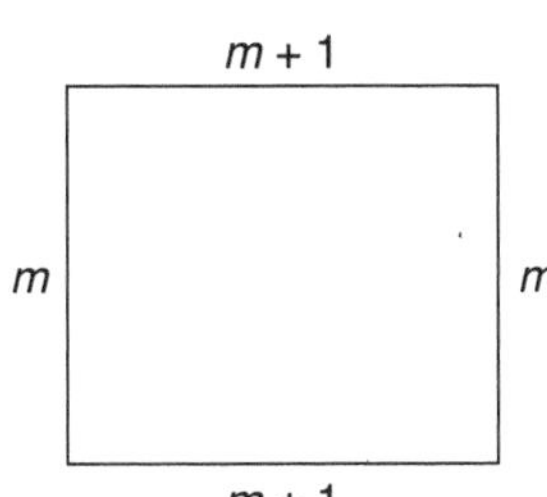

15. Write an expression for the perimeter of the figure.

16. Simplify the expression.

17. What is the value of the expression when $m = 4.5$?

18. Find the value of the perimeter when $m = 18$.

Use the square to solve each problem.

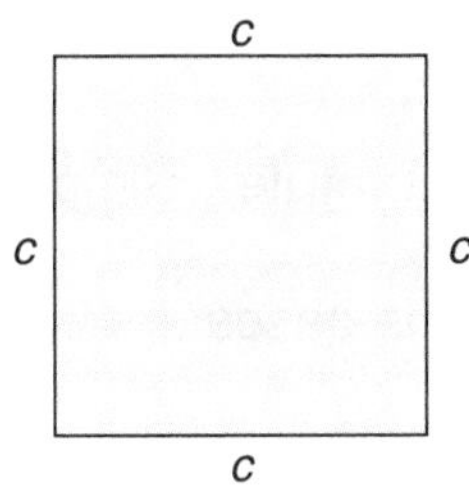

19. Write an expression for the perimeter of the figure.

20. Simplify the expression.

21. Find the value of the perimeter when c equals 7 cm.

22. If the sides of the square are changed to $c - 3$, what is the new perimeter of the square if c equals 7 cm?

Solve as directed.

23. John is n years old. His sister is $n + 12$ years old. His brother is $n - 2$ years old. Write and simplify an expression that could be used to find the sum of their ages. (***Hint:*** The word *sum* indicates addition.)

24. A plumber has three pieces of pipe. The first piece is x inches long. The second piece is 5 inches shorter than the first piece. The third piece is 9 inches longer than the second piece.

    a. Write an expression for the third piece of pipe.

    First: x Second: $x - 5$ Third: ____________

    b. Simplify an expression that shows the total length of the three pieces.

Answers start on page 184.

THE RULES OF EXPONENTS

Exponents are used to show repeated multiplication of a number called the **base.**

For example, 2^5 means $2 \times 2 \times 2 \times 2 \times 2$. The number 2 is the base, and the exponent is 5. There are five 2s in the multiplication problem. To find the value, complete the multiplication: $2 \times 2 \times 2 \times 2 \times 2 = 32$

Variables can also be raised to a power. n^5 means $n \times n \times n \times n \times n$.

You can use the rules of exponents to simplify expressions with exponents. The rules are written with variables to show that they apply in all situations. They work whether the base is a number or a variable.

Study the rules and the examples that follow. Knowing how to simplify expressions with variables can make your work easier and save you valuable time on tests.

Rule	Meaning
$x^a \bullet x^b = x^{a+b}$	When multiplying the same bases, keep the same base and add the exponents.
$\frac{x^a}{x^b} = x^{a-b}$	When dividing the same bases, keep the same base and subtract the exponents.

Example Simplify $y^3 \times y^2$.

The bases are the same. Keep the same base and add the exponents. $y^3 \times y^2 = y^{3+2} = y^5$

Example Simplify $n^6 \div n^4$.

The bases are the same. Keep the same base and subtract the exponents. $n^6 \div n^4 = n^{6-4} = n^2$

The second rule can cause two special situations to occur.

$\frac{4^3}{4^2} = 4^{3-2} = 4^1$ What does a number raised to the first power equal? The exponent tells you to write the base only one time. A number raised to the first power equals itself. $4^1 = 4$

$\frac{2^3}{2^3} = 2^{3-3} = 2^0$ What does a number raised to the zero power equal? Any number divided by itself equals 1. $2^0 = 1$

Simplify each expression.

1. $x^2 \cdot x$ $\qquad$ $a^4 \times a^2 \times a^1$ $\qquad$ $3^5 \div 3^2$

2. $\frac{4^4}{4 \times 4^2}$ $\qquad$ $\frac{3^5}{3^2 \times 3^0}$ $\qquad$ $\frac{x^3 \times x^2}{x^5}$

3. $\frac{2b^4 \times 3b}{b^4}$ $\qquad$ $\frac{m^3 \times 8m^3}{4m^4}$ $\qquad$ $5^6 \times 5^2 \div 5^5$

Rule	Meaning
$(x^a)^b = x^{a \times b}$	When a base with an exponent is raised to a power, keep the same base and multiply the exponents.
$(xy)^a = x^a y^a$ $(\frac{x}{y})^a = \frac{x^a}{y^a}$	When a product or a quotient is raised to a power, you can distribute the exponent.

Simplify each expression.

4. $(2^3)^4$ $\qquad$ $(x^2 \cdot x^3)^4$ $\qquad$ $(b^2c^4)^3$

5. $\frac{(3^4)^5}{3^2}$ $\qquad$ $\frac{2k^3 \times (k^4)^2}{k^3}$ $\qquad$ $\frac{n^5 \times n^5}{(n^2)^5}$

Simplify first. Then evaluate each expression. Let $a = 2$, $b = -3$, and $c = 5$.

6. $\frac{2a^3}{a^2}$ $\qquad$ $\frac{4b^3c}{b^2}$ $\qquad$ $\left(\frac{c^3}{c^2}\right)^2$

7. $b^2 \times b^0 \times (bc)^2$ $\qquad$ $\frac{a^0 \times a^2}{a}$ $\qquad$ $\frac{b^4 \times b^4}{(b^2)^3}$

8. $\frac{3a^3 \times 3a}{9a^2}$ $\qquad$ $\frac{2c \times 3c^2}{(2c^4)^0}$ $\qquad$ $\frac{4c^4}{2c^2 \times c}$

9. Explain Does the expression $(3n)^2$ equal $9n^2$ or $3n^2$? What rule of exponents did you use to find the answer?

Answers start on page 184.

NEGATIVE EXPONENTS

When following the rules of exponents, you may get an answer with a negative exponent. At first glance, a negative exponent doesn't make sense. How can you raise a number to a negative power? In this lesson, you will learn how to interpret a negative exponent.

The first example is solved in two ways. As you can see, the rules of exponents are connected to canceling.

Example 1

Using the rules of exponents: $\frac{a^5}{a^3} = a^{5-3} = a^2$

Using canceling: $\frac{\cancel{a} \cdot \cancel{a} \cdot \cancel{a} \cdot a \cdot a}{\cancel{a} \cdot \cancel{a} \cdot \cancel{a}} = a^2$

What happens when the exponent in the denominator is greater than the exponent in the numerator? The exponent is negative. Use canceling to find its meaning.

Example 2

Using the rules of exponents: $\frac{a^3}{a^5} = a^{3-5} = a^{-2}$

Using canceling: $\frac{\cancel{a} \cdot \cancel{a} \cdot \cancel{a}}{\cancel{a} \cdot \cancel{a} \cdot \cancel{a} \cdot a \cdot a} = \frac{1}{a^2}$

From the second example, you can see that $a^{-2} = \frac{1}{a^2}$.

The second example reveals a key idea. You can change a negative exponent to a positive exponent by moving the base number and its exponent to the other side of the fraction bar.

Examples x^{-3} becomes $\frac{1}{x^3}$. $\frac{1}{2^{-4}}$ becomes $\frac{2^4}{1}$, which equals 16.

Write each expression using a negative exponent. The first one is done for you.

1. $\frac{1}{3 \times 3 \times 3 \times 3} = 3^{-4}$ $\frac{1}{x \cdot x \cdot x}$ $\frac{1}{2 \cdot 2 \cdot 2 \cdot 2 \cdot 2}$

2. $\frac{1}{a^2}$ $\frac{1}{5^6}$ $\frac{1}{x^7}$

Write in simplest form.

3. 6^{-2} 5^{-3} 2^{-6}

4. 4^{-3} 3^{-4} $\frac{1}{1^{-9}}$

5. $\frac{1}{3^{-2}}$ $\frac{1}{4^{-3}}$ $\frac{1}{5^{-2}}$

When evaluating an expression, first change negative exponents to positive exponents. Simplify the expression as much as possible. Then find the value.

EVALUATING EXPRESSIONS WITH NEGATIVE EXPONENTS

Example Find the value of $\frac{8ab^{-2}}{2a^2b}$ when $a = 2$ and $b = -1$.

Step 1
Move the negative exponent to the other side of the fraction bar.

$$\frac{8ab^{-2}}{2a^2b} = \frac{8a}{2a^2b \cdot b^2} = \frac{8a}{2a^2b^3}$$

Step 2
Simplify.

$$\frac{{}^{4}\cancel{8}\cancel{a}}{{}_{1}\cancel{2}a \cdot \cancel{a} \cdot b \cdot b \cdot b} = \frac{4}{ab^3}$$

Step 3
Substitute the given values, and evaluate the expression.

$$\frac{4}{ab^3} = \frac{4}{2 \cdot (-1)^3} = \frac{4}{2 \cdot -1} = \frac{4}{-2} = -2$$

The value is **–2.**

Evaluate using the given variables.

6. Let $x = -4$ and $y = -2$.

a. $\left(\frac{x^2}{y^3}\right)^{-1}$ **b.** $(xy^2)^{-2}$ **c.** $\frac{x}{y^{-3}}$

7. Let $a = -1$ and $b = 3$.

a. $6a \cdot 3a^2b^{-2}$ **b.** $\left(\frac{a^3}{b^{-2}}\right)^2$ **c.** $a^2b^{-2} \cdot a^{-2}b^2$

8. Let $m = 5$ and $n = 2$.

a. $\frac{20mn^{-2}}{(mn)^2}$ **b.** $\left(\frac{m^3n^3}{m^3n^2}\right)^{-2}$ **c.** $\left(\frac{m^{-1}}{n^{-2}}\right)^{-2}$

CORE CONNECTIONS: Test Your Thinking

Even the best students sometimes forget how the rules work. If you aren't sure whether you are allowed to do something within the rules of algebra, create a test situation using numbers.

Example Does $(x + y)^2 = x^2 + y^2$?

In other words, can you distribute an exponent over addition?
Replace the variables with numbers and try it. Try using $x = 2$ and $y = 3$.

$(2 + 3)^2 = 5^2 = 25$ $\qquad$ $2^2 + 3^2 = 4 + 9 = 13$

The expressions are *not* equal. You can't distribute an exponent over addition.

Create a test for each situation.

1. Does $x^2 - y^2$ equal $(x - y)^2$?

2. Does $x^{-2} + y^{-2}$ equal $\frac{1}{x^2} + \frac{1}{y^2}$?

Answers start on page 184.

SCIENTIFIC NOTATION

Scientific notation is a system for writing very large or very small numbers. This system is based on the powers of ten. The chart below shows some of the powers of ten. Do you notice any patterns in the numbers?

In each case, the exponent tells you how many zeros are in the number or how many places come after the 1.

$10^5 = 100{,}000$	$10^2 = 100$
$10^4 = 10{,}000$	$10^1 = 10$
$10^3 = 1{,}000$	$10^0 = 1$

A number in scientific notation includes a number part and a power of ten. The number part has a digit in the ones place followed by a decimal point and any other important digits. The exponent is the number of places the decimal point had to move.

WRITING A NUMBER IN SCIENTIFIC NOTATION

Example Write 2,800,000 in scientific notation.

Step 1
Move the decimal point from the end of the number to the place directly after the first non-zero digit. Write the number part as 2.8.

2.800,000.
6 places

Step 2
Count the number of places you moved the decimal place to the left. Write the power of ten as 10^6.

The decimal point moved left 6 places. Use 6 for the exponent.

2,800,000 is written **2.8×10^6.**

Example Write 0.000056 in scientific notation.

Step 1
Move the decimal point from the start of the number to one place after the first non-zero digit. Write the number part as 5.6.

0.00005.6
5 places

Step 2
Count the number of places you moved the decimal place to the right. Write the power of ten as 10^{-5}. Note that smaller values are written in scientific notation using a negative exponent.

The decimal point moved right 5 places. Use –5 for the exponent.

0.000056 is written **5.6×10^{-5}.**

To change a number from scientific notation, work backward. Move the decimal point to the right for a positive exponent and to the left for a negative exponent. Add zeros for placeholders as needed.

Remember, if the exponent is positive, the actual number is much larger. If it is negative, the actual number is much smaller.

Examples

3.14×10^7 Move the decimal point 7 places to the right. 3.1400000. (7 places) $3.14 \times 10^7 = 31,400,000$

2.6×10^{-4} Move the decimal point 4 places to the left. .0002.6 (4 places) $2.6 \times 10^{-4} = 0.00026$

Scientific calculators use scientific notation to display any answer that has more than ten digits. Try these operations on a calculator.

Multiply 3,000,000 by 40,000.
Press: 3000000 × 40000 [enter] The display reads: $1.2*10^{11}$

Divide 0.00029 by 1,000,000.
Press: .00029 ÷ 1000000 [enter] The display reads: $2.9*10^{-10}$

Write these numbers in scientific notation.

1.	19,000	735,000	6,400,000
2.	35,000,000	560,000,000	0.0035
3.	0.00048	0.000005	0.0000000014

Change these numbers from scientific notation to regular form.

4.	8.1×10^4	6.314×10^6	1.85×10^3
5.	2.5×10^5	3.6×10^1	9.1×10^{-5}
6.	7.42×10^{-7}	1.4×10^{-3}	2.7×10^{-2}

Solve as directed.

7. The surface area of Earth is about 1.97×10^8 square miles. Write the number in standard notation.

8. Earth orbits the sun at a rate of about 6.7×10^4 miles per hour. Write the number in standard notation.

9. The average distance from Earth to the moon is 2.39×10^5 miles. Write the number in standard notation.

10. A grain of sand is about 2.1×10^{-5} meters in diameter. Write the number in standard notation.

Answers start on page 185.

SIMPLIFYING RADICALS

A **radical** is an expression that contains the symbol $\sqrt{}$. You already know how to simplify some radicals.

Example $\sqrt{81} = 9$ because $9 \times 9 = 9^2 = 81$.

You can find the square root of 81 because 81 is a **perfect square.** A perfect square is formed when you raise a number to the second power. The first 12 perfect squares are 1, 4, 9, 16, 25, 36, 49, 64, 81, 100, 121, and 144.

Most numbers are not perfect squares. Without a calculator, you may not be able to find the exact value, but you can estimate the value.

Example Estimate the value of $\sqrt{70}$.

$\sqrt{70}$ is between $\sqrt{64}$ and $\sqrt{81}$. You know that $\sqrt{64} = 8$ and $\sqrt{81} = 9$, so you can conclude that the value of $\sqrt{70}$ is **between 8 and 9.**

As you continue learning about algebra, you will need to be able to write a radical in simplest form. You should memorize the properties in the box below. The properties are true only for numbers that are greater than or equal to zero.

Properties of Square Roots $a \geq 0$ and $b \geq 0$

Product property $\sqrt{ab} = \sqrt{a} \times \sqrt{b}$

Quotient property $\sqrt{\frac{a}{b}} = \frac{\sqrt{a}}{\sqrt{b}}$

SIMPLIFYING EXPRESSIONS WITH RADICALS

Example Write $\sqrt{54}$ in simplest form.

Step 1
Use the product property. Factor the number inside. Look for a perfect square factor.

$\sqrt{54} = \sqrt{9} \times \sqrt{6}$

Step 2
Find the square root of the perfect square: $\sqrt{9} = 3$
Write it outside the bracket. $3\sqrt{6}$ means $3 \times \sqrt{6}$

$3\sqrt{6}$

The expressions $\sqrt{54}$ and $3\sqrt{6}$ have equal value.

Example Write $\sqrt{\frac{7}{25}}$ in simplest form.

Step 1
Use the quotient property. Write the quotient using two radicals.

$\sqrt{\frac{7}{25}} = \frac{\sqrt{7}}{\sqrt{25}}$

Step 2
Find the square root of the perfect square: $\sqrt{25} = 5$

$\frac{\sqrt{7}}{5}$ or $\frac{1}{5}\sqrt{7}$

The expressions $\sqrt{\frac{7}{25}}$ and $\frac{1}{5}\sqrt{7}$ have equal value.

A scientific calculator can be used to simplify radicals and to find their value.

Example Simplify $\sqrt{72}$ and find its value to the nearest tenth.

Simplify the expression. Press: [2nd] $\sqrt{\ }$ 72 [enter]

The display reads: $\sqrt{72}$ $6\sqrt{2}$

Find its value. There is no need to re-enter the information from the first step.

Press: [◄ ►]

The display adds a new line: $\sqrt{72}$ $6\sqrt{2}$
$6\sqrt{2}$ ◄►
8.485281374

The expression $\sqrt{72}$ is equal to $6\sqrt{2}$ and rounds to **8.5.**

Estimate the approximate value of each radical expression.

1. $\sqrt{30}$ is between
A. 3 and 4
B. 4 and 5
C. 5 and 6
D. 6 and 7

2. $\sqrt{120}$ is between
A. 10 and 11
B. 11 and 12
C. 12 and 13
D. 13 and 14

3. $\sqrt{95}$ is between
A. 8 and 9
B. 9 and 10
C. 10 and 11
D. 11 and 12

Simplify each expression. Do not use a calculator. The first one is done for you.

4. $\sqrt{63}$ $\sqrt{8}$ $\sqrt{32}$

5. $\sqrt{45}$ $\sqrt{24}$ $\sqrt{112}$

6. $\sqrt{80}$ $\sqrt{50}$ $\sqrt{175}$

7. $\sqrt{810}$ $\sqrt{108}$ $\sqrt{900}$

Use a calculator to simplify each radical and find the value to the nearest tenth.

8. $\sqrt{304}$ $\sqrt{5,202}$ $\sqrt{1,152}$

9. $\sqrt{1,587}$ $\sqrt{1,440}$ $\sqrt{3,920}$

Answers start on page 185.

Mixed Review

Write each statement using mathematical symbols.

1. The difference of 13 and 5 times a number is 29.

2. The quotient of 25 and the sum of 3 and a number.

3. The sum of 6 and the product of 12 and a number is equal to 31.

4. The product of 2 and the sum of a number and 8.

5. 15 less than the quotient of a number and 3.

6. The quotient when 7 times *n* is divided by 11 less than *n*.

Evaluate.

7. Find the value of $a - (b^2 + c)$ when $a = 9$, $b = -2$, and $c = 6$.

8. Find the value of $\frac{xy}{6} \cdot 3y$ when $x = 10$ and $y = 3$.

9. Find the value of $|\ m\ | - (n + 3)^2$ when $m = -17$ and $n = 3$.

10. Find the value of $(7 - x)^4$ when $x = 4$.

11. Find the value of $2(m + (m - n)^2)$ when $m = -8$ and $n = -2$.

12. Find the value of $b - 4 \cdot |\ \frac{a}{3+c}\ |$ when $a = -21$, $b = 5$, and $c = 0$.

Simplify each expression.

13. $x^5 \cdot x^2$ $\qquad (3^3)^6 \qquad a^4 \div a^1$

14. $\frac{2^7}{2^3 \cdot 2^0}$ $\qquad \frac{(x^5)^4}{x^{12}} \qquad \left(\frac{b^1}{c^4}\right)^2$

15. $(2m^0n^3)^3$ $\qquad (3k^2)^0 \qquad \frac{4y^2 \cdot (2y)^3}{8y^5}$

16. $\frac{1}{3^{-3}}$ $\qquad x^3y^{-2} \cdot x^{-4}y^2 \qquad \left(\frac{m^{-4}}{m^{-5}}\right)^{-1}$

Use the triangle to solve problems 17–19.

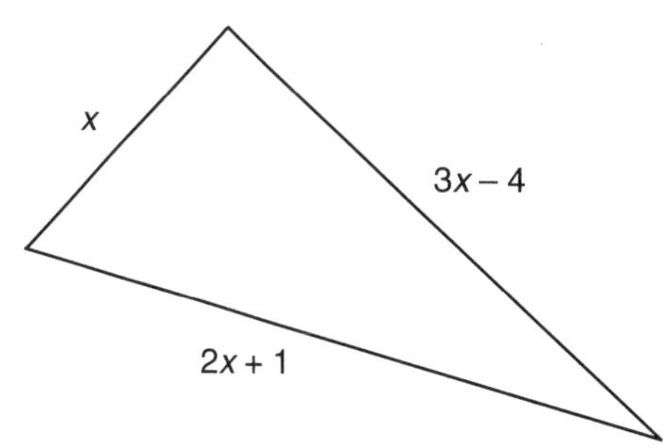

17. Write an addition expression for the perimeter of the triangle.

18. Simplify the expression.

19. Find the value of the perimeter when $x = 4$.

Solve as directed.

20. Jalen cuts 3 lengths of ribbon. The first piece is n inches long. The second piece is twice as long as the first piece. The third piece is 6 inches shorter than the second piece.

a. Write an expression for the third length of ribbon.

b. Simplify an expression that shows the total length of the three pieces.

21. The area of Mexico is about 1,970,000 square miles. Express this number in scientific notation.

22. The diameter of a virus is 2.7×10^{-8} meters. Write this number in standard notation.

23. Mercury's maximum distance from the sun is about 4.35×10^{7} miles. Write this number in standard notation.

24. A human hair is about 0.00254 centimeters thick. Write this number in scientific notation.

25. Simplify the expression $-5k + 4m - k + 15 + 8m$.

26. Evaluate $4m^3n^1 \cdot 6m^{-6}n^5$ when $m = 4$ and $n = -1$.

27. Simplify the expression $9a - 14 - 15a - 8$.

Write in simplest form.

28. $\sqrt{72}$ $\sqrt{96}$ $\sqrt{120}$

29. $\sqrt{\frac{5}{36}}$ $\sqrt{\frac{16}{49}}$ $\sqrt{\frac{21}{144}}$

30. $\sqrt{117}$ $\sqrt{200}$ $\sqrt{192}$

Answers start on page 185.

READING AND WRITING EQUATIONS

Algebra is a language you can use to describe operations with numbers even when some of the numbers are unknown. Good test takers are comfortable reading and writing equations. In this lesson, you will explore the relationship between words and the symbols of algebra.

Example A number increased by seven is twelve.
$x \quad + \quad 7 \quad = \quad 12$

The number sentence $x + 7 = 12$ is an equation. An **equation** is a mathematical statement that two expressions are equal. The = sign separates the two sides of the equation.

$x + 7$	=	12
left side	equal sign	right side

In this equation, the letter x represents an unknown number. Letters used in equations are called **variables.** Any letter can be used as a variable. Study the next examples carefully. Notice how the word *is* corresponds to the = sign.

Verbal Expressions	**Algebra**
The product of five and a number is thirty.	$5c = 30$
Ten less than a number is three.	$y - 10 = 3$
A number divided by eight is seven.	$\frac{a}{8} = 7$
Fifteen increased by a number is twenty.	$15 + w = 20$
Ten decreased by a number is four.	$10 - n = 4$
Three times a number decreased by five is thirteen.	$3m - 5 = 13$

Choose the correct equation for each problem.

1. Twelve less than a number is twenty-five.
A. $12 - x = 25$ B. $x - 12 = 25$ C. $25 - x = 12$ D. $12x = 25$

2. Sixty divided by a number is fifteen.
A. $\frac{60}{n} = 15$ B. $\frac{n}{15} = 60$ C. $\frac{n}{60} = 15$ D. $\frac{60}{15} = n$

3. A number increased by nine is twenty.
A. $9a = 20$ B. $20 + a = 9$ C. $a + 9 = 20$ D. $a - 9 = 20$

4. Two less than three times a number is ten.

A. $3w - 2 = 10$ B. $2 - 3w = 10$ C. $3 - 2w = 10$ D. $3(w - 2) = 10$

5. The product of five and a number increased by two is twelve.

A. $2b + 5 = 12$ B. $5b + 2 = 12$ C. $b + 2 + 5 = 12$ D. $5(2) + b = 12$

6. Ten divided by a number is three decreased by that number.

A. $\frac{10}{z} = 3 - z$ B. $\frac{z}{10} = z - 3$ C. $\frac{10}{2} = 3 - z$ D. $\frac{10}{z} = z - 3$

Write a verbal expression for each equation.

7. $5 + x = 8$ ______________________________

8. $\frac{12}{d} = 6$ ______________________________

9. $4y - 5 = 7$ ______________________________

Choose an equation for each situation described below.

10. Warren has \$320 in his checking account. After making a deposit (d), he has \$400 in the account.

A. $\$320d = \$400$

B. $\$320 + d = \$400$

C. $\$320 - d = \$400$

D. $\$320 + \$400 = d$

11. Four times the measure of the side (s) of a square equals a perimeter of 12 inches.

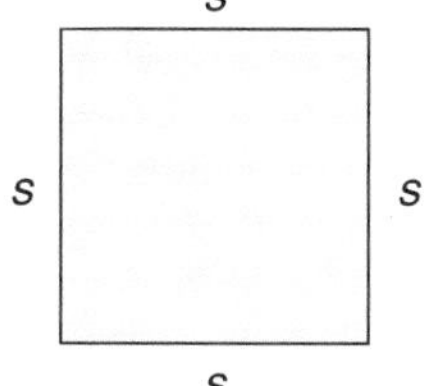

A. $\frac{4}{s} = 12$

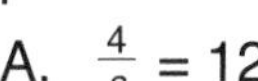

B. $4 + s = 12$

C. $4s = 12$

D. $4 = 12s$

12. The sale price of a coat, which is \$85, is \$35 less than the original price (p).

A. $p + \$35 = \$85$

B. $p - \$35 = \$85$

C. $\$35 - p = \$85$

D. $\$85 - \$35 = p$

13. Socks sell for \$1.15 per pair. The total cost before tax for a number of pairs (n) of socks is \$5.75.

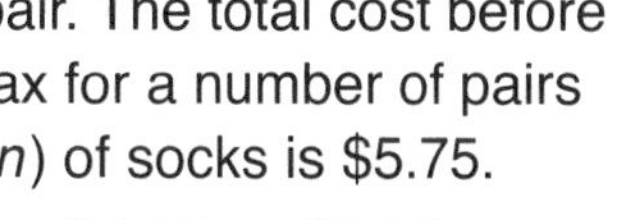

A. $\$1.15n = \$5.75$

B. $\$1.15 + n = \$5.75$

C. $\frac{\$1.15}{n} = \$5.75$

D. $\$5.75n = \$1.15$

14. For her job, LeeAnn drove the same distance (d) each day for 5 days for a total distance of 1,650 miles.

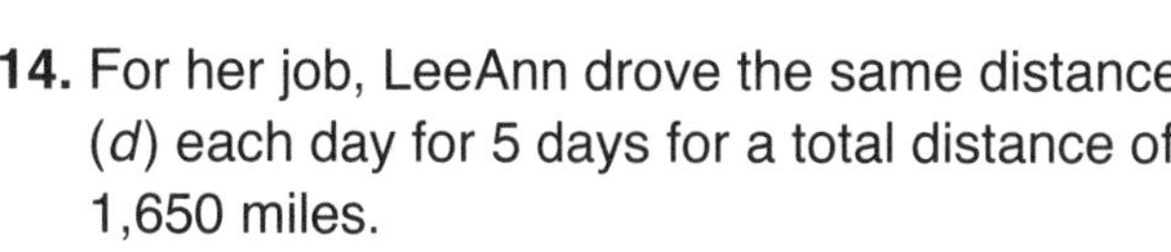

A. $5d = 1{,}650$

B. $5 + d = 1{,}650$

C. $\frac{5}{d} = 1{,}650$

D. $5(1{,}650) = d$

15. **Explain** Two students, Sam and Jin, are given this situation: The \$120 charge for repairs is \$30 more than twice the worker's hourly rate (r). Sam writes the equation $\$120 = \$30 + 2r$. Jin writes the equation $2r + \$30 = \$120$. Explain why both students are correct.

Answers start on page 186.

SOLVING ADDITION AND SUBTRACTION EQUATIONS

Think about this equation: $5 + x = 9$. Since you know that the sum of 5 and 4 is 9, you know the value of x must be 4. It is not difficult to see the solution to an equation with small whole numbers and one operation. But to find the solution to a complicated equation, you need a method.

An equation is solved when you find the value for the variable.

A solution can take either of these forms:

x	=	10	or	10	=	x
unknown		value		value		unknown

To solve an equation, you want to get the variable alone on one side of the equal sign. To do this, use inverse operations.

For example, if you have \$100 in savings and you spend \$20 (subtract), how do you get back to your original balance? You must deposit (add) \$20.

Addition and subtraction are inverse operations. If you subtract 20, you can undo the operation by adding 20.

The important thing to remember is that whatever you do to one side of an equation, you need to do the same to the other side to keep things equal. Think of an equation as a balance scale that must be balanced.

USING INVERSE OPERATIONS

Example 1 Solve for y in the equation $y + 16 = 64$.

Think: You want to get y alone. The operation in the equation is addition. The inverse of addition is subtraction.

Do: Subtract 16 from both sides.

$$\begin{aligned} y + 16 &= 64 \\ -16 \quad & \quad -16 \\ y \quad &= 48 \end{aligned}$$

The solution is ***y* = 48.**

Check: Substitute 48 for y in the equation.

$$\begin{aligned} 48 + 16 &= 64 \\ 64 &= 64 \end{aligned}$$

Example 2 Solve for n in the equation $3.25 = 2.4 + n - 9.2$.

Think: You want to get n alone.

First, combine like terms: $2.4 - 9.2 = -6.8$
The operation in the equation is subtraction.
The inverse operation is addition.

Do: Add 6.8 to both sides.

$$\begin{aligned} 3.25 &= n - 6.8 \\ +6.8 \quad & \quad +6.8 \\ 10.05 &= n \end{aligned}$$

The solution is ***n* = 10.05.**

Check: Substitute 10.05 for n in the equation.

$$\begin{aligned} 3.25 &= 2.4 + 10.05 - 9.2 \\ 3.25 &= 3.25 \end{aligned}$$

Solve and check each equation.

1. $a - 15 = 78$ | $5.3 = x + 0.6$ | $532 = 189 + n$

2. $b + 3\frac{1}{2} = 9$ | $10 = w - 8.2$ | $d - 11 = 33$

3. $x + 6.4 = 100$ | $1{,}050 + g = 8{,}000$ | $9\frac{1}{2} = y - 3\frac{1}{2}$

Simplify each equation by combining numerical terms. Then solve the equation. The first one is started for you.

4. $c + 28 - 7 = 84$ | $h + 1.5 + 8.75 = 12.5$

   $c + 21 = 84$

5. $95 - 25 + 15 + x = 105$ | $5.375 = e - 0.9 + 2.05$

6. $7 + x - (-10) = 46$ | $-18.1 = 2.9 + x - 2.4$

For each problem below, first write an equation. Then solve for the unknown.

7. According to the map below, Leon has driven 265 miles of a 770-mile trip. Let *m* equal the remaining miles he has to drive. Solve for *m*.

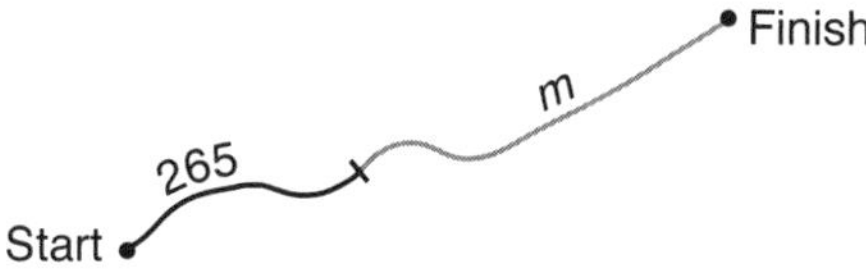

9. The perimeter (distance around) the triangle shown below is 6.5 centimeters. What is the measure of side *a*?

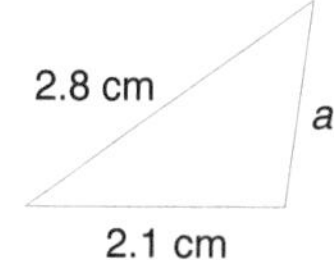

8. Nita earns \$580 per week. The total of her and her husband Craig's weekly salaries is \$1,124. Let c equal Craig's weekly earnings. How much does Craig earn per week?

10. Explain The difference between the high and low temperatures for Provo on January 9 was 24°. The high temperature was 18°F. Let *l* represent the low temperature. Explain how you know that *l* will be a negative number. Solve for *l*.

Answers start on page 186.

SOLVING MULTIPLICATION AND DIVISION EQUATIONS

Multiplication and division are opposite operations.

Look at the price tag on the jacket in the drawing. The original price is 3 times the sale price. You can write two equations using this information.

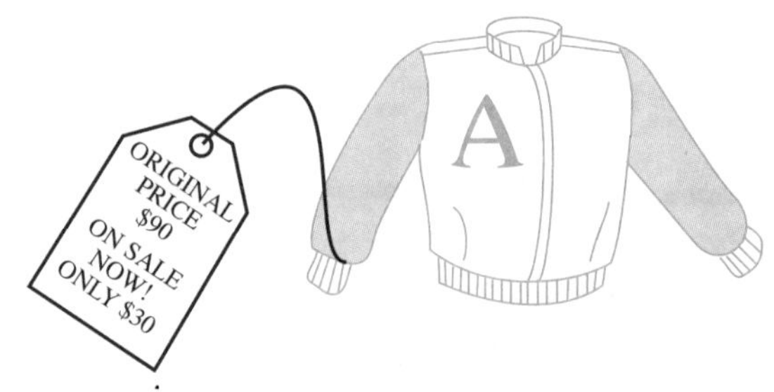

$30 × 3 = $90 $90 ÷ 3 = $30

USING INVERSE OPERATIONS

Example 1 Solve for z in the equation $4z = 32.8$.

Think: You want to get z alone. The operation in the equation is multiplication. The inverse of multiplication is division.

Do: Divide both sides of the equation by 4. (Remember, $4z \div 4 = 1z$ and $1z = z$.)

$\frac{4z}{4} = \frac{32.8}{4}$

$z = 8.2$

The solution is $\boldsymbol{z = 8.2}$.

Check: Substitute 8.2 for z in the equation. $4(8.2) = 32.8$, and $32.8 = 32.8$

Example 2 Solve for t in the equation $15 = -\frac{t}{9}$.

Think: You want to get t alone. The operation in the equation is division. The inverse operation is multiplication.

Do: Multiply both sides by –9.

$15(-9) = (-\frac{t}{9})(-9)$

$-135 = t$

The solution is $\boldsymbol{-135 = t}$.

Check: Substitute –135 for t in the equation. $15 = -(\frac{-135}{9})$, and $15 = 15$

Solve and check each equation.

1.	$\frac{w}{6} = 9$	$12n = 600$	$\frac{z}{16} = 128$
2.	$1.5x = 45$	$\frac{p}{-2} = 56$	$25r = 40$
3.	$50c = 3{,}000$	$\frac{y}{0.5} = 150$	$\frac{h}{32} = -3$
4.	$-126 = -18x$	$\frac{n}{2} = -4$	$-15k = 45$
5.	$2 = \frac{b}{17}$	$-200 = 10c$	$\frac{y}{6} = -9$

Some equations involve fractions. In the equation $\frac{3}{4}x = 12$, the variable x is multiplied by a fraction. Normally, you would divide to undo multiplication. With fractions, multiply by the **reciprocal.** The reciprocal is the number you multiply a fraction by to get a product of 1. The reciprocal of a fraction is found by switching the numerator and the denominator.

Examples The reciprocal of $\frac{1}{3}$ is 3 because $\frac{1}{3} \cdot \frac{3}{1} = \frac{3}{3} = 1$.

The reciprocal of $\frac{3}{4}$ is $\frac{4}{3}$ because $\frac{3}{4} \cdot \frac{4}{3} = \frac{12}{12} = 1$.

You can use reciprocals to solve problems.

USING RECIPROCALS

Example Solve for a in the equation $\frac{3}{5}a = 30$.

Step 1
Multiply both sides by the reciprocal of $\frac{3}{5}$. The reciprocal of $\frac{3}{5}$ is $\frac{5}{3}$.

$$\frac{3}{5}a = 30$$
$$\frac{5}{3} \cdot \frac{3}{5}a = 30 \cdot \frac{5}{3}$$
$$\frac{15}{15}a = \frac{150}{3}$$
$$a = \mathbf{50}$$

Step 2
Check.

$$\frac{3}{5}a = 30$$
$$\frac{3}{5} \cdot 50 = 30$$
$$\frac{150}{5} = 30$$
$$30 = 30$$

Solve and check each equation.

6. $\frac{2}{3}n = 12$ $\frac{2}{5}y = 10$ $-\frac{4}{9}b = -16$

7. $\frac{3}{7}a = -45$ $\frac{7}{10}b = 56$ $\frac{1}{4}m = -9$

Write an equation and solve for the variable.

8. Haskell paid \$6.72 for 6 pens. How much did he pay per pen? (***Hint:*** Total cost equals the number of items multiplied by the price for one item.)

9. A number divided by –5 is 4. What is the number?

10. **Explain** Emily says you can solve the equation below using multiplication. Is it possible? Explain your thinking.

$4a = -32$

Answers start on page 186.

SOLVING MULTISTEP EQUATIONS

Some problems require more than one inverse operation to find a solution. When an equation uses more than one operation, reverse the order of operations. In most situations, undo addition or subtraction first. Then undo multiplication or division.

An equation is like a balance scale. If you perform the exact same operation on both sides of the equation, the two sides will remain balanced. The balance scale shows the equation $3x + 5 = 26$.

To solve, first subtract 5 from both sides of the equation.

$3x + 5 - 5 = 3x$ $\qquad 26 - 5 = 21$

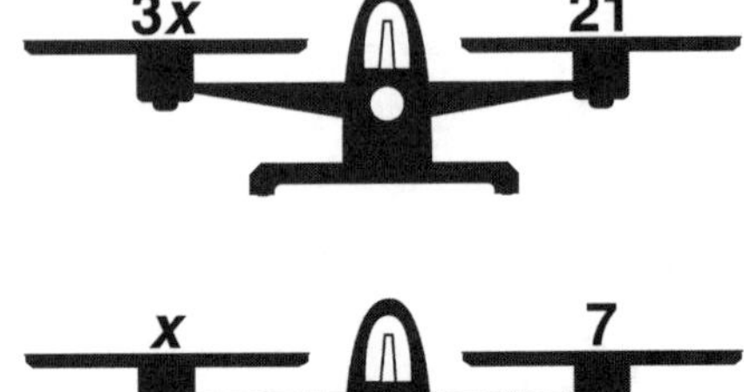

Next, divide both sides by 3.

$\frac{3x}{3} = x$ $\qquad \frac{21}{3} = 7$

The value of x is **7.**

Remember, the goal in solving an equation is to isolate the variable on one side of the equation. Keep the equation balanced by always performing the same operation on both sides of the equation.

USING TWO INVERSE OPERATIONS

Example Solve for x: $9 = \frac{x}{4} + 7$

Step 1
Since 7 is added on the right side of the equation, subtract 7 from both sides.

$9 = \frac{x}{4} + 7$
$9 - 7 = \frac{x}{4} + 7 - 7$

Step 2
The variable is divided by 4, so multiply both sides by 4.

$2 = \frac{x}{4}$
$4 \cdot 2 = 4 \cdot \frac{x}{4}$
$8 = x$

$8 = x$ is the same thing as $x = 8$. The solution is **8.**

Check: $9 = \frac{8}{4} + 7$
$9 = 2 + 7$
$9 = 9$

Solve for the variable in each equation.

1.	$3m + 2 = 62$	$-8 = -3x + 7$	$-3 = \frac{x}{4} - 1$
2.	$4x - 7 = -83$	$4 = 3 + \frac{x}{12}$	$\frac{s}{2} - 9 = -19$
3.	$8x + 1 = -55$	$-1 = 2 + \frac{m}{5}$	$\frac{w}{5} - 3 = 0$
4.	$\frac{b}{2} - 4 = -7$	$-9 - 7x = 5$	$-4n + 9 = -35$
5.	$\frac{a}{3} - 1 = 1$	$10 = 8 - \frac{k}{8}$	$-3 + 7n = 137$
6.	$-8 = -5 + \frac{m}{3}$	$\frac{n}{5} - 9 = -6$	$-3 - 9y = 69$

CORE CONNECTIONS: Working Backward

Not every problem needs to be solved by writing an equation. Some problems can be solved by working backward through the events in the problem.

Example Jenna earned $5 more than twice the amount her brother Greg earned yesterday. If Jenna earned $85, how much did Greg earn?

If you knew Greg's earnings, you could double it and add $5 to find Jenna's earnings. Work backward through the steps.

Step 1
Subtract $5 from Jenna's earnings. $85 – $5 = $80

Step 2
$80 must be 2 times Greg's earnings. Divide by 2. $80 ÷ 2 = $40

Greg must have earned **$40.**

Solve by working backward.

1. A number is increased by 9. The result is multiplied by 3. If the product is 63, what is the number?

2. Kira earns $8 per hour as a cashier. She is saving money to buy a new phone. She has $150 saved so far. If the phone costs $414, how many more hours will she need to work to buy the phone?

Answers start on page 187.

SOLVING EQUATIONS WITH SEPARATED TERMS

In algebraic expressions and equations, terms are separated by addition and subtraction symbols. A term can consist of a number alone, a variable alone, or the product of a number and a variable: 12, y, or $3x$.

Like terms have exactly the same variables. Constants are also like terms. You've already learned how to simplify expressions by combining like terms. Now, you want to simplify the sides of an equation so that you can solve it.

Example Solve: $-6 + 2n = 7n + 1 - 4n$

Step 1
Combine like terms on each side of the equation.

The right side of this equation can be simplified.

$$-6 + 2n = 7n + 1 - 4n$$
$$-6 + 2n = 7n - 4n + 1$$
$$-6 + 2n = 3n + 1$$

Step 2
Isolate the variable on one side of the equation. It doesn't matter which side you choose.

Subtract $2n$ from each side.

$$-6 + 2n = 3n + 1$$
$$-6 + 2n - 2n = 3n - 2n + 1$$
$$-6 = n + 1$$

Subtract 1 from each side.

$$-6 - 1 = n + 1 - 1$$
$$-7 = n$$

$-7 = n$ is the same as $n = -7$.

Substitute -7 for n in the original equation to check.

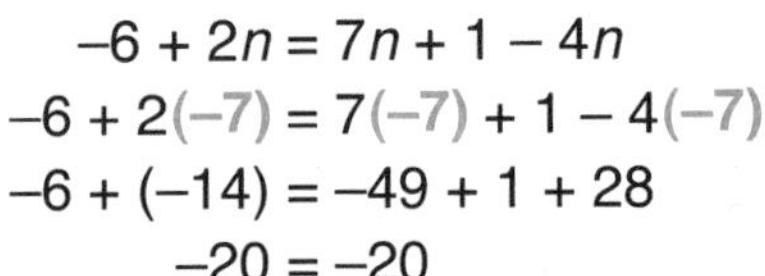

$$-6 + 2n = 7n + 1 - 4n$$
$$-6 + 2(-7) = 7(-7) + 1 - 4(-7)$$
$$-6 + (-14) = -49 + 1 + 28$$
$$-20 = -20$$

The equation checks. The answer is $\boldsymbol{n = -7}$.

Use these steps for solving equations:

1. Simplify each side of the equation.
2. Isolate the variable on one side of the equation using inverse operations.

Students often assume that if an answer is a whole number, then it must be right. They also assume that if the answer is a fraction or a decimal, it must be wrong. These are false assumptions. Many correct answers in real life are fractions or decimals.

The only way to be sure your answer is correct is to substitute your solution into the equation. Good test takers think about whether their answers make sense, and they check their work if they have enough time.

Solve for the variable in each equation. Check your work.

1. $-5x + 7 = 3 - 6x$ $2m - 16 - m = -m - 6$ $-19 + 5a = -40 + 8a$

2. $1 - 5k = 10k - 14$ $10 - 5c + 21 = 3c + 7$ $2 + 10x = 9x - 16 - 7$

3. $5b + 30 = -b$ $12 + 7p = 2p + 4 + p$ $8 - 6m = 5 - 18m + 3$

4. $20 + a - 33 = 3 + 9a$ $25 + 30d = d - 19 + 7d$ $21 + 2n = 4n - 63 + 5n$

5. $52 + 5x = 12x - 4$ $-2a + 60 + 2a = -8a + 140$ $13n + 9 = 14n + 104 - 96n$

CORE CONNECTIONS: Apply a Rule

Algebra provides a way to write a rule that can be applied to numbers. For example, the expression $5n - 9$ tells you to multiply a number by 5 and then subtract 9. In the chart below, the rule in the second row is applied to different values for n.

Values for *n*	1	2	3	4	5	6
Rule: 5*n* – 9	–4	1	6	11	16	21

Rules create patterns. Notice that the numbers in the second row increase by the same number. The pattern shows that you have applied the rule correctly.

Apply the rule to complete each chart.

1.

Values for *n*	5	6	7	8	9	10
Rule: 4*n* + 7						

2.

Values for *n*	–2	–1	0	1	2	3
Rule: 9*n* + (–*n*) – 1						

Answers start on page 188.

SOLVING EQUATIONS WITH PARENTHESES

When an equation contains parentheses, you must remove them before you can solve the equation. On page 24, you learned about the distributive property. Use the distributive property to remove parentheses and other grouping symbols.

REMOVING PARENTHESES IN AN EQUATION

Example Solve for *m*. $4 - 3m = 2m + 7(m - 8)$

As it is written, $7(m - 8)$ is a product. You need to separate the product into terms so that you can combine like terms and use inverse operations to solve the equation.

Step 1
Use the distributive property.

$4 - 3m = 2m + 7(m - 8)$
$4 - 3m = 2m + 7m - 56$

Step 2
Combine like terms.

$4 - 3m = 2m + 7m - 56$
$4 - 3m = 9m - 56$

Step 3

Use inverse operations.	$4 - 3m = 9m - 56$
Add $3m$ to both sides.	$4 = 12m - 56$
Add 56 to both sides.	$60 = 12m$
Divide both sides by 12.	$5 = m$

The solution to the equation is $\boldsymbol{m = 5}$.

Don't be fooled when you see a subtraction sign before parentheses. To find the value of an expression like $-(x - 3)$, imagine there is a 1 before the parentheses. Then multiply the terms in the parentheses by -1. $-(x - 3) = -1(x - 3) = -x + 3$

Solve.

1. $8(x + 5) = 96$ $\quad$ $-6(6y - 1) = -102$ $\quad$ $2(4 - 6k) = 92$

2. $2 + 4(1 - 3a) = 42$ $\quad$ $4(3n + 3) + 2 = 50$ $\quad$ $-64 = 4(-3m - 4)$

3. $4(1 - d) = 3(d - 1)$ $\quad$ $2(4 - m) + 4m = -(2 + 3m)$

4. $4(m + 5) = 2(m - 1)$ $\quad$ $4(3 - 2x) + 2 = -6(x + 1)$

A fraction bar is another kind of grouping symbol. You can eliminate a fraction by multiplying both sides of the equation by the denominator of the fraction.

WORKING WITH A FRACTION BAR

Example Solve for *x*. $\frac{3(8x-1)}{5} = x + 7$

Step 1
Use the distributive property to eliminate the parentheses in the numerator.

$$\frac{3(8x-1)}{5} = x + 7$$
$$\frac{24x-3}{5} = x + 7$$

Step 2
The denominator is 5. Multiply both sides of the equation by 5. The 5s cancel. Use the distributive property on the right side of the equation.

$$\frac{\cancel{5}}{1} \cdot \left(\frac{24x-3}{\cancel{5}}\right) = 5(x + 7)$$
$$24x - 3 = 5x + 35$$

Step 3
Use inverse operations.
Add 3 to both sides.
Subtract 5*x* from both sides.
Divide both sides by 19.

$$24x - 3 = 5x + 35$$
$$24x = 5x + 38$$
$$19x = 38$$
$$x = 2$$

The solution to the equation is $\boldsymbol{x = 2}$.

Solve.

5. $\frac{3m+1}{2} = 2m + 1$ $\qquad$ $n + 3 = \frac{8n}{5}$ $\qquad$ $\frac{-3a-11}{7} = a - 3$

6. $\frac{7-5x}{-3} = x - 7$ $\qquad$ $6p + 8 = \frac{2(p-12)}{7}$ $\qquad$ $\frac{1+n}{2} = 2(n + 4)$

7. $\frac{3k+5}{2} = 6k - 2$ $\qquad$ $-8m + 5 = \frac{30+m}{6}$ $\qquad$ $4 + b = \frac{b+9}{2}$

8. $\frac{7(n-4)}{2} = n - 4$ $\qquad$ $a + 10 = \frac{a+40}{6}$ $\qquad$ $5(1 - x) = \frac{5(x+3)}{-3}$

Answers start on page 189.

GRAPHING INEQUALITIES

You have already used four symbols to compare numbers.

$5 > 3$ means 5 is greater than 3.
$-4 < -1$ means -4 is less than -1.
$5 \geq -1$ means 5 is greater than or equal to -1.
$-1 \leq 3$ means -1 is less than or equal to 3.

TIP
Think of the symbol as an arrow that points to the smaller number.

You can easily determine that these statements are true. Compare their locations on the number line. Values to the right are greater than values to the left.

When an inequality contains a variable, the variable represents a range of values.

Think about the statement $x < 3$. The variable x represents a value that is less than 3. There are many values that will make the statement true. The variable could represent 2, 0, –50, or even a fractional quantity such as $\frac{1}{2}$ or 1.75.

The **solution set** of an inequality is the set of all the values that can make the inequality true. One way to show a solution set is to graph it on a number line.

GRAPHING AN INEQUALITY

1. Draw a circle on the number line to represent the number in the inequality. Draw an *open circle* if the number is not a solution. Draw a *closed circle* if the number is a solution.
2. Darken the line and the arrow to show that all the values in that direction are solutions.

Example	Graph	Explanation
$x < 4$	0 4	4 is not a solution.
$x > -1$	–1 0	–1 is not a solution.
$x \geq 0$	0	0 is a solution.
$x \leq 3$	0 3	3 is a solution.

Graph each inequality.

1. $x \geq 1$ 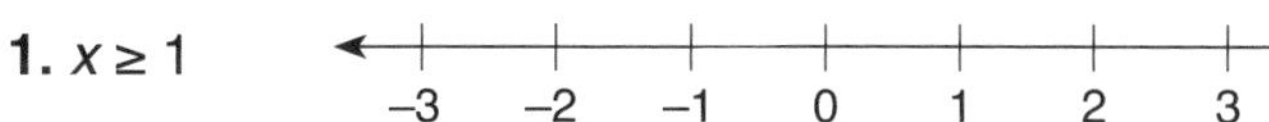

4. $x < 3$ 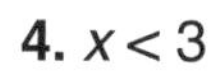
–3 –2 –1 0 1 2 3

2. $x < -2$
–3 –2 –1 0 1 2 3

5. $x \geq -1$
–3 –2 –1 0 1 2 3

3. $x \geq 0$
–3 –2 –1 0 1 2 3

6. $x > 0$ 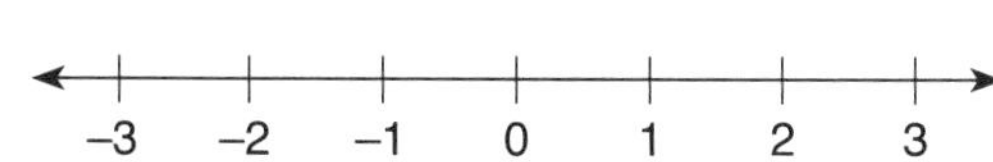

Decide whether each given value is within the solution set of the inequality shown on the graph. Write Yes or No.

7. –4 –3 –2 –1 0 1 2 3 4
   a. –2 b. 10 c. –1

8. –4 –3 –2 –1 0 1 2 3 4
   a. 1 b. –5 c. 0

9. –4 –3 –2 –1 0 1 2 3 4
   a. –3 b. –4 c. 7

10. Explain Compare the graphs in problems 7–9. Are there any values that would belong in all three solution sets? Explain your thinking.

A **compound inequality** combines two inequalities. Suppose a friend says that a restaurant has meals ranging in cost from \$8 to \$15. You would expect the cost to be greater than or equal to \$8 ($c \geq 8$) and less than or equal to \$15 ($c \leq \$15$). You can put both ideas in the same inequality: $\$8 \leq c \leq \$15$

Study the table below to understand the two kinds of compound inequalities.

Example	Graph	Explanation
$-1 < x \leq 4$	–4 –3 –2 –1 0 1 2 3 4	*x* is both greater than –1 AND less than or equal to 4.
$x > 2$ or $x < -2$	–4 –3 –2 –1 0 1 2 3 4	*x* is either greater than 2 OR less than –2. It can't be both.

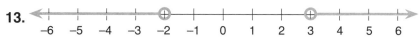

Write a compound inequality to match the information on the graph.

11. 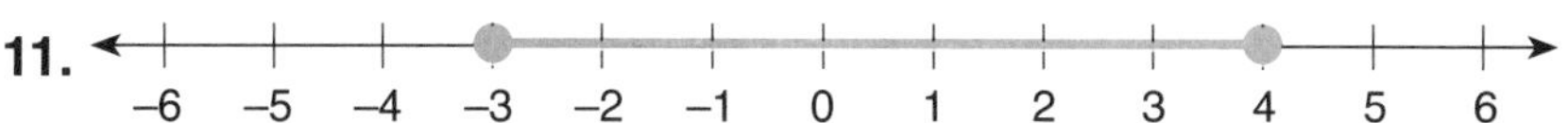

12. –6 –5 –4 –3 –2 –1 0 1 2 3 4 5 6

13. –6 –5 –4 –3 –2 –1 0 1 2 3 4 5 6

14. 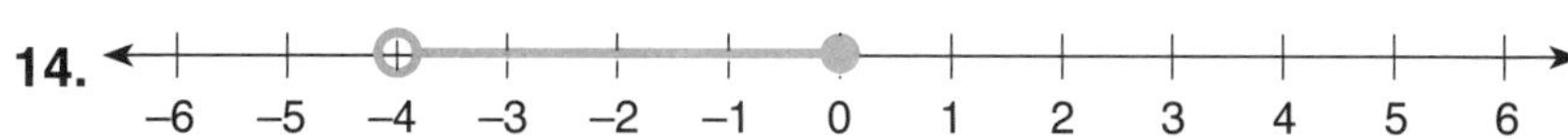

Answers start on page 190.

SOLVING INEQUALITIES

Solving inequalities is much like solving equations. The goal is to use inverse operations to isolate the variable on one side of the inequality.

There is one difference. If you multiply or divide both sides by a negative number, you must change the direction of the inequality symbol.

Can you see why? This statement is true: $7 > 4$
Now multiply both sides by –1. The statement is now false: $-7 > -4$
To make it true, flip the sign: $-7 > -4$ becomes $-7 < -4$.

SOLVING INEQUALITIES

Example 1 Solve: $4x - 7 > 5$

Step 1
Add 7 to both sides.

$$4x - 7 + 7 > 5 + 7$$

$$4x > 12$$

Step 2
Divide both sides by 4.

$$\frac{4x}{4} > \frac{12}{4}$$

The solution is ***x* > 3.**

$$x > 3$$

Example 2 Solve: $-9x + 8 < 26$

Step 1
Subtract 8 from both sides.

$$-9x + 8 - 8 < 26 - 8$$

$$-9x < 18$$

Step 2
Divide both sides by –9 AND flip the inequality symbol.

$$\frac{-9x}{-9} > \frac{18}{-9}$$

The solution is ***x* > –2.**

$$x > -2$$

Solve each inequality.

1. $8x - 1 < 7$ $5(a + 2) \geq 45$ $18 > 3c + 4 - c$

2. $-2n - 3 > 9$ $4(m - 3) < 20$ $36 \leq 9(y - 6)$

3. $8(m + 2) < 6(m + 5)$ $81 \geq -3(1 - 7x)$ $-2(7n + 2) \geq 108$

4. $17 - 3a > -4(6a + 1)$ $-8n + 2 > 6(7n - 8)$ $-3(1 + 4k) > -7k + 32$

A compound inequality combines two statements. You can use inverse operations to solve compound inequalities. Whatever you do to one part of the inequality, you must do to every part.

A graph of the solution to a compound inequality makes it easier to understand the answer. To make a graph, draw a short line and mark the important numbers from the solution. Then shade the part of the line that contains the solution set.

SOLVING COMPOUND INEQUALITIES

Example 1 $-6 < x + 3 < -4$

Subtract 3 from each part of the inequality. $-6 - 3 < x + 3 - 3 < -4 - 3$

The solution is $\mathbf{-9 < x < -7}$. $-9 < x < -7$

The graph of the solution is:

-9 -7

Example 2 $a + 4 \geq 10$ or $a - 1 < -5$

Solve the inequalities separately.

$a + 4 \geq 10$ $a - 1 < -5$

$a + 4 - 4 \geq 10 - 4$ $a - 1 + 1 < -5 + 1$

The solution is $\mathbf{a \geq 6}$ or $\mathbf{a < -4}$. $a \geq 6$ $a < -4$

The graph of the solution is:

-4 6

Solve and graph the solution set on the number line.

5. $-2 < n + 4 < 9$

$y - 2 \leq -12$ or $-8y < -72$

6. $6 + a \geq 4$ or $-2a \geq 20$

$-3 < n - 5 \leq 2$

7. $0 > -7x \geq -7$

$k - 2 < -2$ or $k - 2 > 7$

8. $\frac{a}{10} \leq 0$ or $a - 6 > 0$

$-5 < \frac{m}{2} < -4$

Answers start on page 190.

TRY THE ANSWER CHOICES

When you answer multiple-choice questions, sometimes it can be easier to check the answer choices than to do the algebra. When you are given an equation or an inequality, use your calculator to test each answer choice. Only one choice will make the equation or inequality true.

TRYING ANSWER CHOICES WITH EQUATIONS

Example Solve for *x*.
$5x - 12 = 2x + 9$

A. 4
B. 7
C. 10
D. 12

Substitute each answer choice for *x* into the equation.

A. $5(4) - 12 = 2(4) + 9$
$20 - 12 = 8 + 9$
$8 \neq 17$

B. $5(7) - 12 = 2(7) + 9$
$35 - 12 = 14 + 9$
$23 = 23$

C. $5(10) - 12 = 2(10) + 9$
$50 - 12 = 20 + 9$
$38 \neq 29$

D. $5(12) - 12 = 2(12) + 9$
$60 - 12 = 24 + 9$
$48 \neq 33$

Only **choice B** makes the equation true.

You can also try the answer choices with word problems. Set up a percent equation, a proportion, or a simple equation and substitute the answer choices for the missing value.

TRYING ANSWER CHOICES WITH WORD PROBLEMS

Example Danielle receives a 15% commission on every sale she makes. At the end of the month, she receives a $510 commission check. What were her total sales for the month?

A. $2,100
B. $2,600
C. $3,400
D. $3,800

Step 1
Set up a percent equation.

$0.15 \times w = \$510$

Step 2
Substitute each answer choice for the whole in the percent equation.

A. $0.15 \times \$2{,}100 = \$315$
B. $0.15 \times \$2{,}600 = \$390$
C. $0.15 \times \$3{,}400 = \$510$
D. $0.15 \times \$3{,}800 = \$570$

Only **choice C** gives the correct answer.

When you're taking a test, you can stop checking answer choices when you find the right one. Remember, you don't have to check the choices in order. If you check choice A and it seems far too low, skip to a higher choice.

Try the answer choices to solve the following problems. You may use a calculator.

1. The sum of a number and 3 divided by 5 is 5. What is the number?
   A. 12
   B. 17
   C. 22
   D. 27

2. A poll says that $\frac{2}{3}$ of grocery store customers buy cereal. On Friday, 460 customers bought cereal. How many customers visited the store on Friday?
   A. 360
   B. 420
   C. 540
   D. 690

3. Devon has scores of 73 and 82 on his first two tests. What score would he need to get on his third test to have an average of 80?
   A. 76
   B. 79
   C. 82
   D. 85

Use the diagram for problem 4.

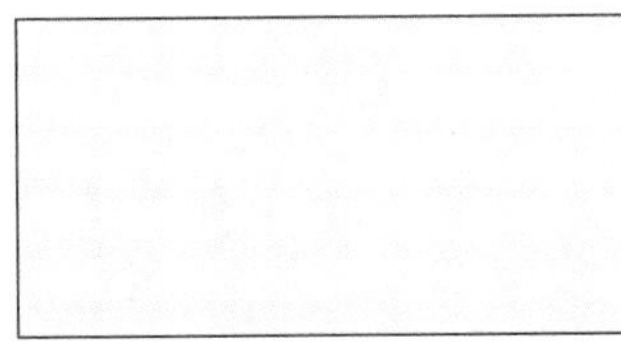

4. The area of the rectangle is 68.44 square centimeters. How many centimeters long is the rectangle? (***Hint:*** The area of a rectangle equals length times width.)
   A. 9.1
   B. 11.6
   C. 12
   D. 13.2

5. Solve: $3(x - 1) + 12 = 24$
   A. 5
   B. 6
   C. 7
   D. 8

6. A can of mixed nuts contains 75% peanuts. If a can has 12 ounces of peanuts, how many total ounces does the can hold?
   A. 12
   B. 14
   C. 16
   D. 18

Use the diagram for problem 7.

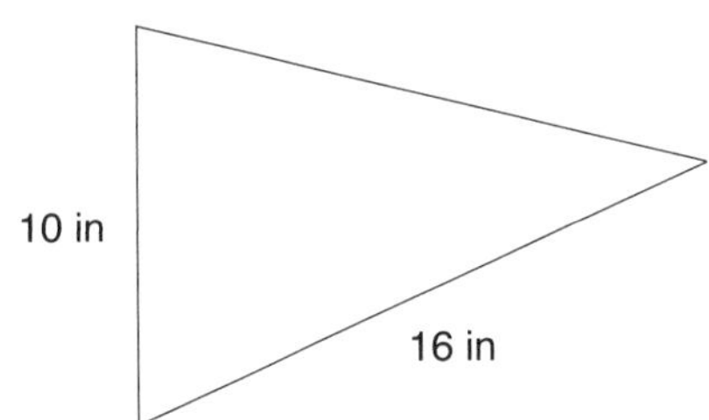

7. The perimeter of the triangle is between 40 and 45 inches. Which of the following could be the measure of the missing side?
   A. 12 in
   B. 15 in
   C. 21 in
   D. 25 in

8. Last week, Chantal received $358.75 in pay. If her hourly rate is $10.25, how many hours did she work?
   A. 25
   B. 30
   C. 35
   D. 40

Answers start on page 191.

Unit 2 Review

Solve the following problems.

1. Solve for x.

   $3(5 - x) + 3 = 6(x - 3)$

   A. 0
   B. 4
   C. 8
   D. 12

2. Choose the correct expression.

   The sum of 17 and the quotient of a number and 9.

   A. $17 + \frac{n}{9}$
   B. $\frac{17 + n}{9}$
   C. $n + \frac{17}{9}$
   D. $9 + \frac{n}{17}$

3. DeAndre spends $45.86 at the grocery store. He pays with a $50 bill. Let c equal his change. Which equation could be used to find the amount of change DeAndre receives?

   A. $\$45.86 - c = \$50$
   B. $c - \$50 = \$45.86$
   C. $\$45.86 + c = \$50$
   D. $\$45.86 + \$50 = c$

4. Solve for y.

   $y + 5 = \frac{2y - 8}{4}$

   A. 2
   B. 6
   C. –8
   D. –14

5. The radius of a hydrogen atom is about 0.000000000025 meters. Which of the following is the number written in scientific notation?

   A. 0.25×10^{-13}
   B. 2.5×10^{-11}
   C. 25×10^{-12}
   D. 250×10^{-10}

6. Rent for an apartment is split between 4 people. If each person pays $610, what is the total rent for the apartment?

   A. $152.50
   B. $610
   C. $1,970
   D. $2,440

Decide whether the values are part of the solution set of the inequality shown on the graph.
Select your answer.

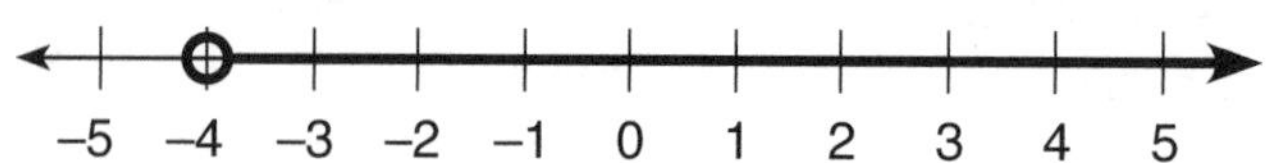

7. 0

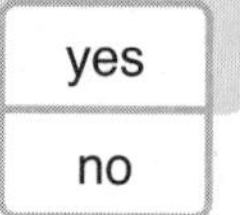

8. –8

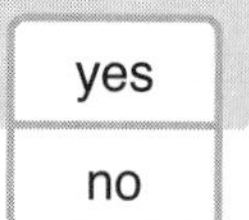

9. –4

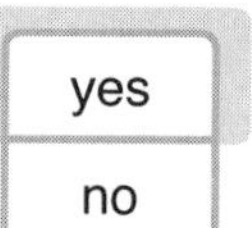

10. 6

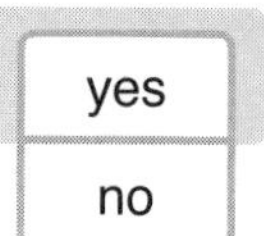

Solve as directed.

11. Solve: $12 = -10 - \frac{x}{2}$

$x =$ 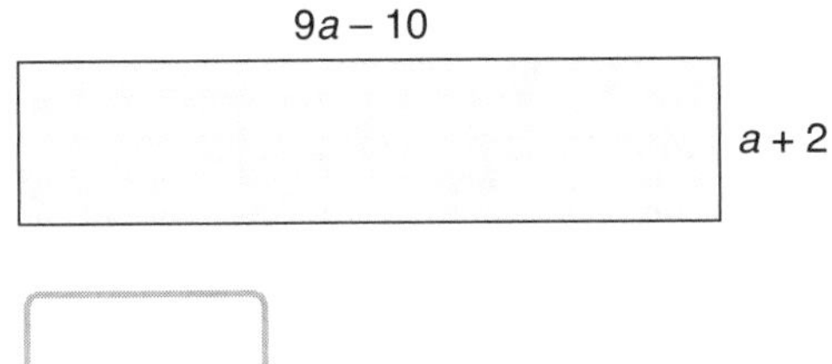

12. Simplify: $\sqrt{900}$

A. $3\sqrt{100}$
B. $10\sqrt{9}$
C. $10\sqrt{90}$
D. 30

13. The perimeter of the rectangle is 64. Find a.

9a – 10

a + 2

$a =$

14. Solve: $-4(y - 1) = 40$

$y =$

15. Solve the inequality, and graph the solution set on the number line.

$-7(x + 3) \geq 4x + 12$

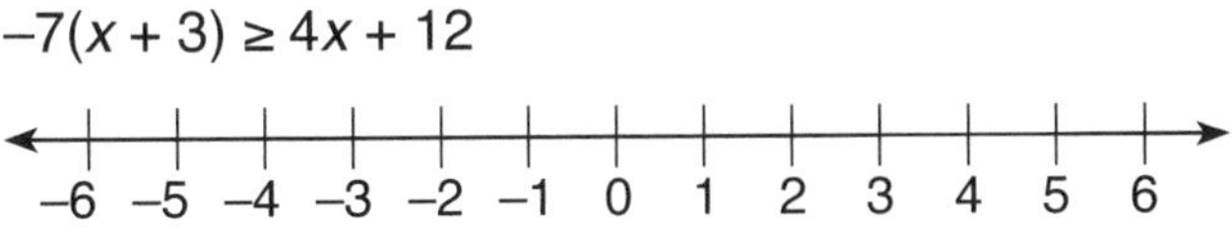

For problems 16 and 17, write an expression using mathematical symbols.

16. 18 less than the product of a number and 9.

17. The sum of 5 times a number and 8.

18. Solve: $5 + 15a = -17 - a - 10$

A. –6
B. –2
C. 1
D. 4

19. Simplify: $\frac{(2x^2y)^4}{(4xy^3)^2}$

A. $\frac{x^6}{y^2}$
B. $\frac{x^4}{y^3}$
C. x^6y^2
D. $16x^{10}y^{10}$

20. Solve: $\frac{2(m-12)}{-5} = -(m + 6)$

$m =$

21. Solve the inequality, and graph the solution set on the number line.

$4 + 5n > 24$

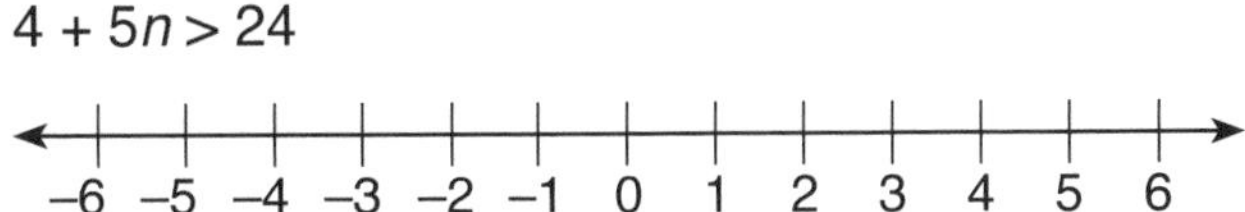

22. A game store expects customers will pay no more than \$60 for the latest video game release. The store must sell the game for at least \$45 to make a profit. Let x be the price of the video game. Write an inequality to represent the range of prices for the video game. Which symbols did you use? Explain your thinking.

Answers start on page 192.

SOLVING PROBLEMS WITH ALGEBRA

SKILLS

- Translating words to equations
- Solving motion, value, and work problems
- Simplifying radicals
- Rewriting formulas

TOOLS AND STRATEGIES

- Solving problems with fractions
- Using inequalities to solve problems
- Using formulas

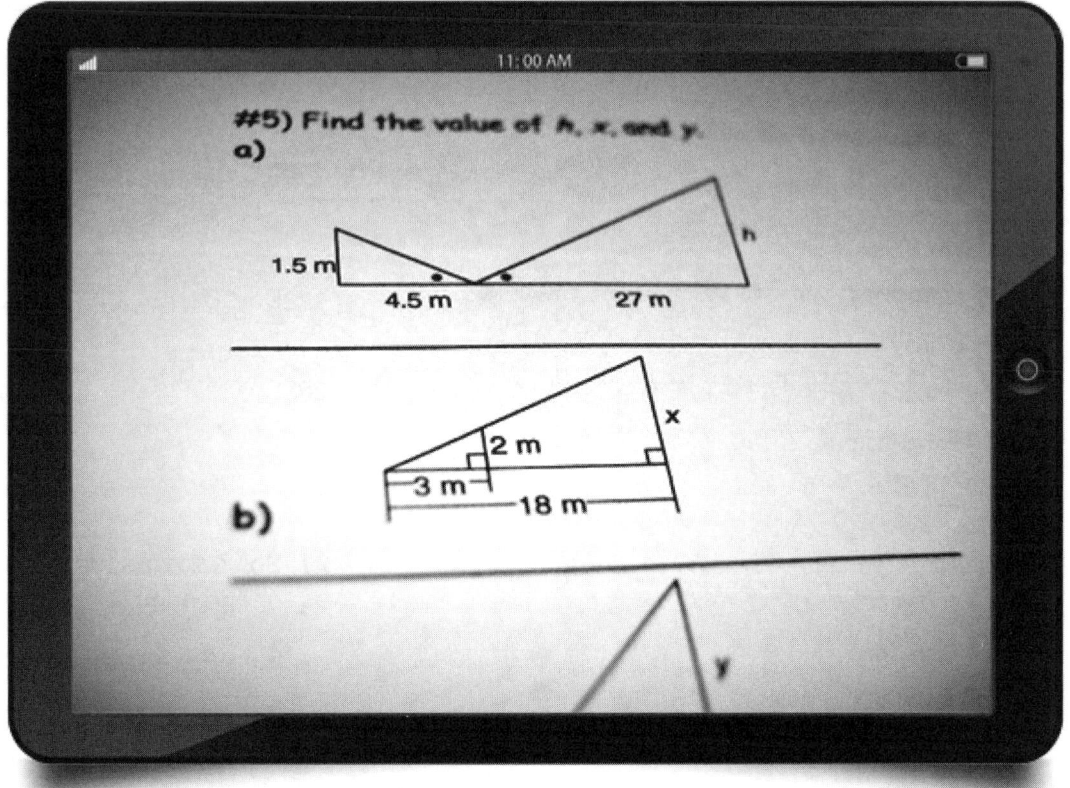

YOU HAVE ALREADY LEARNED how to solve word problems that require you to choose which operations to use. Sometimes, word problems require you to use algebra to find an unknown value.

In this unit, you'll learn how to translate the words in the problem into an equation. Certain types of word problems are very common. You'll learn how to solve each of these types of problems. You'll also learn how to use algebra to rewrite important formulas.

Remember, there isn't one right way to solve a word problem. In this unit, you should learn how to think about word problems and put to use the basics of algebra you've already learned.

USING ALGEBRA IN WORD PROBLEMS

You solve problems with algebra when you:

- Listen to a mathematical explanation and use algebra to take notes
- Use a formula
- Set up a spreadsheet to calculate values
- Write computer programs
- Estimate how long a job will take

Read the following items. Describe some of your experiences in writing or discuss them with a partner.

1. When your math teacher is explaining something, how do you take notes? Do you write down only words? Do you use symbols?

2. Have you ever worked on a project with friends or classmates? How did you figure out how long it would take? How much faster is it to work as a group compared to working alone?

3. When you go shopping, do you set a limit on how much you can spend? How do you decide what your limit should be? If you're buying several items, how do you make sure you stay below your limit?

4. How do you find the value of loose change? Do you organize the coins? Do you count them one by one or in groups?

MATH TALK

Formulas are equations that show the relationship between different variables. Some relationships are so common that memorizing the formulas saves time.

You have probably already learned several formulas. For example, you may have learned the formula to find the area of a rectangle. Make a list of the formulas you have learned. With a partner, describe what each formula says using words.

For example, the formula for the area of a rectangle is $A = bh$. You could explain this formula by saying, "Find the area of a rectangle by multiplying the base by the height. This means the same as multiplying the length by the width."

TRANSLATING WORDS TO EQUATIONS

Word problems tell a story. The words give you the facts you need to solve the problem. The words also show how the facts are related. In an algebra problem, one or more of the numbers are unknown.

For some problems, organizing the information in a chart before writing an equation is helpful. Study the example below to see how to use a chart to write an equation.

USING A CHART TO ORGANIZE INFORMATION

Example Chelsea, Robin, and Dan start a dog obedience school. Because they will not be investing equal amounts of time and money, they will not split the profits evenly. They agree that Robin will receive twice as much as Dan, and Chelsea will receive twice as much as Robin. How much is Robin's share of $3,500?

Step 1
Create a chart showing what you know. You know the least about Dan's share. Let x represent his share. Fill out the rest of the chart using information from the problem.

Dan's Share	Robin's Share (2 times Dan's share)	Chelsea's Share (2 times Robin's share)	Total
x	$2x$	$2(2x)$	$3,500

Step 2
Write an equation based on the chart.

$$x + 2x + 2(2x) = \$3{,}500$$

Step 3
Solve for x.

$$x + 2x + 4x = \$3{,}500$$
$$7x = \$3{,}500$$
$$x = \$500$$

Step 4
Answer the question asked in the problem. You need to find Robin's share. Go back to the chart. Robin's share is represented by $2x$.

Substitute $500 for x: 2($500) = $1,000

Robin's share of $3,500 is **$1,000.**

Check to see whether your answer makes sense. Chelsea earned twice Robin's share, so Chelsea must have earned $2,000. Does the total equal $3,500?

$500 + $1,000 + $2,000 = $3,500   The answer makes sense.

In this unit, you will explore common kinds of word problems. As you explore each type, study how the information is presented and how to organize your work. Then write and solve an equation. Good test takers know that it is impossible to memorize how to do every kind of word problem. Instead, they learn the process that applies to all word problems.

Create a chart for each problem and solve.

1. Ethan, Anna, and Cole work at the same store. Last week, Ethan worked 6 hours more than twice Anna's hours. Cole worked 10 hours more than Anna. Together, they worked 96 hours. How many hours did Ethan work last week?

Ethan	Anna	Cole	Total

2. A board is 104 inches long. Jun needs to cut the board into two pieces so that one piece is 12 inches longer than the other piece. Find the lengths of both pieces.

Piece 1	Piece 2	Total Length

3. In an election, 4,800 people voted for mayor. Ron Reyes received 600 more votes than Barbara Glass. Len Tynan received twice as many votes as Glass. How many votes were for Tynan?

Reyes	Glass	Tynan	Total Votes

4. A washer and dryer combo is on sale for $1,600. Individually, the washer is $60 more than the dryer. What is the price of the dryer?

Washer	Dryer	Total

5. Over a 3-year period, a basketball team won 164 games. The team won 15 more games the second year than it did the first year. The team won 8 more games the third year than the second year. How many games did the team win in the third year?

First Year	Second Year	Third Year	Total Wins

6. Mike is 3 years less than 4 times as old as his son Jacob. The difference in their ages is 33. How old is Jacob? (***Hint:*** Subtract to find the difference between two numbers.)

Mike	Jacob	Difference

7. Rosa and Zoila drove 870 miles in 3 days. They drove 150 more miles the second day than they did the first day. They drove 60 miles less the third day than the first day. How many miles did they drive on the third day?

First Day	Second Day	Third Day	Total Miles

8. The difference of two numbers is 18. The sum of the two numbers is 102. What are the two numbers? (***Hint:*** One number must be 18 more than the other.)

First Number	Second Number	Sum of the Numbers

Answers start on page 193.

NUMBER PUZZLES AND AGE PROBLEMS

A number puzzle gives clues to help you find an unknown number. To solve number puzzles, you need to understand the words that indicate operations.

sum → add   difference → subtract   product → multiply   quotient → divide

SOLVING A NUMBER PUZZLE

Example Twelve less than the product of a number and 3 is 4 more than twice the number. What is the number?

Step 1
Let n equal the unknown number. The clue describes two series of operations that can be performed using n. The word *is* tells us that the results of each series are equal.

Write each part of the sentence as an expression.

- 12 less than the product of a number and 3
  $3n - 12$
- 4 more than twice the number
  $2n + 4$

Step 2
Write and solve an equation.

$$3n - 12 = 2n + 4$$

Add 12 to both sides. $3n - 12 + 12 = 2n + 4 + 12$

$$3n = 2n + 16$$

Subtract $2n$ from both sides. $3n - 2n = 2n - 2n + 16$

$$n = 16$$

The number is **16.**

After finding an answer, good test takers read the problem one more time to make sure the answer makes sense.

Solve.

1. Five times the sum of a number and 11 is 75. What is the number?

2. The sum of three consecutive numbers is 90. What are the numbers? (***Hint:*** Consecutive numbers are in counting order. If the first number is n, the second is $n + 1$, and the third is $n + 2$.)

3. The quotient of a number and 9 is equal to the same number decreased by 40. What is the number?

4. The product of a number and 4 is decreased by 9. The result is 39. What is the number?

5. Barry opens a book. He says, "I'm looking at two pages. The sum of their page numbers is 345. What are the two pages? (***Hint:*** Book pages are consecutive.)

6. Multiplying a number by 8 and decreasing that product by 8 gives the same result as multiplying the number by 5 and adding 10. What is the number?

7. One odd number is 6 more than another odd number. The sum of the numbers is 160. What are the numbers?

Age problems seem tricky because time passes. To organize the information in an age problem, you need a more complex chart.

SOLVING AGE PROBLEMS

Example Fred is 5 times as old as his grandson Joe. In 10 years, the sum of their ages will be 92. How old is Fred now?

Step 1
Make a chart to organize the facts.

- Let x represent Joe's age now.
- Fred's age now is 5 times Joe's.
- In the future, they will each be 10 years older than they are now.

	Age Now	Age in 10 Years
Joe	x	$x + 10$
Fred	$5x$	$5x + 10$

Step 2
Write and solve an equation. The sum of their ages in 10 years will be 92.

$$(x + 10) + (5x + 10) = 92$$
$$6x + 20 = 92$$
$$6x + 20 - 20 = 92 - 20$$
$$6x = 72$$
$$x = 12$$

Step 3
Answer the question.

The variable x equals 12. The question asks for Fred's age now, which is $5x$ Joe's age. Fred is $5(12) = 60$

Fred is **60 years old.**

Solve.

8. Rhonda's age is 2 more than 3 times her son Greg's age. In 9 years, the sum of their ages will be 60. How old will Greg be in 9 years?

	Age Now	Age in 9 Years
Rhonda		
Greg		

9. The sum of the ages of Lucy and her sister Laura is 34. Eight years ago, Lucy's age was half of Laura's age. How old is Lucy now?

10. Samantha is 3 years older than her twin sisters. Next year the sum of the ages of all 3 girls will be 45. How old is Samantha now?

11. The Johnsons' house is 35 years old, and the Moys' house is 25 years old. How many years ago was the Johnsons' house twice as old as the Moys' house? (***Hint:*** The variable is how many years you are subtracting from the ages of the houses.)

	Age Now	Age x Years Ago
Johnsons'	35	$35 - x$
Moys'		

12. In 2 years, Cal and Phil will have worked a total of 50 years in their father's car repair shop. Phil has worked there 6 years longer than Cal has. As of this year, how many years has each of them worked at the shop?

Answers start on page 193.

SOLVING EQUATIONS WITH FRACTIONS AND DECIMALS

Real situations often involve more difficult numbers. The examples below demonstrate useful tips for working with fractions and decimals.

Although you can solve problems using fractions, most problems are easier to solve without them. To eliminate the fractions from a problem, multiply both sides of the equation by the reciprocal of a common denominator.

SOLVING EQUATIONS WITH FRACTIONS

Example $\frac{1}{4} + \frac{5}{2}x = \frac{9}{4}x - 2$

Multiply both sides by 4, or $\frac{4}{1}$.

$$\frac{4}{1} \times (\frac{1}{4} + \frac{5}{2}x) = \frac{4}{1} \times (\frac{9}{4}x - 2)$$

Use the distributive property.

$$(\frac{4}{1} \times \frac{1}{4}) + (\frac{4}{1} \times \frac{5}{2}x) = (\frac{4}{1} \times \frac{9}{4}x) - (4 \times 2)$$

Finish by using inverse operations.

$$1 + 10x = 9x - 8$$
$$1 + x = -8$$
$$x = -9$$

The solution is $\mathbf{x = -9}$.

You can also eliminate the decimals from an equation. Find the decimal with the greatest number of decimal places. Multiply each term by a power of ten with that same number of zeros.

Remember, when multiplying by a power of ten, the number of zeros in the power of ten dictates how many places to move the decimal point to the right.

SOLVING EQUATIONS WITH DECIMALS

Example $5.22 + 0.6n = 1.5n$

The term 5.22 has two decimal places. Multiply both sides by 100 to eliminate the decimals.

$$5.22 + 0.6n = 1.5n$$
$$100 \times (5.22 + 0.6n) = 100 \times 1.5n$$

Use the distributive property.

$$(100 \times 5.22) + (100 \times 0.6n) = 100 \times 1.5n$$

Finish by using inverse operations.

$$522 + 60n = 150n$$
$$522 = 90n$$
$$5.8 = n$$

The solution is $\mathbf{n = 5.8}$.

Eliminate the fractions or decimals and then solve for the variable.

1.	$-\frac{11}{4} = \frac{1}{2}x - \frac{1}{4}$	$\frac{1}{3} + \frac{3}{2}a = \frac{11}{6}$	$\frac{1}{3}m - 1 = -\frac{1}{3}$
2.	$\frac{13}{3} = -\frac{8}{3} - \frac{7}{2}y$	$\frac{5}{2}n - \frac{1}{3} = 8$	$-\frac{3}{2}x + \frac{7}{3} = \frac{11}{24}$
3.	$0.48 = 2.4 - 1.6a$	$-9.28 - 3.2n = 0.736$	$18.12 = -2.8x + 4.4$
4.	$-2.5 + 2.6m = -5.1$	$-0.036 = 3.6 + 4.04k$	$0.8 - 1.7x = -4.13$

Solve. Use the method that seems best to you.

5. A tree grows at an average rate of $5\frac{3}{4}$ inches per year. How many years will it take for the tree to grow 92 inches?

6. In a game, Sean scored $\frac{1}{2}$ as many points as Carrie scored. Carrie scored $\frac{1}{2}$ as many points as Silas scored. Altogether, they scored 560 points. How many points did Carrie score?

7. When $\frac{3}{5}$ of a number is decreased by 9, the result is 15. What is the number?

8. A runner ran the same distance for 3 days. On the fourth day, she ran 2.8 miles. If she ran a total of 22 miles during the 4 days, how many miles did she run on the first day?

9. A patio is 600 square feet. The homeowner wants to increase the size by 15% and resurface the entire patio. The total job will cost $2,346. Based on the size of the new patio, how much will the homeowner pay per square foot?

10. Art bought 20 shares of a stock. During the first month, the price of the stock fell by 10%. At the end of the first month, Art's shares were worth $176.40. How much did Art pay per share in the beginning?

11. If a number is multiplied by 1.5 and then decreased by 70, the result is 25 less than the original number. What is the number?

12. When a number is multiplied by $\frac{2}{3}$, the result is 5 less than the number. What is the number?

Answers start on page 194.

SOLVING MOTION PROBLEMS

Motion problems use the formula $r \times t = d$, or *rate × time = distance.*
Let's see how the formula works.

Example Imagine you drove 60 miles per hour for two hours. How many miles did you drive?

The rate is 60 miles per hour. The time is 2 hours. Use the formula: 60 × 2 = 120
The distance traveled is **120 miles.**

Solve using the distance formula.

1. Elaine needs to make a trip of 175 miles. If she averages 50 miles per hour, how long will the trip take?

2. Driving a winding mountain road, Jeff can average only 20 miles per hour. How far can he drive in $2\frac{1}{2}$ hours?

3. A model airplane traveled 60 feet in 12 seconds. What was the speed of the plane in feet per second?

4. An airliner traveled 1,800 miles at the average speed of 600 miles per hour. How many hours did it take to travel the distance?

You can use this formula to solve more complicated problems using algebra.

SOLVING MOTION PROBLEMS

Example Two trains leave a station at the same time. One heads west at an average speed of 75 miles per hour, and the other heads east at an average speed of 60 miles per hour. How far apart will the trains be at the end of 2 hours?

Step 1
Draw a diagram to help you picture what is happening in the problem. The trains are going in opposite directions. The distance apart is the sum of the distances.

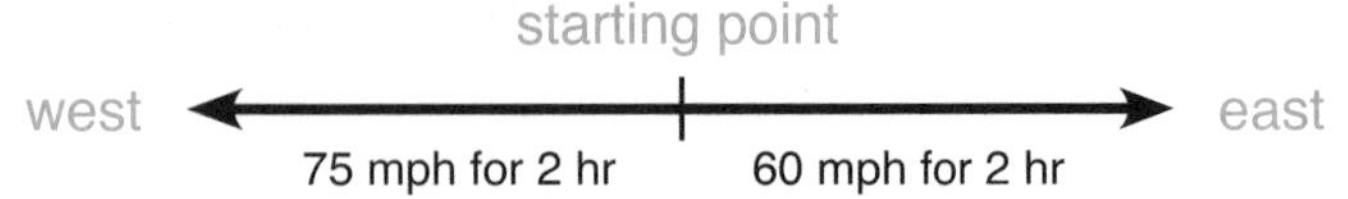

Step 2
Write and solve an equation.

train 1	+	train 2	= distance apart
(75 × 2)	+	(60 × 2)	= d
150	+	120	= 270 miles

After 2 hours, the trains will be **270 miles apart.**

In algebra problems about motion, there will usually be two objects that are moving. The key to solving motion problems is to figure out how the objects are connected. In order to write an equation, something must equal something else.

Solve. The first one is started for you.

5. Lee and Ned started driving at the same time. Lee drove west and Ned drove east. Ned drove at an average rate of 10 miles per hour faster than Lee. At the end of 3 hours, they were 318 miles apart. Find Lee's average speed.

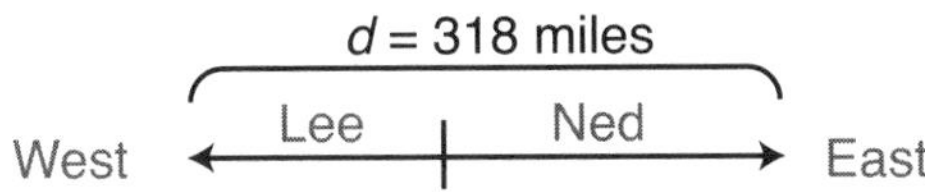

   a. The total distance was 318 miles. Write expressions that multiply rate (r) and time for each driver.

      Lee: $r \times 3$

      Ned: $(r + 10) \times 3$

   b. Write and solve an equation to find r.

6. Marcus and Diego started bicycling north at 9 a.m. at an average speed of 16 miles per hour. After 2 hours, Marcus turned around and headed back home while Diego continued on. Assuming no change in speed, how far apart were they at noon?

   a. Draw a diagram to represent the problem.

   b. Think about rate, time, and distance. Which elements remain equal for the two riders?

   c. Write and solve an equation to find the answer to the problem.

Solve. You may find it helpful to organize information in a chart.

7. At 6:30 a.m., Nita starts walking along a trail at an average speed of 4 miles per hour. At 6:40 a.m., Pat begins jogging after her. How fast must Pat run in order to catch Nita by 7 a.m.?

	Rate	Time	Distance
Nita			
Pat			

8. Frank and Dave started driving at the same time from the same place. They went in the same direction, but Frank drove at an average speed of 45 miles per hour and Dave drove 55 miles per hour. How long did it take them to be 25 miles apart? (***Hint:*** Dave will drive 25 miles farther than Frank. The difference in the distances will be 25 miles.)

9. Brent ran 2 laps around the park in 54 minutes. He ran the first lap at 4 mph and the second at 5 mph. How long did it take him to run each lap?

	Rate	Time	Distance
1st Lap	4 mph	t	
2nd Lap	5 mph	$\frac{9}{10} - t$	

(***Hint:*** 54 minutes equals $\frac{9}{10}$ hour. Since *mph* means miles per *hour,* express the time in hours, not minutes.)

10. At 8:30 a.m., the Garcias started driving north at a speed of 48 miles per hour. Twenty minutes later, the Parkers began driving north from the same point. If the Parkers drive 60 miles per hour, at what time will they catch up with the Garcias?

Answers start on page 195.

SOLVING VALUE PROBLEMS

A value problem is one where the counted objects have a value. You need to consider the total number of objects and the amount they are worth.

SOLVING VALUE PROBLEMS ABOUT MONEY

Example Brad has 20 coins in his pocket, all either quarters or dimes. If he has exactly \$2.90, how many of the coins are quarters?

Step 1
Use a chart.

Let x represent the number of dimes.
If there are x dimes, there must be $20 - x$ quarters.

Now complete the value column. Multiply the number by the value for that coin. Dimes are worth \$0.10 each. Quarters are worth \$0.25 each.

	Number	Value
Dimes	x	$0.1x$
Quarters	$20 - x$	$0.25(20 - x)$

Step 2
Write and solve an equation.

Use the distributive property.
Combine like terms.
Use inverse operations to isolate the variable.
There are 14 dimes.

$$0.1x + 0.25(20 - x) = 2.90$$
$$0.1x + 5 - 0.25x = 2.90$$
$$5 - 0.15x = 2.90$$
$$-0.15x = -2.10$$
$$x = 14$$

Step 3
Answer the question. How many of the coins are quarters?

$20 - 14 =$ **6 quarters**

Solve.

1. Doug has quarters, dimes, and nickels in his pocket for a total of \$3.40. He has twice as many quarters as nickels, and 3 times as many dimes as nickels. How many of each coin does he have?

	Number	Value
Nickels	x	
Dimes	$3x$	
Quarters	$2x$	

2. A cashier handed Morgan 12 bills. Some were \$5 bills, and some were \$10 bills. If the bills totaled \$100, how many were \$5 bills?

3. Mark is paid \$14 an hour during the week and double on the weekends. Last week he earned \$672. He worked 4 times as many hours during the week as he did over the weekend. How many hours did he work during the week?

4. Grace has 8 more dimes than quarters. If she has \$5.35 in change, how many dimes does she have?

5. Emma and John have the same number of coins. Emma has dimes and John has quarters. If John has \$1.80 more than Emma has, how many coins does each have?

Not all value problems are about money. As you read the next example, ask yourself, "How can I tell this is a value problem?"

SOLVING OTHER VALUE PROBLEMS

Example A restaurant has 30 tables. The small tables seat 2 people, and the large tables seat 5 people. When the restaurant is completely filled, there are 117 customers seated. How many small tables are in the restaurant?

Step 1
Use a chart.

Let x represent the number of small tables.
There must be $30 - x$ large tables.

In the value column, multiply the number by how many chairs are at a table of that size.

Tables	Number	Value
Small	x	$2x$
Large	$30 - x$	$5(30 - x)$

Step 2
Write and solve an equation.

$$2x + 5(30 - x) = 117$$
$$2x + 150 - 5x = 117$$
$$-3x = -33$$
$$x = 11$$

Step 3
Answer the question.

There are **11 small tables.**

Solve.

6. At an amusement park, you get 20 points if you hit the center ring of a target. You lose 5 points if you miss the center ring. After 15 attempts, you have 25 points. How many times did you hit the center ring?

7. In basketball, shots can be worth 1, 2, or 3 points. Klay made twice as many 2-point shots as 3-point shots. He made 2 more 3-point shots than he did 1-point shots. If he scored 38 points, how many 3-point shots did he make?

8. A costumer is making vests and shirts for a play. A vest uses $\frac{3}{4}$ yard of fabric, and a shirt uses $2\frac{1}{4}$ yards. The costumer made the same number of vests and shirts. If he used exactly 24 yards of fabric, how many vests did he make?

9. An art school purchased 120 canvas panels. The panels come in small boxes with 5 panels or large boxes with 9 panels. If there are 16 boxes of panels in all, how many are small boxes?

10. A math quiz has some questions worth 3 points and some worth 8 points. The quiz is worth 100 points in all. If there are exactly 20 questions, how many questions are worth 3 points?

11. Jacob bought 2 dozen breakfast muffins on his way to work. The bakery sells regular muffins for $1.00 each and deluxe muffins for $1.75. If Jacob spent $35.25, how many regular muffins did he buy?

Answers start on page 196.

SOLVING WORK PROBLEMS

In some ways, work problems are like motion problems. In a motion problem, you know that the *rate* of travel multiplied by the *time* traveled is equal to the *distance*: rate × time = distance

In a work situation, the *rate* at which someone works multiplied by the *time* worked is equal to how much *work* can be done: rate × time = work

Work problems often use fractions because the time worked is enough to complete only a fraction of the job. For example, a mover estimates that he can completely load a truck in 4 hours. After 1 hour, he should have $\frac{1}{4}$ of the job done.

SOLVING WORK PROBLEMS BASED ON EQUAL TIME

Example Samuel is a house painter. He can finish a job in 6 hours. Working alone, his assistant Scott could finish the job in 8 hours. If they work together, how long will the job take?

The problem is about 2 people who work at different rates. When they work together, they will work the same amount of time, even though one is working faster.

Step 1 Use a chart.

If it takes Samuel 6 hours, he can finish $\frac{1}{6}$ of the job in 1 hour. If Scott can do the job in 8 hours, he can finish $\frac{1}{8}$ of the job in 1 hour.

	Rate: Fraction of Job per Hour	**Time Worked**	**Work Done per Time Worked**
Samuel	$\frac{1}{6}$	x	$\frac{1}{6}x$
Scott	$\frac{1}{8}$	x	$\frac{1}{8}x$

Step 2
Write an equation. The equation is set equal to 1 whole job.

$\frac{1}{6}x + \frac{1}{8}x = 1$

Step 3
Solve the equation.

$\frac{1}{6}x + \frac{1}{8}x = 1$

Find a common denominator and add.

$\frac{4}{24}x + \frac{3}{24}x = 1$

$\frac{7}{24}x = 1$

TIP
You could also multiply each term by 24 to eliminate the fractions.

Multiply by the reciprocal.

$\frac{24}{7} \times \frac{7}{24}x = 1 \times \frac{24}{7}$

Change the answer to a mixed number.

$x = \frac{24}{7}$, which equals $3\frac{3}{7}$ hours

The job will take **$3\frac{3}{7}$ hours.**

It makes sense that by helping each other, Samuel and Scott should be able to do the work faster. Always use common sense to check your work.

In the last example, both people worked the same amount of time. However, things often don't work out so neatly in real life. In this example, see how to handle one person working longer than another.

SOLVING WORK PROBLEMS BASED ON VARYING TIME

Example Working alone, either Karla or her son could clean out the garage in 10 hours. They decide to work together, but her son has to leave after 3 hours, and Karla finishes by herself. How many more hours does Karla work after her son leaves?

Step 1
Let x represent the number of hours worked.

Karla's work per hour: $\frac{1}{10}x$

Her son's work per hour: $\frac{1}{10}x$

After 3 hours, they have finished $\frac{3}{10} + \frac{3}{10} = \frac{6}{10}$ of the job. Only $\frac{4}{10}$ remains.

Step 2
Write an equation to figure out how long it will take Karla to do the final $\frac{4}{10}$ of the job.

$\frac{1}{10}x = \frac{4}{10}$

$x = 4$

Karla will need to work **4 more hours** after her son leaves.

Solve.

1. One copier can finish a copying job in 3 hours. A faster copier can finish the same job in 2 hours. If both copiers run at the same time, how long will it take to complete the job?

	Rate: Fraction of Job per Hour	Time Worked	Work Done per Time Worked
Copier		x	
Faster Copier		x	

2. Pipe A can fill a swimming pool in 12 hours. Pipe B can fill the swimming pool in 15 hours. Pipe A is turned on at 8 a.m. Pipe B is turned on 4 hours later. How many hours will it take to fill the pool?

3. Rafael can clean a suite of offices in 60 minutes. Kim can do the same job in 40 minutes, and Nick can do the work in 30 minutes. If they all work together, how long will it take to do the job? (***Hint:*** Figure the rate as a fraction of the job per minute.)

4. Mike and Vanessa are addressing invitations by hand. Mike can address 1 invitation in 60 seconds. Vanessa can address 1 in 50 seconds. To the nearest minute, how long will it take them to finish 200 invitations? (***Hint:*** Figure out how long it will take them, working together, to address 1 envelope and multiply by 200. Your answer will be in seconds. Convert it to minutes.)

5. **Explain** Elaine needs to send out statements to clients, a job that normally takes her 20 hours. The office has a new employee named Stan who could do the job in 30 hours.

   If they work together, Elaine will have to spend time helping Stan. She figures that she will slow down from a rate of 20 hours to 25 hours for the job. Stan will speed up from a rate of 30 hours to 25 hours for the job.

   Should Elaine do the job alone or work with Stan? Which will take the least amount of time? Explain your thinking.

Answers start on page 197.

USING INEQUALITIES TO SOLVE WORD PROBLEMS

Think about the following situation:
Saul needs an average of 90 to get an A in a class. On his first two tests, he scored 94 and 88. What score does he need on the third test to get an A in the class?

Most people would write and solve an equation to solve the problem. Let x equal Saul's third test score.

$$\frac{94+88+x}{3} = 90$$
$$94 + 88 + x = 270$$
$$182 + x = 270$$
$$x = 88$$

Saul needs a **88** on the third test to get an A.

However, it would be more accurate to say that Saul needs to get *at least* an 88 on the third test. If Saul scores 89 on the test, he will still get an A. Saul's last score needs to be **greater than or equal to 88.** This idea is best expressed using an inequality: $x \geq 88$

In fact, the original equation should have been an inequality: $\frac{94+88+x}{3} \geq 90$

Is it wrong to use an equation to solve an inequality? Not really. You can always adjust after you find a value for the variable. Good test takers don't worry about whether the situation requires an inequality. They solve the problem with an equation, and then think about the situation to see whether an inequality is appropriate.

Another way to solve an inequality on a test is to test some numbers.

Example Melanie needs to save at least $345 within 5 months. Let x represent her average savings per month. On average, how much does Melanie need to save per month to meet her goal? Express the solution set as an inequality.

A. $x < \$69$
B. $x \leq \$69$
C. $x > \$69$
D. $x \geq \$69$

Try some numbers.
- Will exactly $69 work? $69 × 5 = $345. Yes, it works.
- $60 for 5 months is $300. Less than $69 doesn't work.
- $70 for 5 months is $350. Greater than $69 works.

The variable x should be *greater than or equal to* $69. **Choice D** is correct.

Certain words and phrases indicate that an inequality can be used to solve a problem.

Naoko needs to earn *at least* $14 per hour.	$n \geq \$14$
The repair will cost *a maximum* of $325.	$c \leq \$325$
The small theater has *at most* 80 seats.	$s \leq 80$
The *minimum* charge for a repair call is $75.	$r \geq \$75$

Use the menu below to answer problems 1–4. For each problem, write an inequality and solve for the unknown.

Frank is buying food from Zestos for a pot luck dinner. He doesn't want to spend more than $30.

Zestos

Super Burger	$2.19
With Cheese	$2.39
Junior Burger	$1.59
With Cheese	$1.79
Large Fries	$1.39
Small Fries	$.99
Milkshake	$2.49
Large Drink	$1.29
Small Drink	$.99
Junior Meal*	
Burger	$2.49
Chicken	$2.89

*Includes fries, drink, and toy

1. For $30, how many Super Burgers with cheese could Frank buy?

2. Frank doesn't want to spend more than $30. For each burger he buys, he plans to buy an order of small fries and a large drink. If he chooses Junior Burgers without cheese, how many meals can he buy?

3. Frank decides to buy 10 small fries. How many Junior Burgers could he buy with the money that is left?

4. Frank is thinking about buying 10 large drinks. How many small drinks could he buy for the same cost or less?

Solve.

5. Ten more than a number is greater than or equal to 6. What is the number?

   Choose the inequality that represents the solution set to the problem.

   A. $n > -4$
   B. $n < -4$
   C. $n \geq -4$
   D. $n \leq -4$

6. Which value does NOT make the inequality true?

   $2(x - 5) > -2$

   A. 4
   B. 6
   C. 8
   D. 10

7. The product of –4 and a number is increased by 19. The result is less than –1. What is the number?

   Choose the inequality that represents the solution set to the problem.

   A. $n < 5$
   B. $n > 5$
   C. $n < -5$
   D. $n > -5$

8. Which value for x makes both inequalities true?

   $-8 < 5x + 2$ and $4 - x \leq 8$

   A. –6
   B. –4
   C. –2
   D. 0

Answers start on page 197.

USING FORMULAS

Formulas are useful tools for solving certain kinds of problems. A **formula** is an equation that shows a constant relationship between variables.

For example, you have already learned that **perimeter** is the total distance around a figure. You can find the perimeter of any figure by adding its sides. The perimeter of the square in the drawing is 20 because 5 + 5 + 5 + 5 = 20.

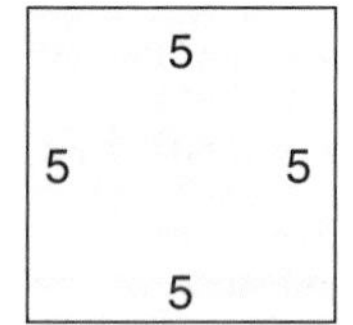

From the example, you can write directions stating how to find the perimeter of a square: *Take 1 side and multiply it by 4.*

You can write those directions as a formula. Let P represent perimeter and s represent a side. Write $P = 4s$.

$P = 4s$
$P = 4(5)$
$P = 20$

On the GED® Math Test, you are expected to know many basic formulas. Good test takers memorize these basic formulas.

When you take the GED Math Test, you will be able to access a formula sheet by clicking on a link during the test. If you need any other formula to answer a question during the test, you will be given it as part of the question.

The formulas provided on pages 220–221 are also available during the test on the GED math formula sheet.

To use a formula, substitute the given values and use the order of operations to find the value that you don't know.

USING FORMULAS TO SOLVE PROBLEMS

Example Barbara borrowed $3,000. She financed the loan using simple interest. She agreed to pay a rate of 4% interest for 5 years. How much interest will she pay on the loan?

simple interest: $I = prt$

The variable p represents principal (the amount borrowed), r represents rate, and t represents time in years.

Step 1
Substitute the given values in the formula.

$3,000 is the principal, 4% is the rate, and 5 years is the time.

$I = prt$
$I = \$3{,}000 \times 0.04 \times 5$

Step 2
Solve.

$I = \$3{,}000 \times 0.04 \times 5 = \$600$
The interest (I) is $600.

Barbara will pay **$600** in interest on the loan.

Solve using the given formula.

1. A toy car traveled at a rate of 24 feet per second for 8 seconds. How far did it travel?

   distance formula: $d = rt$
   where d = distance, r = rate, and t = time

2. In Los Angeles, the outdoor temperature is 77° Fahrenheit. What temperature is it using the Celsius scale?

   temperature conversion formula:
   $C = \frac{5}{9}(F - 32)$
   where C and F are the temperatures in Celsius and Fahrenheit

3. Area is the space inside a figure.

   area of a triangle: $A = \frac{1}{2}bh$
   where A is area, b is the base, and h is the height of the triangle

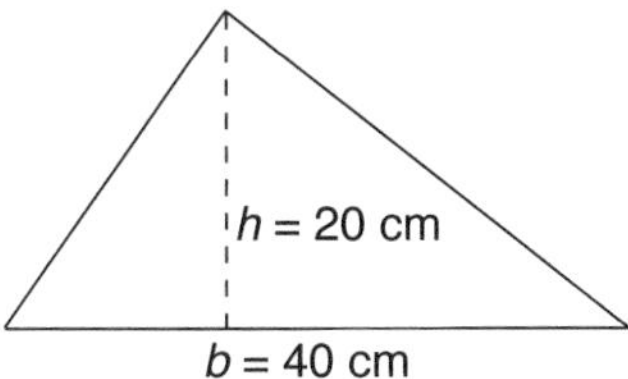

   What is the area of the triangle in square centimeters?

4. Two loans are financed using simple interest. The principal of both loans is $10,000. Which loan charges the least amount of interest?

   Loan A: 4% interest for 6 years
   Loan B: 5% interest for 4 years

   Use the simple interest formula on page 94.

5. What is the area of the parallelogram in square inches?

   area of a parallelogram: $A = bh$
   where A is area, b is the base, and h is the height of the parallelogram

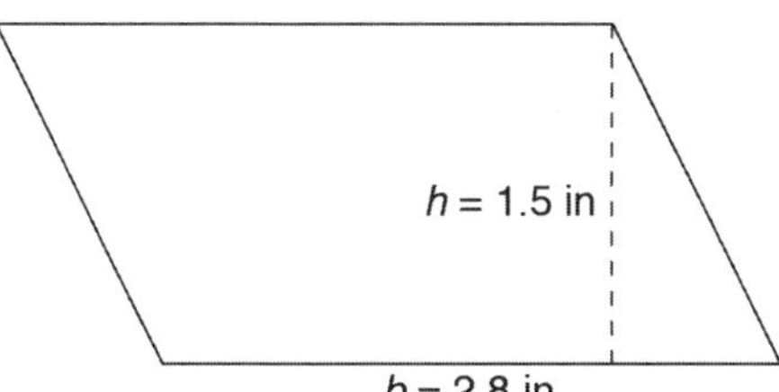

6. An object is dropped by a skydiver. How many meters will the object fall in 8 seconds when $g = 9.8$?

   distance an object has fallen: $d = \frac{1}{2}g(t \times t)$
   where d is distance; g is acceleration produced by gravity; and t is time, the number of seconds the object has fallen

Answers start on page 198.

REWRITING FORMULAS

The distance formula ($d = rt$) states that distance = rate × time.

Example Bill drives at an average rate of 70 mph for 2 hours. How many miles does he travel?

$d = rt$
$= 70 \times 2$
$= 140$ miles

You can use algebra to solve for a different variable.

Example Bill drove 140 miles in 2 hours. What was his average rate of speed in miles per hour?

$d = rt$
$140 = r \times 2$
$70 = r$

To isolate *r*, divide both sides by 2.

You can also use algebra to rewrite the formula so that the formula solves for the rate.

$d = rt$
$\frac{d}{t} = r$

To isolate *r*, divide both sides by *t*.

The new formula solves for rate: $r = \frac{d}{t}$

The two formulas $d = rt$ and $r = \frac{d}{t}$ are equivalent formulas.

The same principles and properties that allow you to solve equations can be applied to rewriting formulas.

To write an equivalent formula, use inverse operations to isolate a variable.

REWRITING FORMULAS

Example A formula for finding the average, *A,* of two numbers can be written as $A = \frac{x+y}{2}$, where A = average and *x* and *y* are the two numbers. Rewrite the formula to solve for *x,* one of the two numbers.

Step 1
Multiply both sides by 2.

$A = \frac{x+y}{2}$
$2A = x + y$

Step 2
Subtract *y* from both sides.

$2A - y = x$

Step 3
Switch the sides of the equation.

$x = 2A - y$

The formula $\boldsymbol{x = 2A - y}$ can be used to find a missing number when the average and one of the numbers are known.

Solve as directed.

1. **a.** The formula for finding the perimeter (P) of a triangle is $P = a + b + c$, where a, b, and c are the sides of the triangle. Write an equivalent formula to solve for c.

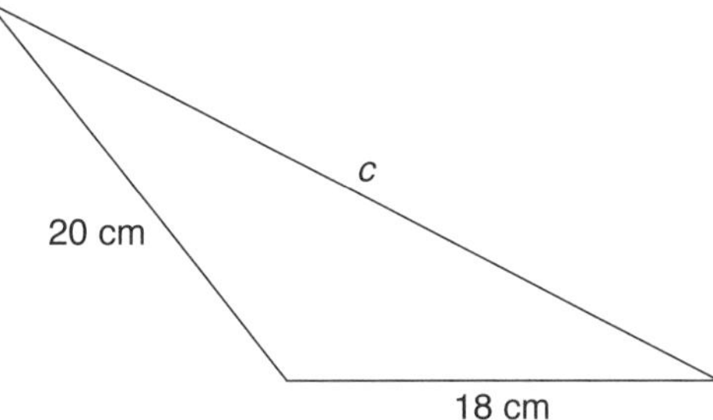

b. The perimeter of the triangle is 72 centimeters. Find the length of side c.

2. **a.** The formula $C = \frac{5}{9}(F - 32)$ converts Fahrenheit degrees to Celsius degrees. Rewrite the formula to solve for F.

b. Find the Fahrenheit temperature that corresponds to 60° Celsius.

3. **a.** The formula for finding the perimeter (P) of a rectangle is $P = 2l + 2w$, where l = length and w = width. Rewrite the formula to solve for w.

b. What is the width of a rectangle if the perimeter is 30 inches and the length is 9 inches?

4. **a.** The average (A) of three numbers can be written $A = \frac{x+y+z}{3}$, where x, y, and z are the three numbers. Rewrite the formula to solve for y.

b. The average of three test scores is 87. What is the third test score if two of the scores are 86 and 81?

5. **a.** The formula for finding the area of a triangle is $A = \frac{1}{2}bh$, where A = area, b = base, and h = height. Write an equivalent formula to solve for b.

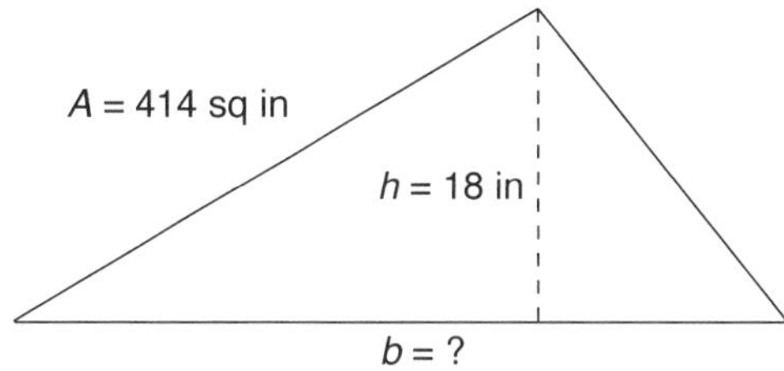

b. Find the length of the base b.

6. **a.** The formula $I = prt$ finds simple interest (I) when the principal (p), annual interest rate (r), and time (t) in years are known. Rewrite the formula to solve for t.

b. Ginny paid her brother $480 in interest on a $4,000 loan. Find the number of years of the loan if she borrowed the money at 4% simple interest.

7. **a.** In the cost formula $C = nr$, C represents total cost, n equals the number of items, and r equals the price (rate) per item. Rewrite the formula to solve for n.

b. Stuart paid $261 to buy custom T-shirts. How many shirts did he buy if each shirt cost $21.75?

8. **Explain** In percent problems, the *whole* (or base) times the *rate* is equal to the *part.* Write three formulas that could be used when working with percent.

Use a real-life situation to prove to a friend that your formulas work.

Answers start on page 198.

Unit 3 Review

Solve as directed.

1. There are 85 students in three classes. Class A has 12 more students than Class B. Class C has 23 fewer than twice the number in Class B.

   a. Use the information from the problem to complete the chart. Let n equal the number of students in Class B.

Class A	Class B	Class C	Total

   b. How many students are in Class B?

   ☐ students

2. Jordan is 4 times as old as Grace. If the difference in their ages is 36 years, how many years old is Jordan?

   A. 12
   B. 32
   C. 48
   D. 60

3. A bank teller handed Serena \$175 in cash using \$5, \$10, and \$20 bills. Serena received 3 times as many \$5 bills as \$10 bills. The number of \$20 bills was 1 less than twice the number of \$10 bills. How many total bills did the teller hand Serena?

   A. 3
   B. 9
   C. 17
   D. 22

4. The total distance around the rectangle below is 110 meters.

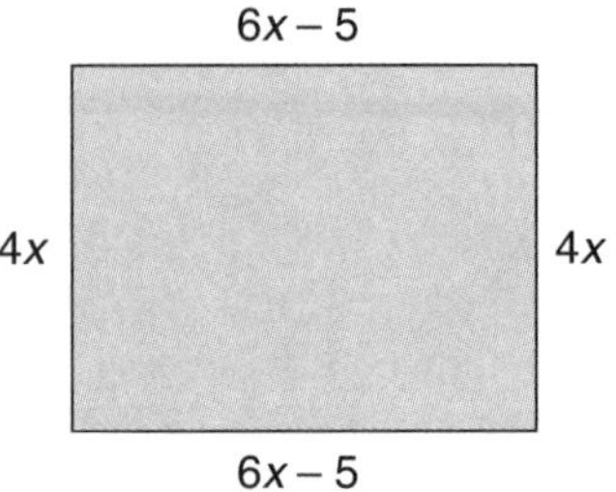

Which choice lists the width and length of the rectangle?

   A. 6 and 24
   B. 24 and 31
   C. 24 and 86
   D. 48 and 62

5. Janice hiked up a hill at a rate of 2 miles per hour and back down at a rate of 4 miles per hour. Her total time hiking was 3 hours.

   a. Complete the chart.

	Rate	Time	Distance
Up	2	x	$2x$
Down			

   b. How many hours did the trip down the hill take?

   A. $\frac{1}{2}$
   B. 1
   C. $1\frac{1}{2}$
   D. 2

6. The Ballpark Souvenir Shop offers the following souvenirs.

Item	Price
Baseball	\$5.00
Bobblehead	\$15.00
Plush mascot	\$19.00
Car flag	\$13.00

A youth club with 20 members attended a baseball game. Each member bought 1 item.

The number of kids who bought car flags is equal to the number who bought plush mascots. The number who bought bobbleheads is 4 times the number who bought car flags. Everyone else bought a baseball.

If the group spent \$162, how many kids bought a baseball?

[ ] kids

7. Bob needs to send out a mailing for his company. Working alone, it will take him 10 hours to get the job done. Ellen can do the job in 8 hours by herself.

They work together for 2 hours, and then Ellen finishes the job by herself. Which choice is the best estimate for how long the job will take in all?

A. between 4 and 5 hours
B. between 5 and 6 hours
C. between 6 and 7 hours
D. between 7 and 8 hours

8. The sum of two numbers is 56. The first number is $2\frac{1}{2}$ times greater than the second number. What is the second number?

[ ]

9. Brandon has 40 coins. Some are nickels and some are quarters. He has at least \$4.80. At most, how many nickels can Brandon have?

[ ] nickels

10. The product of –2 and a number n is increased by 15. The result is greater than 3.

Choose the inequality that represents the solution set to the problem.

A. $n > 6$
B. $n < 6$
C. $n > -6$
D. $n < -6$

11. The formula for finding the volume (V) of a pyramid is $V = \frac{1}{3}bh$, where b represents a side of the base and h represents the height of the pyramid. Rewrite the formula to solve for height.

$h =$ [ ]

12. For one day only, Phil's Footwear is selling all boots at a 30% discount. Let p equal the original price of a pair of boots. Write a formula to find the sale price (s) of a pair of boots.

[ ]

13. Mariah earns \$180 per week plus \$4 per sale. This week she wants to earn at least \$450. Write an inequality to find the number of sales she needs to make.

[ ]

Answers start on page 199.

UNIT
4

GEOMETRY BASICS

SKILLS

- Points, lines, and angles
- Quadrilaterals
- Triangles
- The Pythagorean theorem
- Perimeter
- Area
- Volume
- Surface area
- Working with complex figures

TOOLS AND STRATEGIES

- Using protractors
- Finding patterns
- Choosing formulas

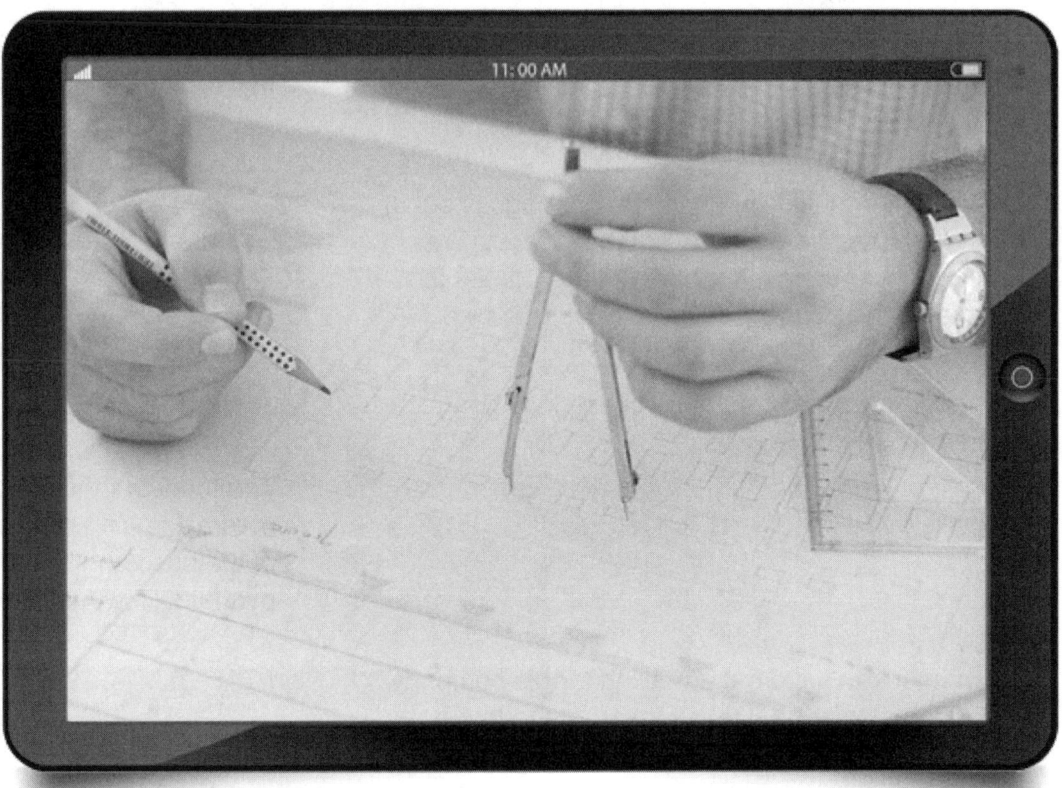

THE WORD GEOMETRY comes from Greek words that mean "to measure the Earth." Everything built by people—the house or apartment you live in, the car you drive, and the bridge you walk across—depends upon geometric principles.

Just as a detective uses clues and evidence to prove a case, you can use the properties of geometry to draw conclusions about shapes and find the measures of unknown angles and sides.

In this unit, you'll learn the very practical skills of figuring perimeter, area, volume, and surface area. These skills will help you take care of your home and apartment.

Geometry is one of the most practical areas of mathematics. Learning geometry will help you develop critical thinking as it applies to the world around you.

USING GEOMETRY

You use the properties of geometry when you:

- Create realistic drawings
- Make home improvements
- Rearrange the furniture in a room
- Reorganize a closet
- Choose a box to mail a package

Read the following items. Describe some of your experiences in writing or discuss them with a partner.

1. Suppose you are going on a trip. How do you pack a suitcase to make sure everything you need for the trip will fit?

2. Have you ever rearranged the furniture in a room? Describe the process you used. Did you measure first, estimate sizes, draw diagrams, or just start moving the furniture?

3. Have you ever painted a room? How did you figure out how much paint to buy?

4. Maintaining a yard or garden requires an understanding of many geometric principles. Brainstorm different measurements you might need to plant and take care of a garden.

MATH TALK

Many words used in geometry have another definition. For each of the words below, write two sentences—one using a math setting and one without. You can find the math definitions in the glossary of this book.

intersect
opposite
adjacent
supplement
complement
parallel

Compare sentences with a friend. Discuss how knowing the nonmathematical definition can help you understand the mathematical definition.

Example A *segment* is part of a line.
Only a small *segment* of the population voted in the election.

Connection In both sentences, *segment* means "part of something."

POINTS, LINES, AND ANGLES

Geometry is concerned with the properties and measurement of points, lines, angles, surfaces, and solids. The first step in learning geometry is to understand its terms. Refer to the drawing as you review the definitions on this page.

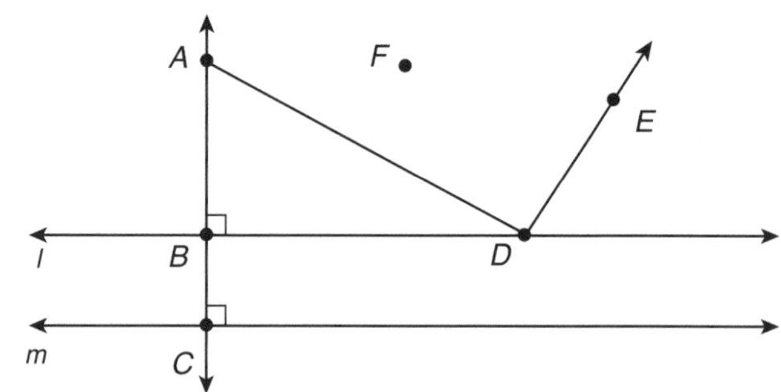

A **point** is a precise location in space. The drawing has six labeled points: A through F.

A **line** is a straight path of points that continues in opposite directions. A line has infinite length shown by an arrow on each end. A line can be named using a single italic letter or by two points on the line.

Line *l* can also be called line *BD,* also written $\overleftrightarrow{BD}$.

A **ray** is a straight path of points that starts at one point and continues infinitely in one direction. Ray *DE,* also written $\overrightarrow{DE}$, starts at point *D,* passes through point *E,* and continues.

A **line segment** is the path of points between two definite points. A line segment is named by its endpoints. Find segment *AD,* also written $\overline{AD}$.

Some lines belong in special categories. **Vertical** lines run straight up and down. **Horizontal** lines run left and right. In the drawing, lines *l* and *m* are horizontal and $\overleftrightarrow{AC}$, the line passing through points *A* and *C,* is vertical.

Two lines **intersect** when they cross at a point. Lines *AB* and *BD* intersect at point *B.* Some lines will never intersect. Two lines that run in the same direction are called **parallel** lines. No matter how far parallel lines are extended, they will never cross. In the drawing, lines *l* and *m* are parallel.

Lines that intersect to form square corners (also called right angles) are called **perpendicular** lines. $\overleftrightarrow{AC}$ is perpendicular to lines *l* and *m.*

Answer the questions about the drawing to the right.

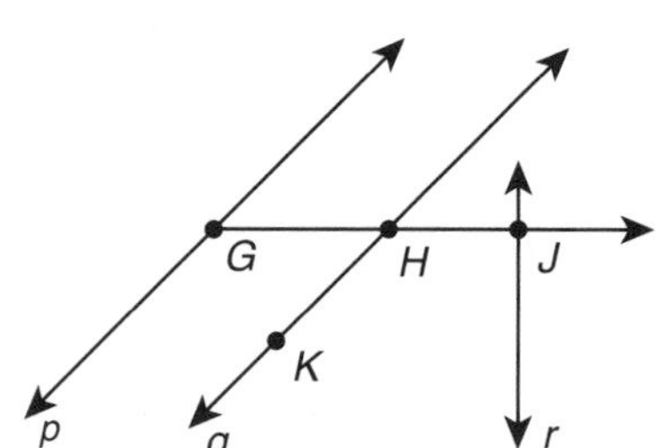

1. How many lines are shown in the drawing?

2. Point *J* lies at the intersection of perpendicular lines. Are lines *r* and *p* perpendicular? Explain your reasoning.

3. Name 4 line segments found in the drawing.

4. There are many rays in the drawing. Name two.

ANGLES

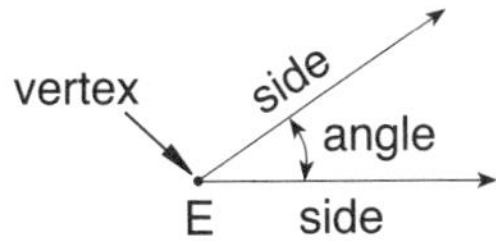

A **vertex** is a point where two rays or line segments intersect. An angle is formed by two rays. The rays that form an angle are called the sides of the angle.

The size of an angle depends on the amount of **rotation** of the sides. Imagine a clock with both hands pointing at the 12. As one hand moves clockwise, the measure of the angle created by the hands increases. Angles are measured in degrees (°). One full rotation (forming a complete circle) is 360°.

The angle increases as the hand moves.

Below are the properties of four angles that you will need to know.

> **TIP**
> *A right angle is indicated by a small box drawn inside the angle.*

Name of Angle	Properties	Examples
right angle	exactly 90°	
acute angle	less than 90°	
straight angle	exactly 180°	
obtuse angle	between 90° and 180°	

Answer each question.

5. Match the illustrations with the descriptions.

_____ an acute angle

_____ a right angle

_____ an obtuse angle

_____ a straight angle

a. b. c. d.

6. Which of the three angles is smallest? Why? (***Hint:*** The size of an angle is based only on the angle, not the length of the sides.)

a. b. c.

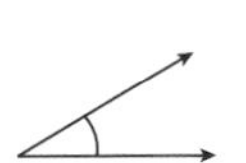
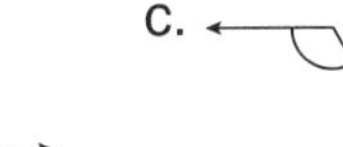

Answers start on page 199.

USING PROTRACTORS

A **protractor** is a tool for measuring angles. A protractor looks like a half circle with a fanlike scale of numbers. One scale runs from left to right; the other from right to left.

To measure an angle, line up one ray of the angle with the baseline of the protractor. Put the center point of the protractor (sometimes marked with crosshairs) on the vertex of the angle. Read the scale at the point where the other ray crosses it.

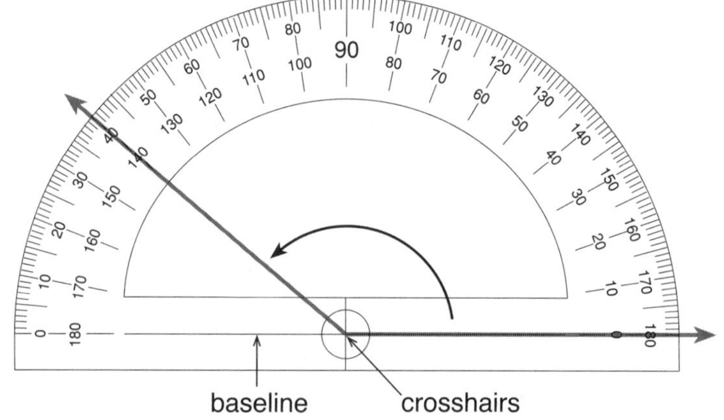

This illustration shows a protractor and an angle of 140°. The symbol ∠ means angle. Angles can be named by the vertex point, by a letter or number within the opening, or by three points.

The angle at the right could be named ∠*A,* ∠1, ∠*BAC,* or ∠*CAB.* When three points are used to name an angle, the vertex is always the middle letter.

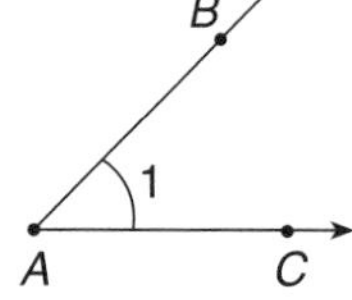

In this illustration, ∠*NOP* is divided into two smaller angles, ∠*x* and ∠*y.* If ∠*x* = 35° and ∠*y* = 30°, we can add to find the measure of ∠*NOP.*

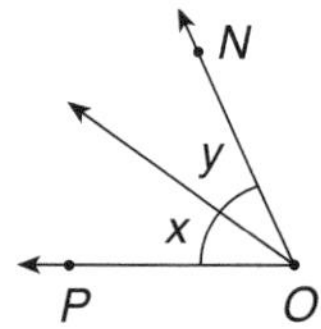

35° + 30° = 65°
∠*NOP* = 65°

Subtraction can be used to find a missing angle. (***Note:*** The *m* before the angle symbol ∠ means "the measure of.")

m∠*EDG* =140°. Find *m*∠*EDF.*

m∠*EDG* —*m*∠*FDG* = *m*∠*EDF*
140°— 58 = 82°

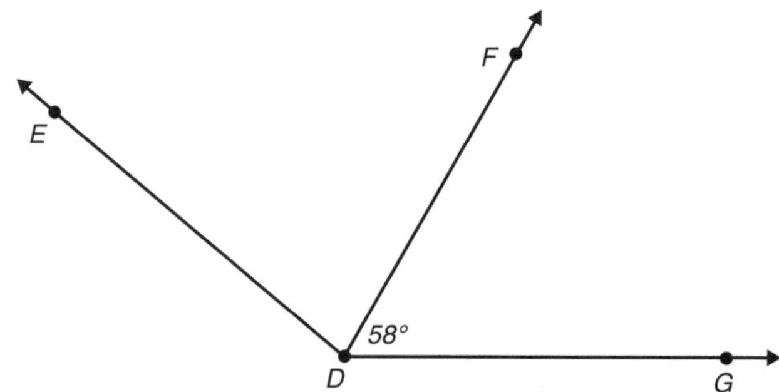

Answer each question.

1. Tell the number of degrees in each of the following angles.

a.

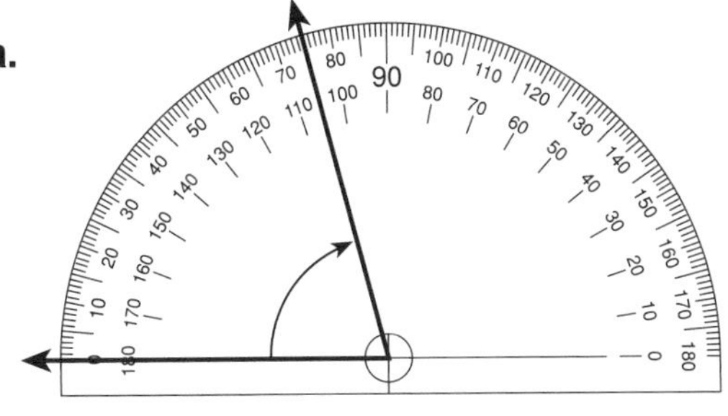

c.

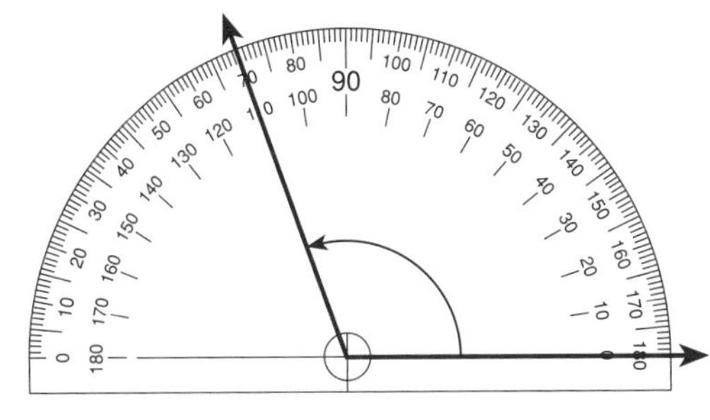

b.

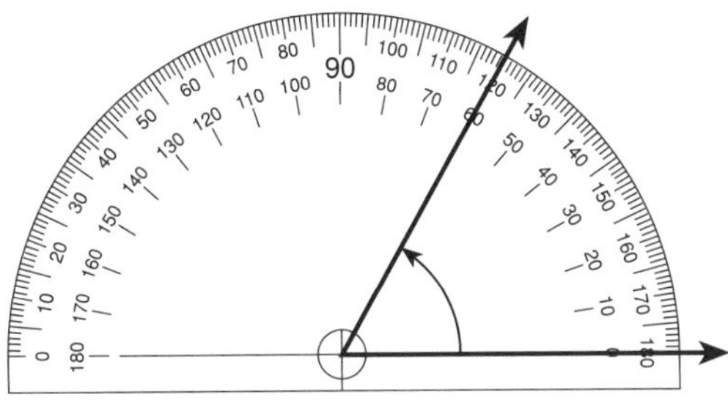

d.

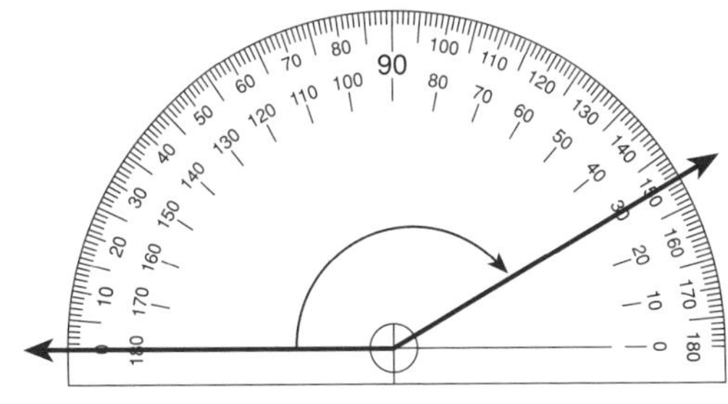

2. Match the angle with the correct number of degrees. Use your judgment or a protractor if you have one.

_____ 180°

_____ 90°

_____ 30°

_____ 135°

a. 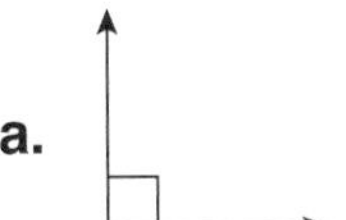

b. 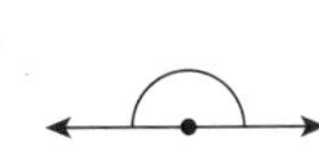

c. 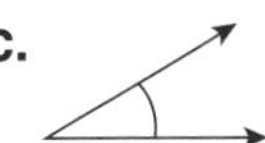

d. 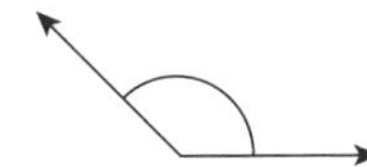

Solve the following problems without using a protractor.

3. $\angle FGH = 160°$. Find the measure of $\angle JGH$.

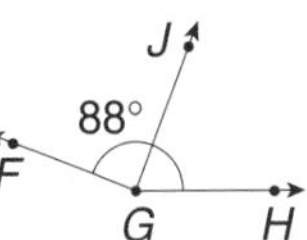

4. Tell the type of angle and number of degrees for each angle:

Angle	Type	Degrees
$\angle POS$		
$\angle QOS$		
$\angle POR$		

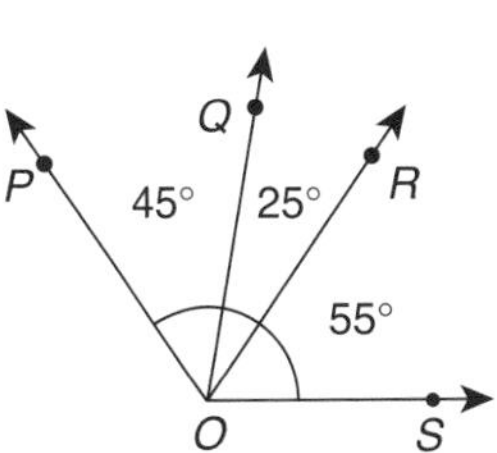

5. $\angle AOB = 120°$ and $\angle c$ is 3 times as great as $\angle d$. Use algebra to find the measurements of both $\angle c$ and $\angle d$. (***Hint:*** Let a variable equal the measurement of $\angle d$.)

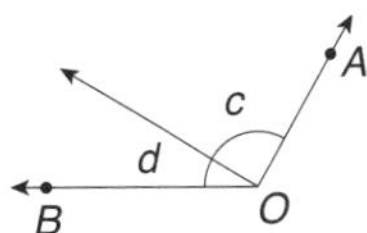

Answers start on page 200.

WORKING WITH ANGLES

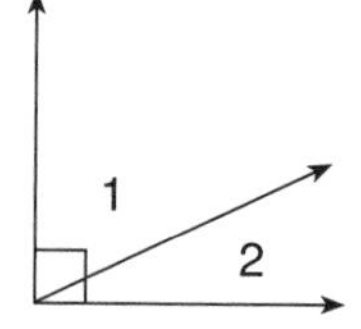

The right angle shown here is divided into two angles, $\angle 1$ and $\angle 2$. The sum of the measures of the two angles must be 90°.

Two angles that add up to 90° are called **complementary angles.** If you know the measure of one angle, you can find the measure of the other.

Example In the drawing, $m\angle 2 = 25°$. What is the measure of $\angle 1$?

You know that $m\angle 1 + m\angle 2 = 90°$. Therefore, $m\angle 1 + 25° = 90°$.
Subtract to find the measure of $\angle 1$: $90° - 25° = 65°$
$\boldsymbol{m\angle 1 = 65°}$

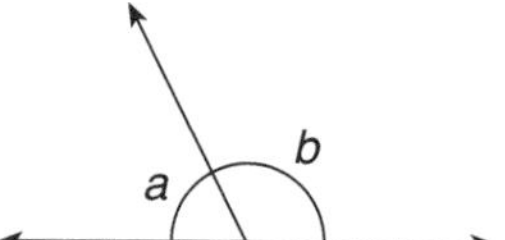

The straight angle shown here is divided into two angles, $\angle a$ and $\angle b$. The sum of the measures of the angles must be 180°. Two angles that add up to 180° are called **supplementary angles.**

Example If $\angle a$ measures 63°, what is the measure of $\angle b$?

Subtract to find the measure of $\angle b$: $180° - 63° = 117°$
$\boldsymbol{m\angle b = 117°}$

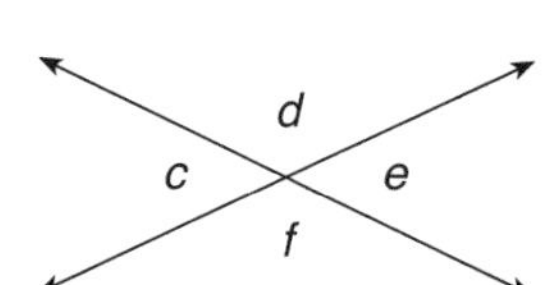

When straight lines intersect, they form pairs of supplementary angles. Look at the drawing. How many pairs of supplementary angles do you see?

There are four pairs: $\angle c$ and $\angle d$, $\angle d$ and $\angle e$, $\angle e$ and $\angle f$, $\angle f$ and $\angle c$.

Each pair of angles can also be described as adjacent. **Adjacent angles** share a side. Angles that do not share a side but are opposite each other are **vertical angles.** Vertical angles have equal measures.

When two lines intersect in this way, you need the measure of only one of the angles to find the measures of the others.

Example If the measure of $\angle c$ is 50°, what is the measure of each of the other angles?

Since $\angle c$ and $\angle d$ are supplementary, the measure of $\angle d$ is $180° - 50° =$ **130°**.
Since $\angle c$ and $\angle e$ are vertical angles, the measure of $\angle e$ is also **50°**.
Since $\angle d$ and $\angle f$ are vertical angles, the measure of $\angle f$ is also **130°**.

In geometry you must have a reason for everything you do. You can't conclude that two angles are equal just because they look equal. You have to have evidence that they are equal. Good test takers learn the definitions of geometry terms, because the definitions can be used as evidence that something is true.

Solve as directed.

1. If $\angle b = 26°$, what is the measure of $\angle a$?

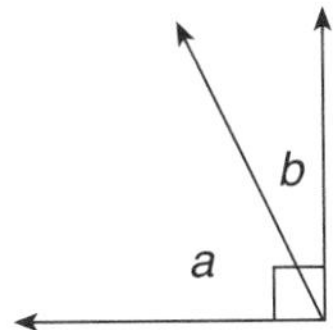

2. If $\angle c = 129°$, what is the measure of $\angle d$?

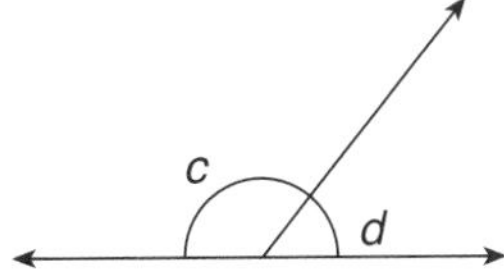

Use the drawing to answer questions 3–5.

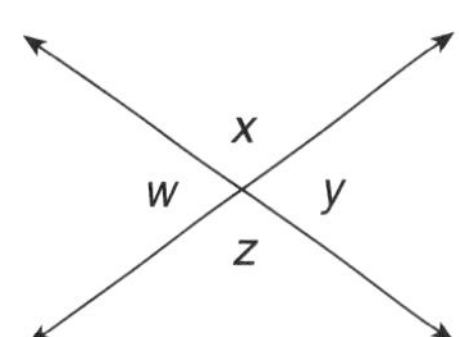

3. Name two pairs of vertical angles.
4. If $\angle z$ measures 110°, what does $\angle w$ measure?
5. $\angle z = 110°$. What does $\angle x$ measure? How do you know?

Use the drawing to answer questions 6 and 7.

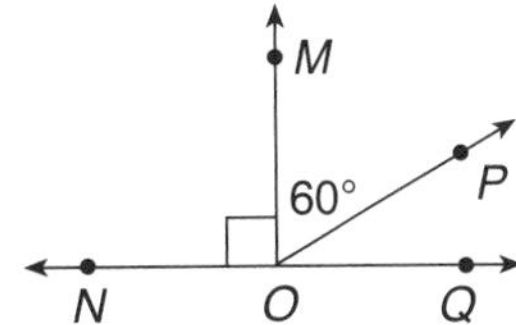

6. Name a supplementary angle to $\angle MON$.
7. What is the measure of $\angle POQ$?

CORE CONNECTIONS: Angle Relationships

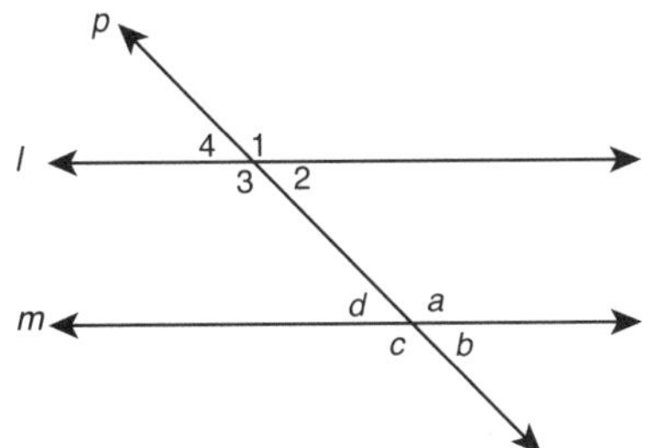

When one line crosses another line, vertical angles are formed. When one line crosses two parallel lines, the line, called a **transversal,** creates vertical angles in two places. These are called **corresponding angles** because they are in the same position on the parallel lines. Corresponding angles are equal. If you know one angle, you can find the others.

Example The measure of $\angle 4$ is 40°. Find all the other angles.

Conclusion	Reason	Conclusion	Reason
$\angle 2 = 40°$	$\angle 4$ and $\angle 2$ are vertical angles.	$\angle d = 40°$	$\angle 4$ and $\angle d$ are corresponding angles.
$\angle 1 = 140°$	$\angle 1$ and $\angle 2$ are supplementary.	$\angle b = 40°$	$\angle b$ and $\angle d$ are vertical angles.
$\angle 3 = 140°$	$\angle 1$ and $\angle 3$ are vertical.	$\angle a = 140°$	$\angle 1$ and $\angle a$ are corresponding angles.
		$\angle c = 140°$	$\angle a$ and $\angle c$ are vertical angles.

1. On the street map, $\angle f = 137°$. Name three other angles with the same measure.

2. What is the measure of $\angle a$? How do you know you are correct?

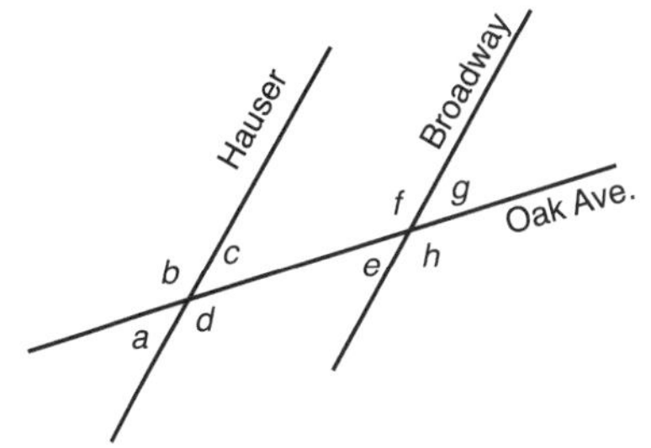

Answers start on page 200.

QUADRILATERALS

A **polygon** is a closed, plane (flat) figure made up of line segments. In this case, *closed* means that the sides meet.

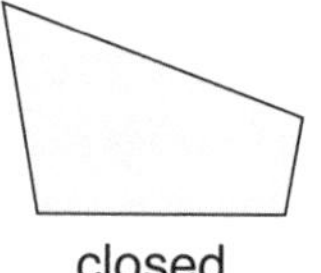
closed

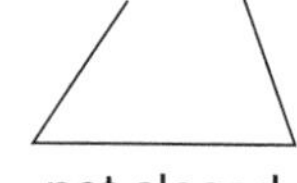
not closed

A **quadrilateral** is a polygon with four sides. Squares and rectangles are the two most common quadrilaterals. If you add the angles inside any quadrilateral, the sum is always 360°.

Look at the quadrilateral *EFGH* shown here. Each time two sides meet, an angle is formed. The point where the sides meet is called a **vertex.** The four labeled points are the **vertices** of this figure.

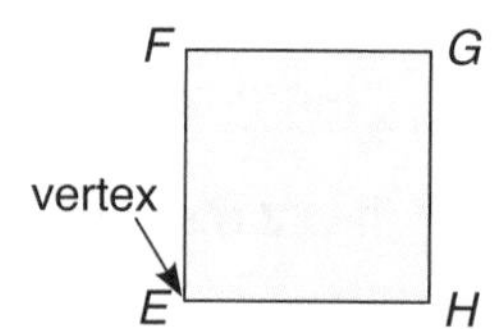

Sides *EF* and *GH* are **opposite** (across from) each other. Sides *FG* and *EH* are also opposites. Sides *EF* and *EH* are **adjacent.** This means they share an endpoint.

A straight line connecting opposite vertices (corners) is called a **diagonal.** Line segment *EG* is a diagonal; so is *FH.*

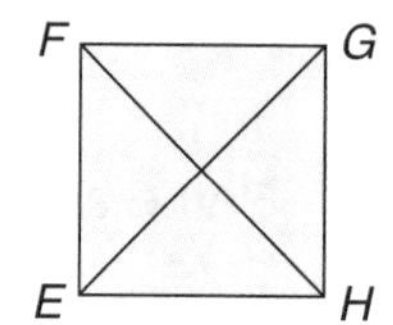

Below are examples and properties of five common quadrilaterals.

Name	Properties	Examples
square	Opposite sides are parallel. All sides are equal. All angles are right angles (90°). Diagonals are equal and perpendicular.	
rectangle	Opposite sides are equal and parallel. All angles are right angles (90°). Diagonals are equal but not necessarily perpendicular.	
rhombus	Opposite sides are equal and parallel. All sides are equal. Diagonals are perpendicular but not necessarily equal.	
parallelogram	Opposite sides are equal and parallel.	
trapezoid	Only *one* pair of sides is parallel.	

Use figure *ABCD* to answer the questions below.

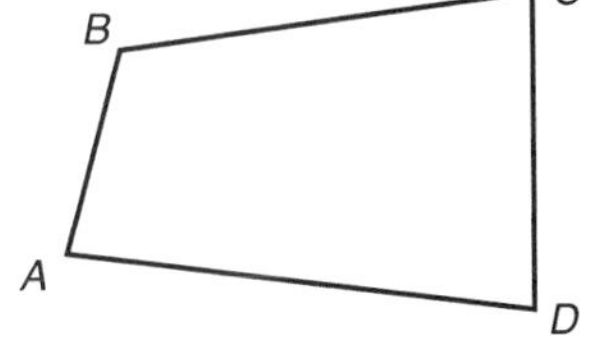

1. Which side is opposite *AB*?

2. Name two sides that are adjacent to *BC*.

3. Name the two diagonals.

4. Which angle is opposite $\angle ABC$?

5. The measure of $\angle DAB$ is 80°. The measure of $\angle ABC$ is 114°. The remaining two angles are equal in measure. What is the measure of $\angle ADC$?

Use the properties of quadrilaterals to answer each question.

6. Name three properties that rectangles and squares have in common.

7. True or False A square, a rectangle, and a rhombus are three examples of parallelograms. Explain your answer.

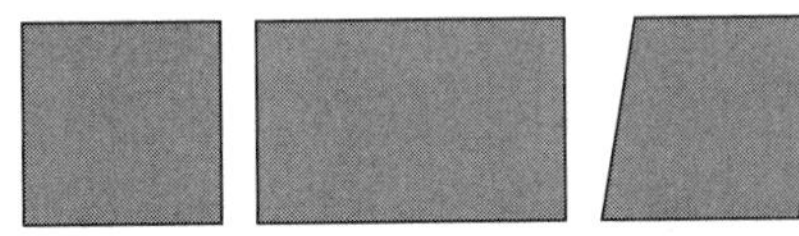

8. A four-sided figure has equal and parallel opposite sides. None of the four angles are right angles, but all four sides are equal in length. What is the name of the figure?

9. True or False A trapezoid can *never* have a right angle. Explain your answer.

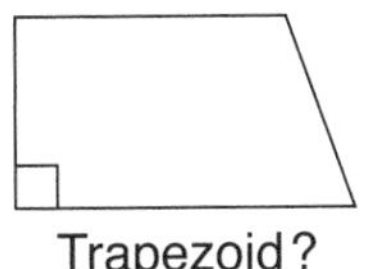
Trapezoid?

Imagine you are viewing the quadrilateral to the right from an angle that distorts the figure. You know that *WX* and *YZ* are equal, *XY* and *WZ* are equal, *XW* and *WZ* are equal, and $\angle XWZ$ is a right angle. Use the information to answer the questions below.

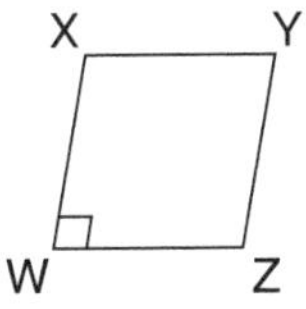

10. Is it possible for this figure to have only one right angle?

    Why or why not?

11. What is the name for this figure?

12. Explore Tiles are often made in the shape of squares because it is easy to fit squares together to cover a surface. Would it be possible to use rhombus-shaped tiles to cover a surface? How about trapezoid tiles?

Answers start on page 200.

TRIANGLES

A **triangle** is a polygon with three sides.

- The sum of the angles in a triangle is 180°.

To see this, draw a diagonal through a square. The square is divided into two equal triangles. Notice that the diagonal divides two of the right angles in half. The sum of the three angles in either of the triangles is 45° + 45° + 90° = 180°.

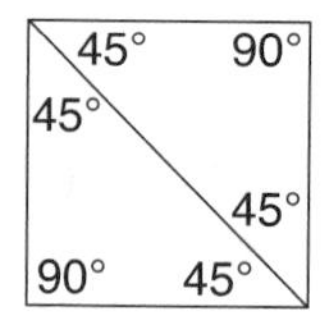

- Equal sides are opposite equal angles.

In the triangle *ABC*, ∠*A* and ∠*C* are equal. Both measure 45°. The sides across from them, *AB* and *BC*, are also equal.

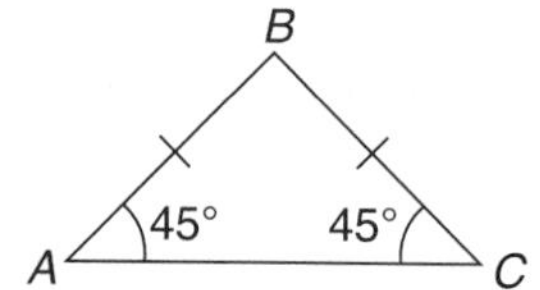

- The longest side is opposite the largest angle.

In triangle *ABC*, ∠*B* is the largest angle. The side across from it, side *AC*, is the longest side.

The names of the triangles come from the relationships among the angles and the sides.

Name	Properties	Examples
equilateral	three equal sides three equal angles	2 cm, 2 cm, 2 cm; 60°, 60°, 60°
isosceles	two equal sides two equal angles	2 cm, 2 cm; 70°, 70°
right	one right angle	
scalene	no equal sides no equal angles	2.1 cm, 1 cm, 2 cm; 55°, 25°, 100°

Identify each triangle.

1. 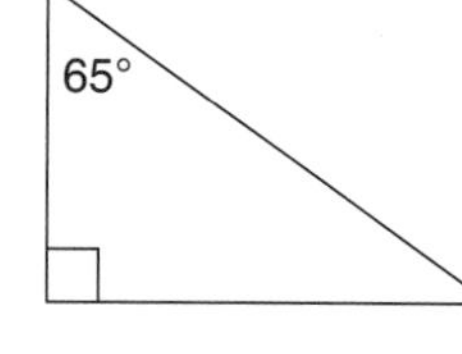

2. 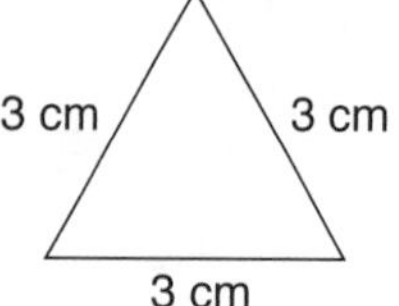

3. 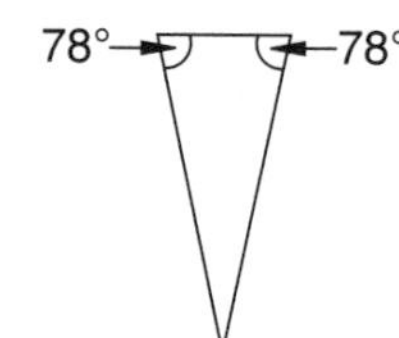

4. 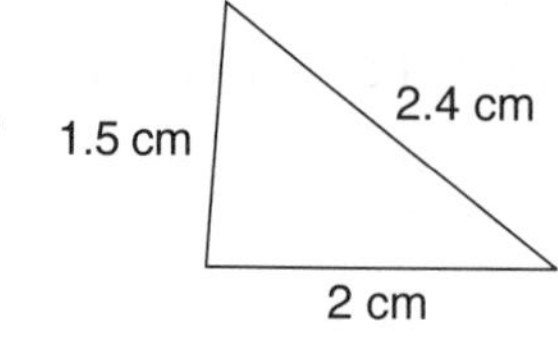

Use your knowledge of triangles to solve problems 5–7.

5. Determine which groups of three angles could form triangles.

_____ 30°, 30°, 90°

_____ 50°, 80°, 50°

_____ 45°, 60°, 75°

_____ 120°, 30°, 45°

_____ 50°, 60°, 70°

6. What is the longest side in triangle *CDE*? Why?

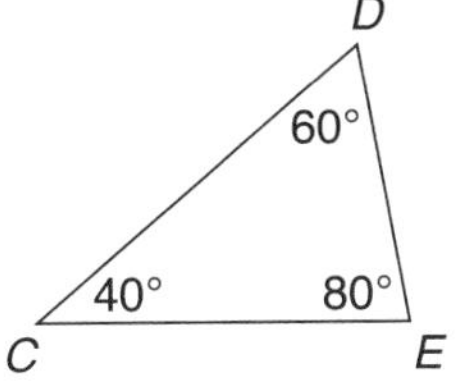

7. What is the largest angle in triangle *MNO*? How do you know?

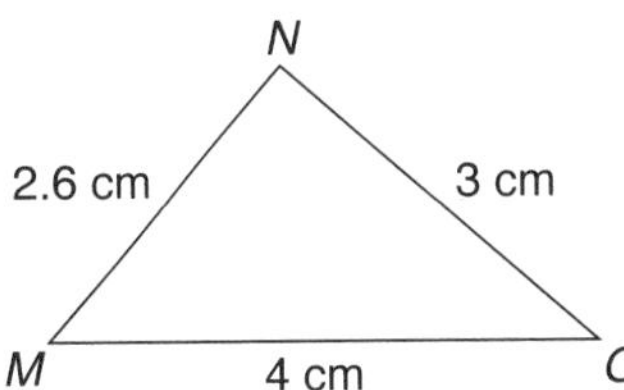

Use algebra to solve for the unknown angle(s).

8. What is the measure of ∠*U*?

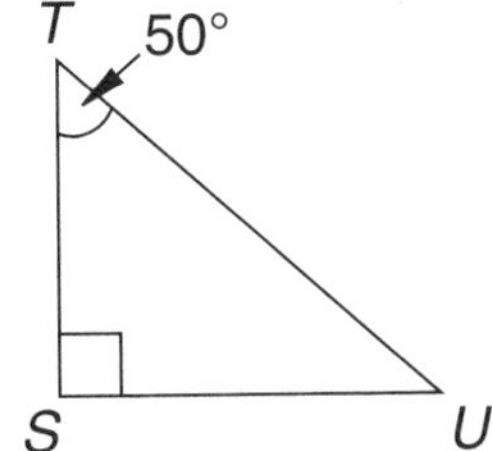

10. In the isosceles triangle *VWX*, ∠*W* measures 50°. What are the measures of ∠*V* and ∠*X*?

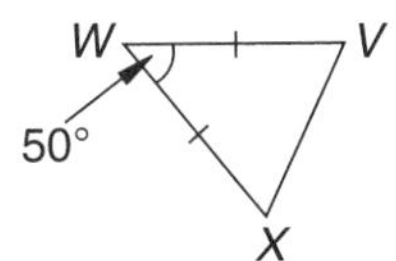

9. ∠*C* is twice the measure of ∠*A*. If ∠*B* measures 120°, what are the measures of ∠*A* and ∠*C*?

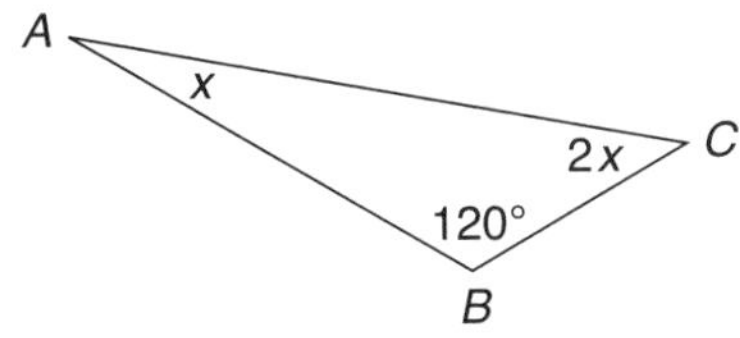

11. **Investigate** The rectangle below is divided into two triangles. Based on your knowledge of triangles, what is the sum of the angles in a rectangle?

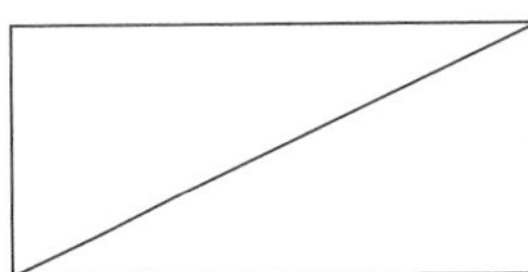

Answer these questions about isosceles triangles.

12. Triangle *BCD* is an isosceles triangle. If sides *BC* and *CD* are equal in length, then ∠*B* must be equal to which other angle?

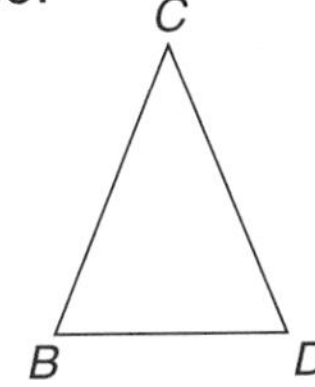

13. **Draw** Can there be a right angle in an isosceles triangle? Create a drawing that proves your answer.

Answers start on page 200.

THE PYTHAGOREAN THEOREM

A right triangle has a right angle, which equals 90°. The two sides that form the right angle are called **legs,** and the side opposite the right angle is the **hypotenuse.** The hypotenuse is always the longest side of a right triangle.

The relationship between the legs and hypotenuse of a right triangle was discovered almost 2,500 years ago by a Greek mathematician named Pythagoras.

Pythagorean theorem $a^2 + b^2 = c^2$
The sum of the squares of the legs of a right triangle equals the square of the hypotenuse.

FINDING THE HYPOTENUSE

Example The lengths of the legs of a right triangle are 9 and 12. What is the hypotenuse?

Step 1
Substitute 9 for *a* and 12 for *b* in the Pythagorean theorem formula.

$a^2 + b^2 = c^2$
$9^2 + 12^2 = c^2$

Step 2
Evaluate the left side of the equation.

$\sqrt{81 + 144} = c$
$\sqrt{225} = c$

Step 3
Find *c*.

$15 = c$

The hypotenuse is **15 units** long.

FINDING THE LEG OF A RIGHT TRIANGLE

Example The hypotenuse of a right triangle has a length of 10 units, and one of the legs is 6 units long. Find the measure of the other leg.

Step 1
Substitute 10 for *c* and 6 for *a* in the Pythagorean theorem formula.

$a^2 + b^2 = c^2$
$6^2 + b^2 = 10^2$

Step 2
Simplify the equation.

$36 + b^2 = 100$
$b = \sqrt{64}$

Step 3
Find *b*.

$b = 8$

The other leg is **8 units** long.

Solve each problem.

1. Find the measurement of side *MN*.

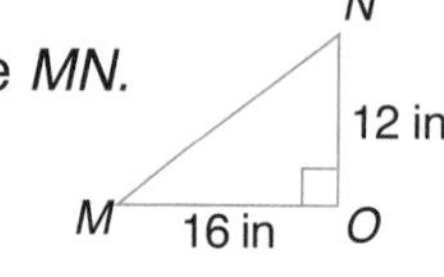

2. What is the measurement of side *PR*?

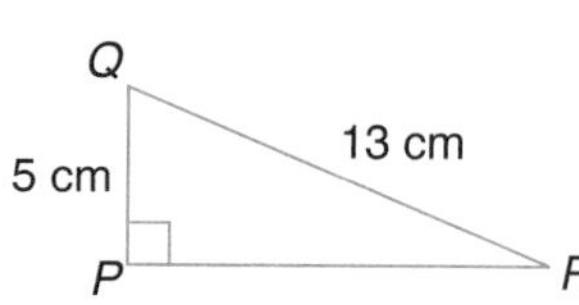

3. The legs of a right triangle measure 10 inches and 24 inches. What is the hypotenuse?

4. What is the measurement of side XZ?

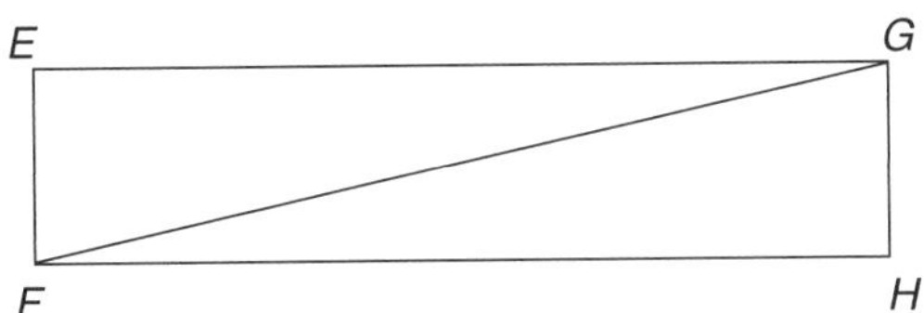

5. In the rectangle, side EF is 9 cm and side FH is 40 cm. Find the measure of the diagonal FG.

E G F H

6. If the lid of a box has a diagonal length of 10 inches and a length of 8 inches, what is the width of the box in inches?

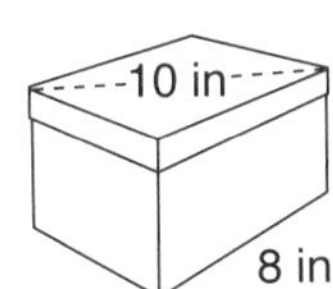

7. For a circus act, an 18-foot pole is braced with a wire that extends from the top of the pole to a stake in the ground 80 feet from the base of the pole. How long is the bracing wire?

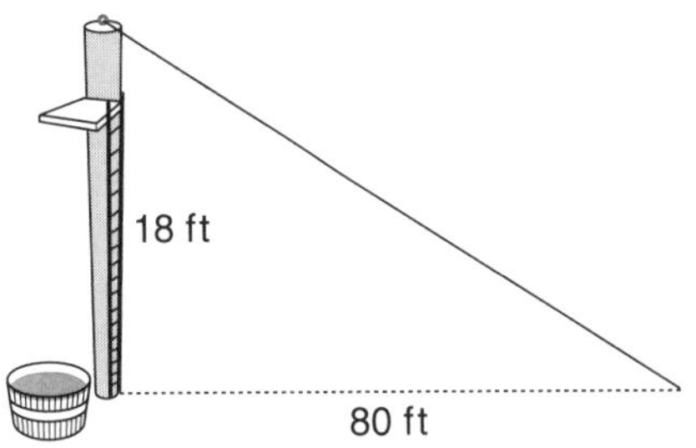

8. The base paths on a baseball diamond form right angles. To the nearest tenth of a foot, what is the distance from home plate to second base?

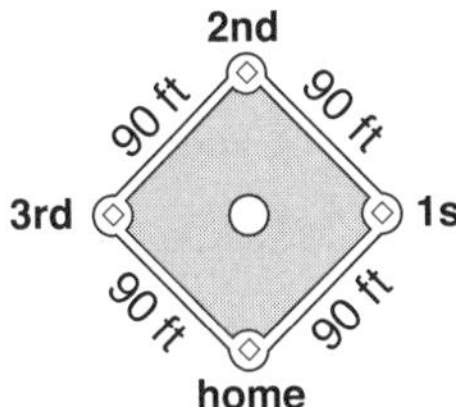

CORE CONNECTIONS: Pythagorean Triples

Most of the numbers you worked with in the examples and problems in this lesson are whole numbers.

A set of whole numbers that forms a right triangle is called a **Pythagorean triple.** Good test takers memorize the basic Pythagorean triples because they are often used on tests.

1. Each row of the table shows a Pythagorean triple. The second row multiplies the first triple by 2. The third row multiplies the first triple by 3. Continue the pattern and complete the next two rows of the table.

a	***b***	***c***
3	4	5
6	8	10
9	12	15

2. Create your own table of Pythagorean triples. Write 5, 12, and 13 as the first set of triples. Multiply each by 2 to find the next row. Fill in two more rows.

Answers start on page 201.

SIMILAR GEOMETRIC FIGURES

Similar figures have the same shape but are different sizes. Imagine using a copy machine to reduce a figure you have drawn. The figure on the copy would be in a smaller scale than the original, but the shape would be the same.

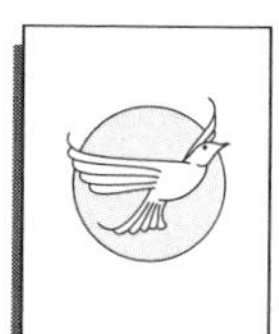

The triangles to the right are similar because the ratios of the lengths of corresponding sides are equal. Each side in the second triangle is half as long as the first.

ABC ~ *DEF* The symbol ~ means "is similar to."

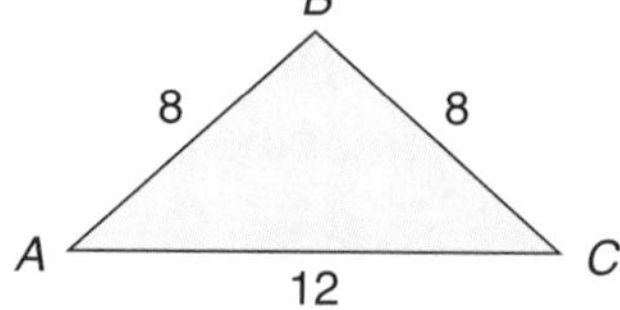

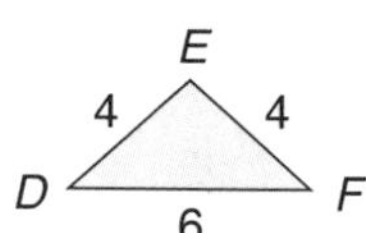

The rectangles shown are not similar.

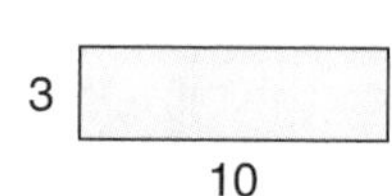

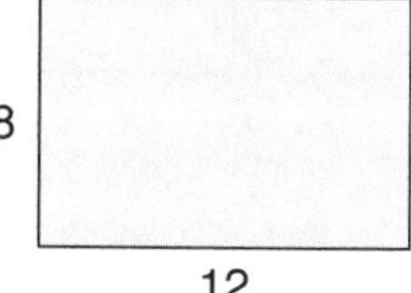

You can use proportion to solve problems about similar figures.

FINDING A MISSING SIDE

Example The plots of land shown here are similar. Find the width of the smaller plot.

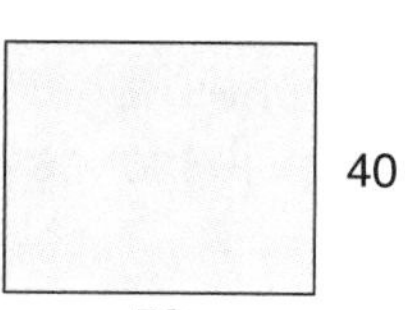

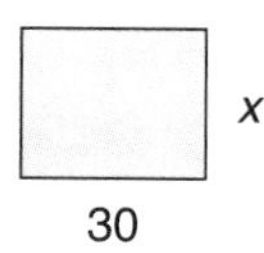

Step 1
Set up a proportion with corresponding sides.

$\frac{\text{length}}{\text{width}} \quad \frac{50}{40} = \frac{30}{x}$

Step 2
Cross multiply and solve for *x*.

$50x = 1{,}200$
$x = 24$

The width of the smaller plot is **24.**

Two triangles are similar if their corresponding angles are equal. When the sun casts the shadow of an object that is perpendicular to the ground, a right triangle is formed. The angle of the sun will be the same for any two objects, creating equal corresponding angles. You can find the height of a tall object by using a smaller object and comparing similar triangles.

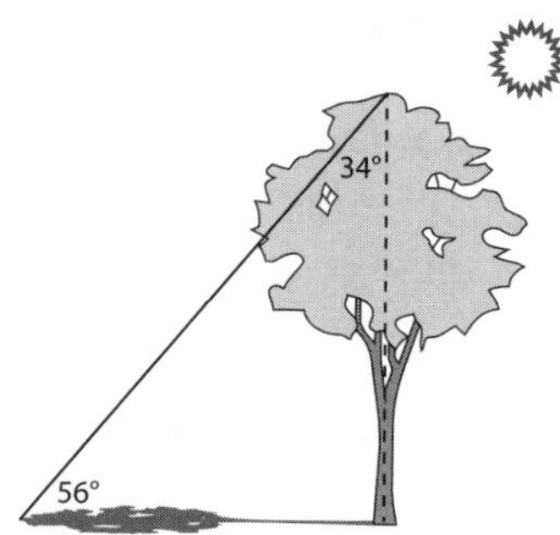

FINDING THE HEIGHT OF A TALL OBJECT

Example A street sign 6 feet high casts a shadow of 4 feet. At the same time, a nearby tree casts a 10-foot shadow. How tall is the tree?

Step 1
Set up a proportion with corresponding sides.

$\frac{\text{height}}{\text{shadow}} \quad \frac{6}{4} = \frac{x}{10}$

Step 2
Cross multiply and solve for x.

$4x = 60$
$x = 15$

The height of the tree is **15 feet.**

Decide whether each pair of figures is similar. Do not rely on the appearance of the drawings.

1.
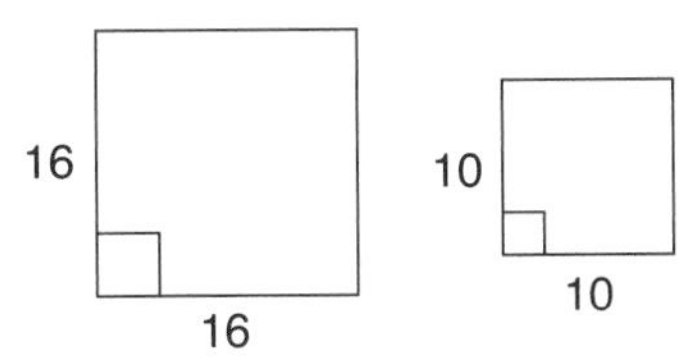

2.
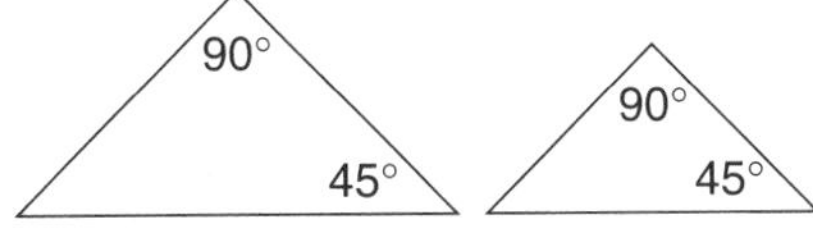

3.
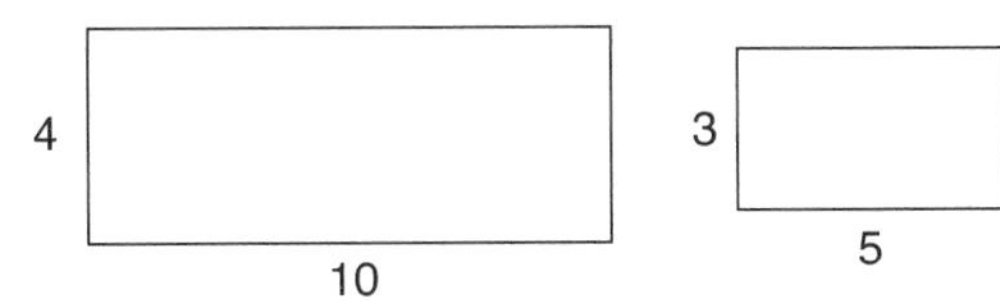

4.
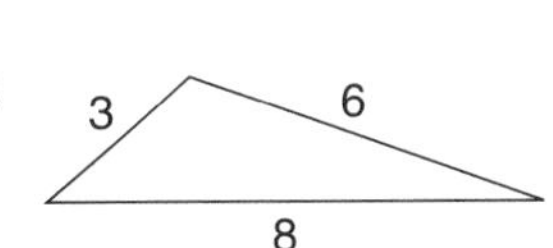

Solve the following.

5. Triangles *ABC* and *DEF* are similar. Find the missing lengths.

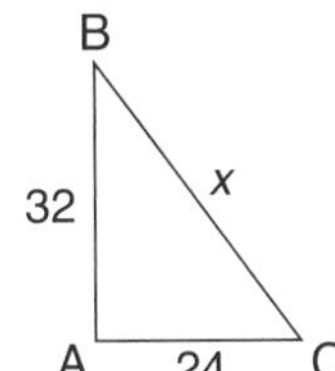

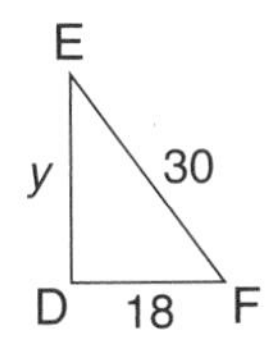

6. Karlene is using a photocopier to enlarge a graph that is 3 inches wide and 5 inches long. If her boss wants the length of the enlargement to be $7\frac{1}{2}$ inches, how wide will the graph be?

7. A billboard casts a shadow of 39 feet when a nearby 4-foot post casts a shadow of 6 feet. Find the height of the billboard.

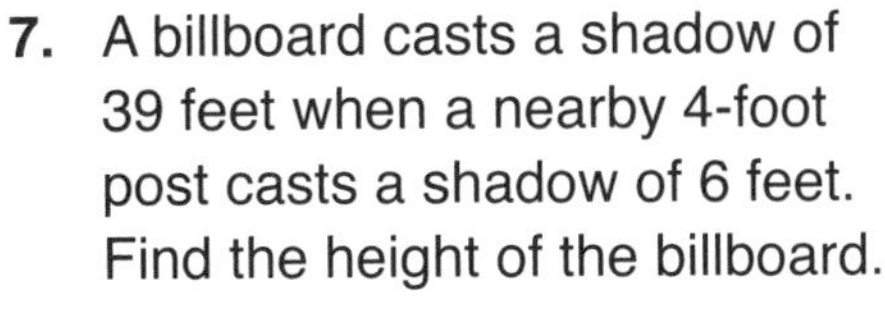
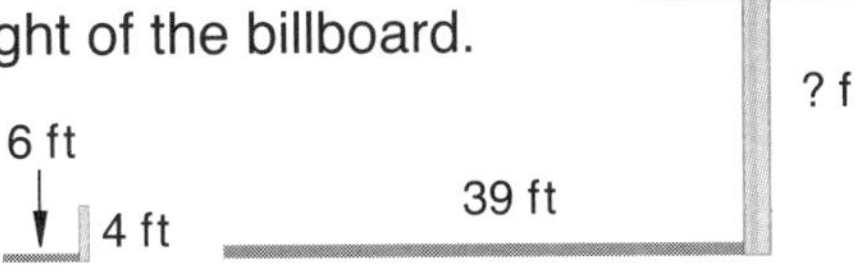

8. On a map, a rectangular park is 1.75 centimeters wide by 2.5 centimeters long. If the park is actually 200 yards long, what is its width in yards?

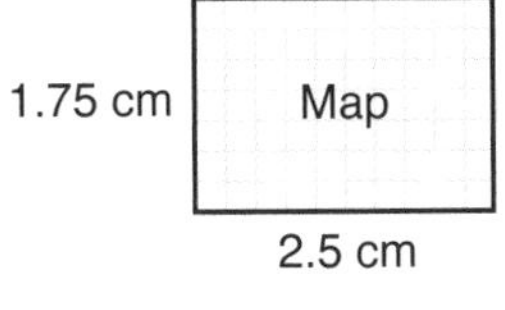

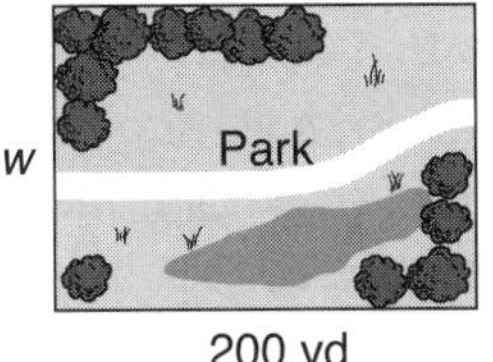

9. Triangles *XYZ* and *XVW* are similar. What is the length of *VW*?

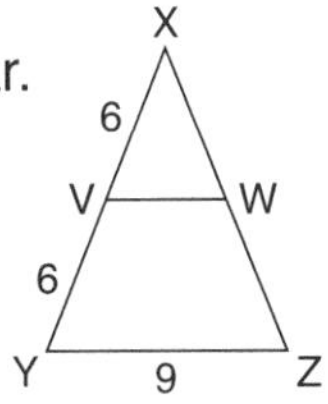

10. A building casts a shadow of 65 feet while a nearby street sign casts a shadow of 5 feet. If the street sign is 6 feet in height, how high is the building?

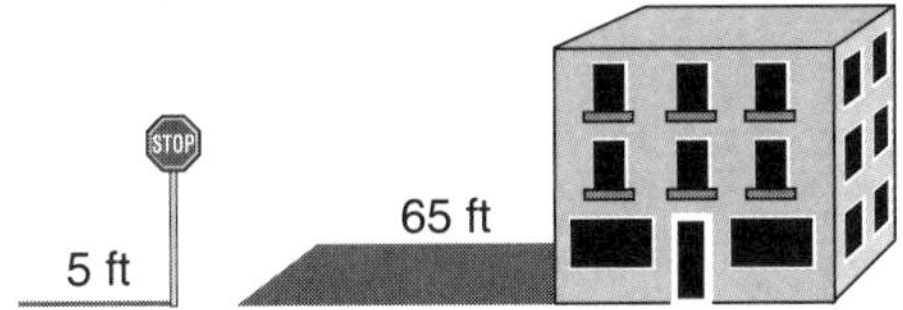

11. Analyze Write *True* or *False* after the following statements. Write one sentence explaining your reasoning for each one.

a. All equilateral triangles are similar.

b. All squares are similar.

c. All rectangles have equal angles; therefore, all rectangles are similar.

d. All right triangles are similar.

Answers start on page 201.

FINDING PATTERNS IN ALGEBRA AND GEOMETRY

Finding a pattern is a useful problem-solving strategy. It can save time you might otherwise spend in lengthy calculations. In this lesson, you will see how patterns can be helpful in solving problems.

One example of patterns in mathematics is the **number series.** A number series is a set of numbers that continues according to a rule.

The counting numbers (1, 2, 3, . . .) are a number series in which each number is 1 larger than the number before it. In the series 1, 4, 7, 10, . . . , each number is 3 more than the preceding number.

Find the next number in each of the following series. Write the rule that determines which number comes next.

1. 3, 6, 9, 12, 15, _____

2. 100, 91, 82, 73, 64, _____

3. 1, 10, 100, 1,000, _____

4. 2, 4, 8, 16, _____

5. 2, 5, 11, 23, 47, _____

6. 1, $\frac{1}{2}$, $\frac{1}{4}$, $\frac{1}{8}$, _____

Complete each series.

7.

8. A, E, I, M, Q, _____

(***Hint:*** Think about the position of each letter in the alphabet.)

9. 1, 4, 9, 16, 25, _____

10. 9 in, 1 ft 6 in, 2 ft 3 in, 3 ft, 3 ft 9 in, _____

11. –2, 4, –8, 16, –32, _____

You have seen how you can use proportion to solve problems that involve similar figures. Finding a pattern can often get the job done just as well. In the next example, the information is organized in a table. Tables and charts can make patterns easier to recognize.

FINDING A PATTERN WITH SIMILAR FIGURES

Example The triangles are similar. Find the measures of the missing sides.

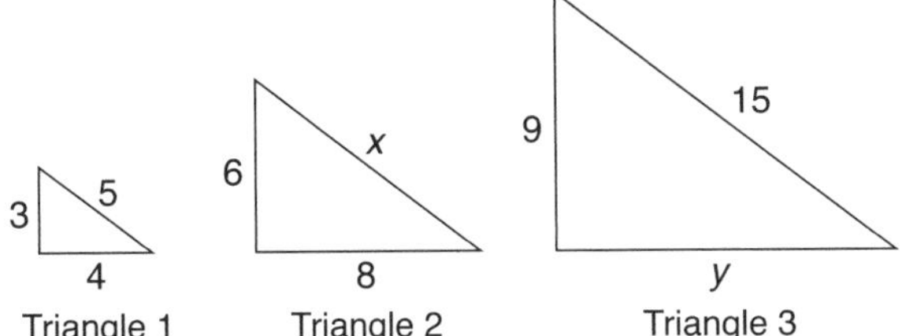

	Vertical Leg	Horizontal Leg	Hypotenuse
Triangle 1	3	4	5
Triangle 2	6	8	*x*
Triangle 3	9	*y*	15

Read down each column to find the pattern. You can quickly see that the sides of Triangles 2 and 3 are multiples of Triangle 1.

The missing side in Triangle 2 is **10.** The missing side in Triangle 3 is **12.**

This table shows the relationship between the length and width of several rectangles and their perimeters. Find the pattern and complete the table. Then solve problems 12–13.

Rectangle	Length	Width	Perimeter
ABCD	2	1	6
EFGH	3	2	10
IJKL	4	3	14
MNOP	5	4	
QRST			
UVWX			

12. Find the perimeter of a rectangle with a length of 6 and a width of 5.

13. Find the length of a rectangle with a width of 7 and a perimeter of 30.

The stair steps below are built with cubes. Count the number of cubes in each set to complete the chart. Then solve the problems.

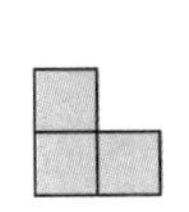
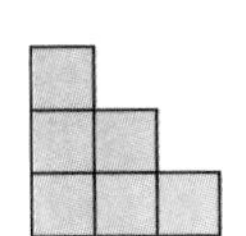
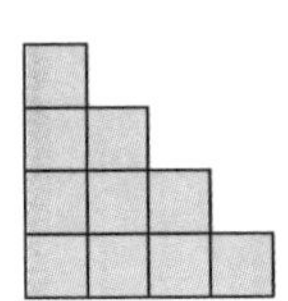
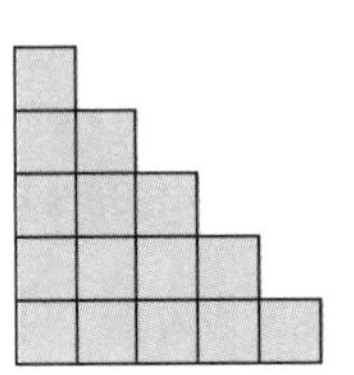
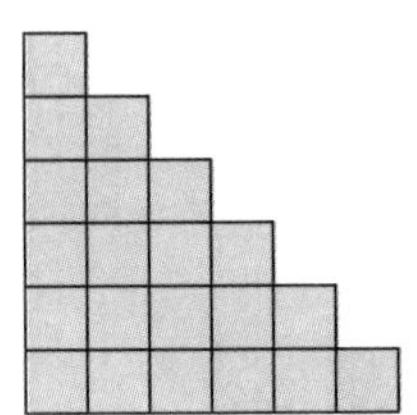

Number of steps	2	3	4	5	6
Number of cubes	3	6			

14. How many cubes are needed to make a stair step with 8 steps?

15. Explain How many blocks would you expect to find on the bottom row of a stair step with 20 steps? How do you know your answer is correct?

Answers start on page 202.

Mixed Review

Find the measure of the angle marked *x* in each drawing.

1.

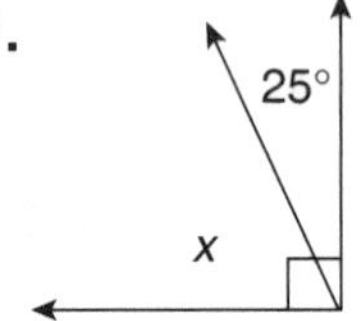

2.

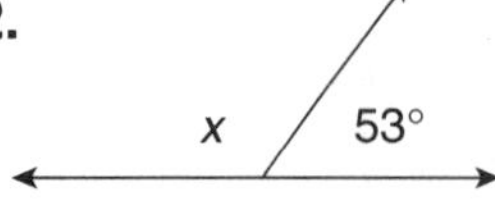

3.

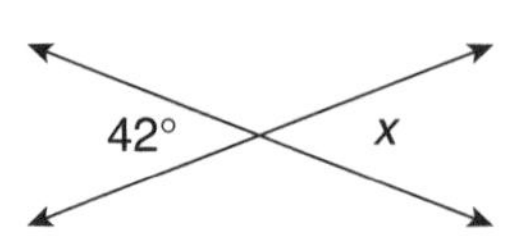

4.

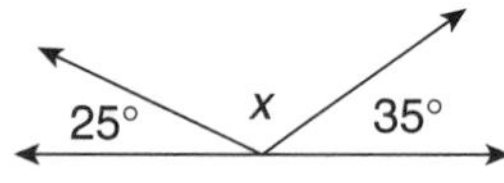

Solve.

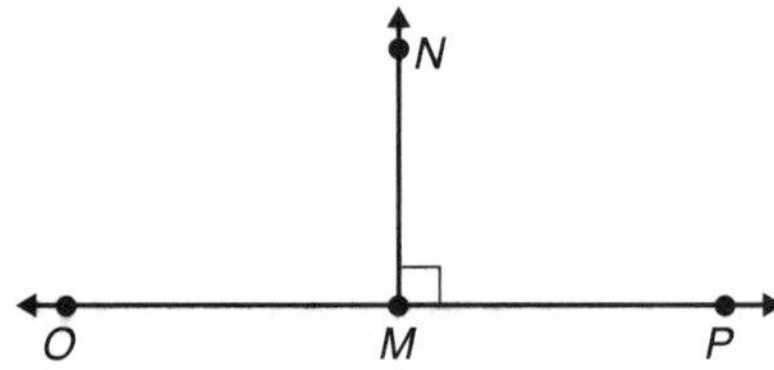

5. Line *OP* and ray *MN* are:

A. vertical
B. parallel
C. perpendicular

6. Angles *NMP* and *NMO* are:

A. acute
B. right
C. obtuse

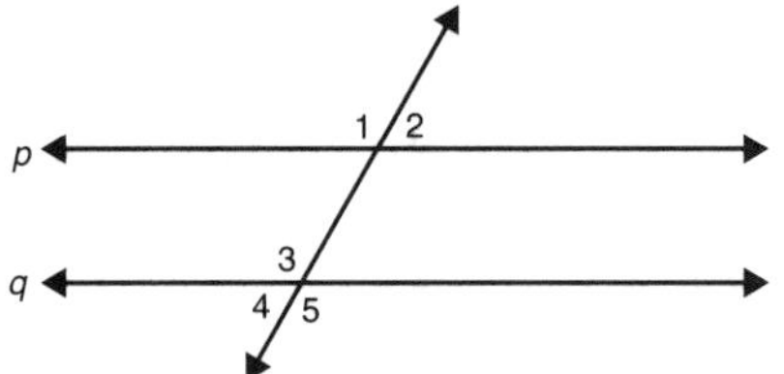

7. Angles 3 and 5 are:

A. vertical
B. parallel
C. perpendicular

8. In the drawing, lines *p* and *q* are parallel. If angle 1 equals 120°, what is the measure of angle 4?

Use the figure to the right to solve problems 9–11.

9. Find the number of degrees in ∠*LON*. What type of angle is it?

10. What kind of angle is ∠*KOM*?

11. Find the number of degrees in ∠*KON*. What type of angle is it?

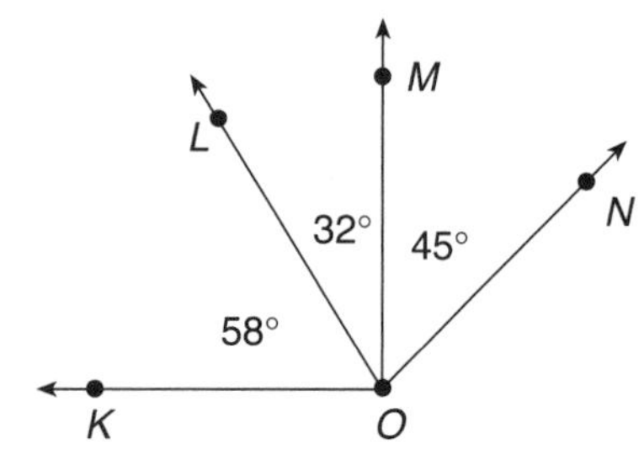

Solve.

12. Which of the combinations of angles cannot form a triangle? Explain your reasoning.

A. 30°, 60°, 90°
B. 50°, 65°, 65°
C. 40°, 50°, 100°
D. 30°, 30°, 120°

13. What is the largest angle in triangle *GHI*? Explain your reasoning.

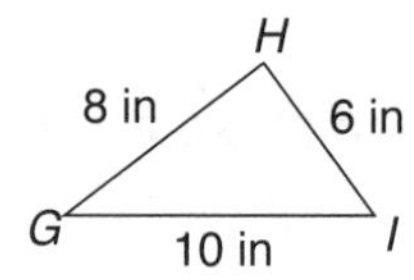

For problems 14–16, tell whether the figures are similar.

14. 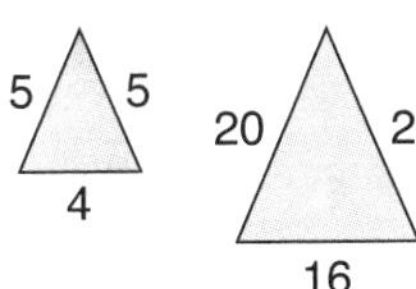

15. 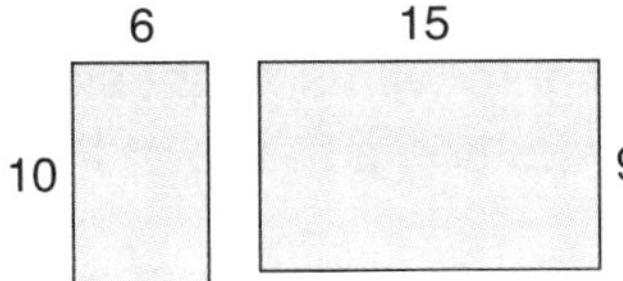

16. 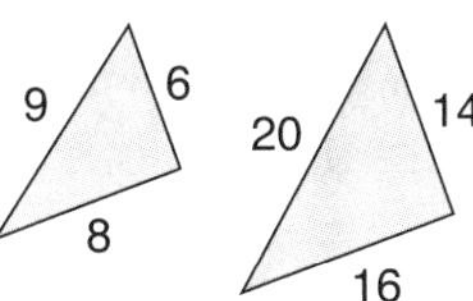

In problems 17–19, each pair of figures is similar. Find x.

17. 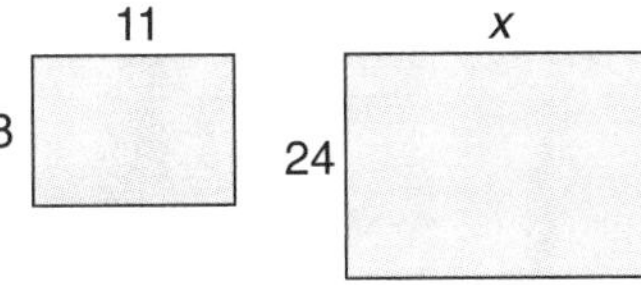

18. 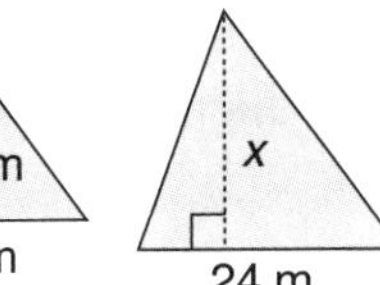

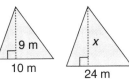

19. 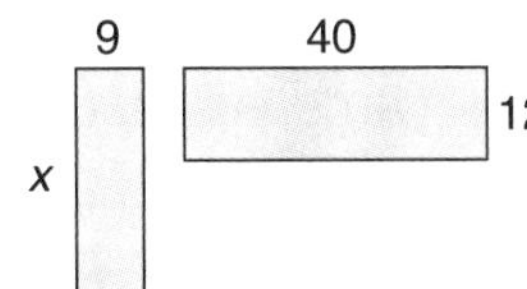

Solve.

20. The tree in the drawing casts a 40-foot shadow. At the same time, a 3-foot stick casts a 2-foot shadow. How tall is the tree?

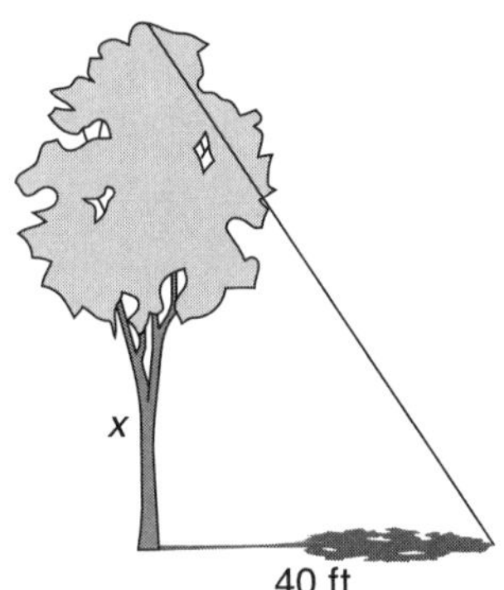

21. *ABCD* is a rectangle.

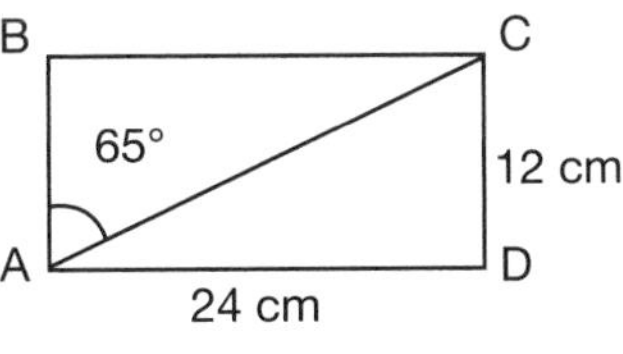

a. If $\angle BAC$ has a measure of 65°, what is the measure of $\angle CAD$?

b. What is the measure of diagonal *AC* to the nearest centimeter?

22. How high up on a wall does a 50-foot ladder reach if the foot of the ladder is 14 feet from the wall?

23. The image to the right is enlarged so that it is 24 inches long. What is the width (the shorter side) of the enlargement?

24. The back of a rectangular frame has a metal support stretching from corner to corner as shown. To the nearest tenth inch, what is the length of the diagonal support?

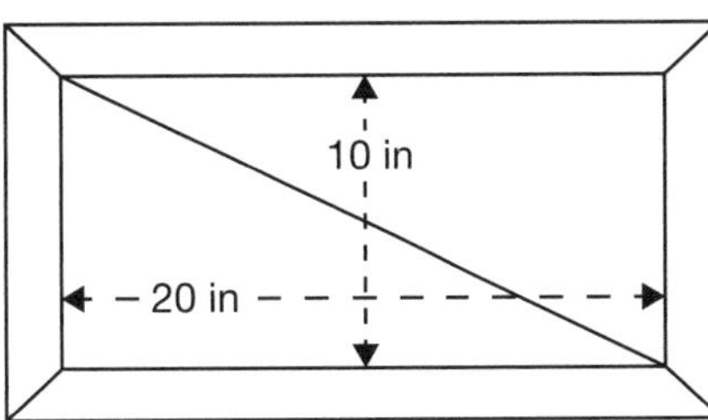

Answers start on page 202.

PERIMETER

Perimeter (P) is the distance around a flat figure with straight sides. Perimeter problems are often about fencing an area or putting a frame or trim around an object.

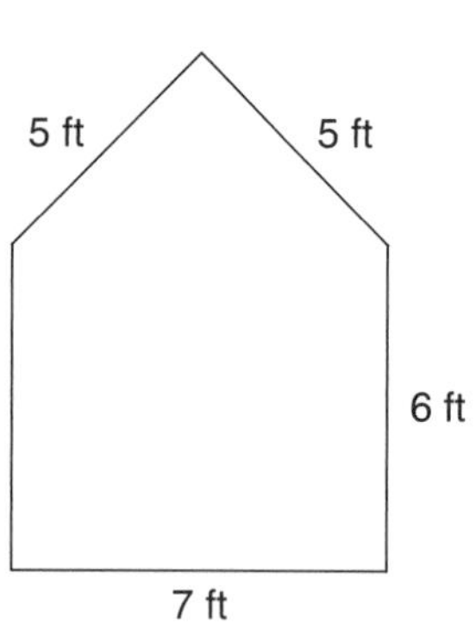

Perimeter formulas exist, but you really don't need them. To find the perimeter of any shape, simply add the lengths of its sides.

The perimeter of this five-sided figure is 5 + 5 + 6 + 6 + 7 = **29 feet.**

Perimeter is a measure of length. Typical units of measure for perimeter are inches, feet, yards, miles, centimeters, meters, and kilometers.

FINDING PERIMETER USING THE PROPERTIES OF A SHAPE

Example What is the perimeter of the parallelogram?

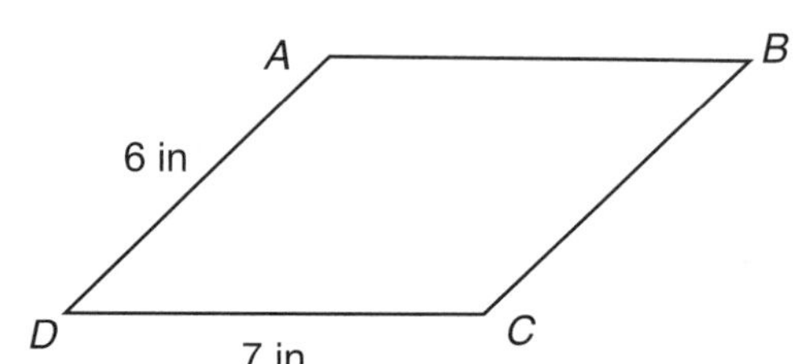

Step 1
Two sides are not labeled. However, since the figure is a parallelogram, you know that opposite sides are equal.

AD and *BC* = 6 inches
DC and *AB* = 7 inches

Step 2
Add to find the perimeter.

6 + 6 + 7 + 7 = 26

The perimeter of the parallelogram is **26 inches.**

Solve.

1. Find the perimeter of rectangle *EFGH.*

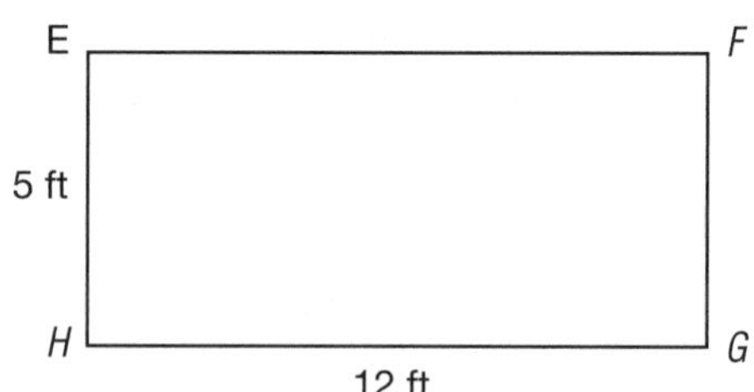

2. One side of a square measures 6.5 centimeters. What is the perimeter of the square?

3. What is the distance around the figure?

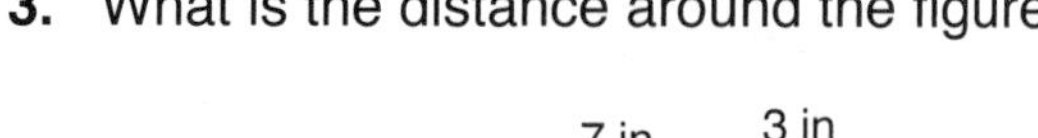

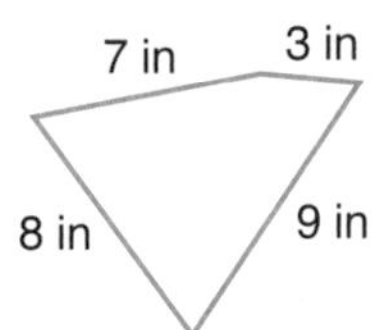

4. What is the perimeter of the six-sided figure?

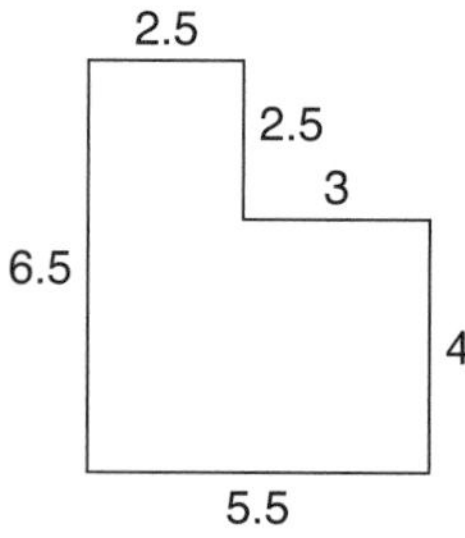

5. The fountain in the diagram is enclosed by a low stone wall. What is the length of the wall?

Sometimes you need to calculate the measure of one or more sides before you can find the perimeter.

FINDING UNKNOWN SIDES

Example The drawing shows a room from a dollhouse with measurements in inches. What is the perimeter of the room?

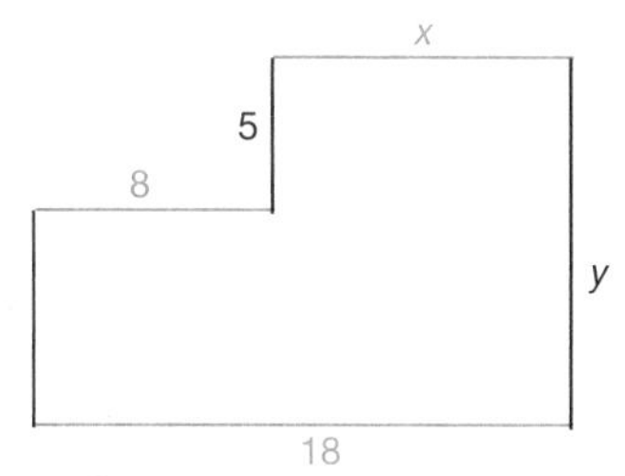

Before you can add all the sides, you need to find the missing sides, *x* and *y*.

Step 1
Look at the horizontal sides. The sum of the sides labeled 8 and *x* is equal to the side labeled 18.

$8 + x = 18$, so $x = 10$

Step 2
Look at the vertical sides. The sum of the sides labeled 7 and 5 is equal to the side labeled *y*.

$5 + 7 = y$, so $y = 12$

Step 3.
Add the sides.

$8 + 5 + 10 + 12 + 18 + 7 = 60$

The perimeter of the room is **60 inches.**

Find the perimeter of the following figures.

6.

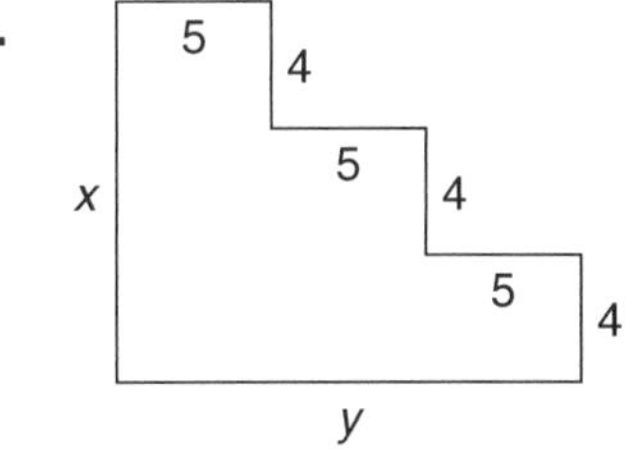

7.

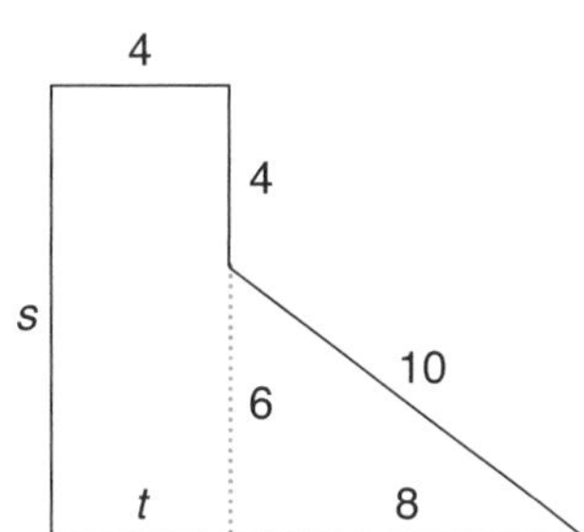

8.

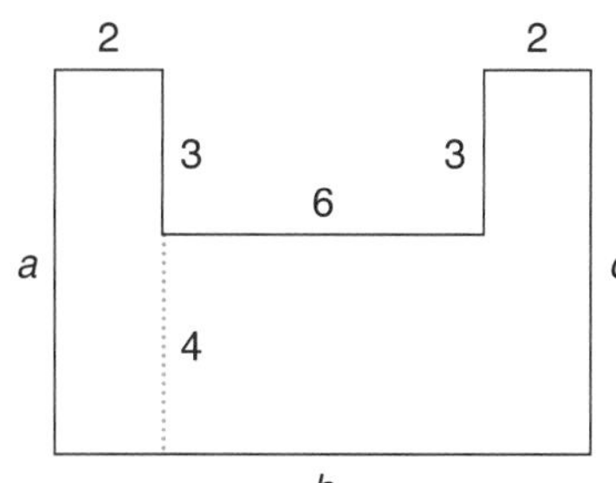

Solve.

9. Find the perimeter of the isosceles triangle.

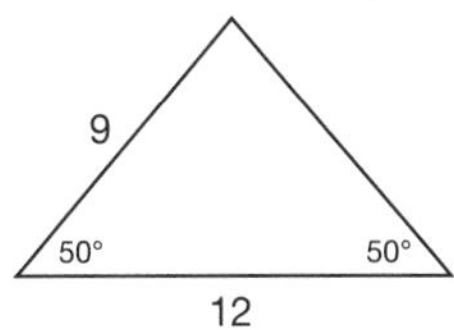

10. The rectangle is two stacked squares. What is the perimeter of the rectangle?

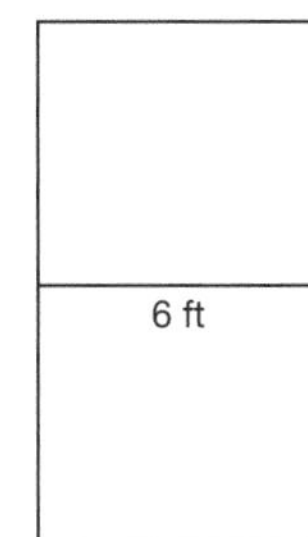

11. Use Algebra A rectangular landscape is three times as long as it is wide. If the perimeter of the landscape is 64 inches, what is the length?

12. Explain The stage area shown consists of two rectangular platforms and a triangular one. Suppose you need to find the perimeter of the stage. Explain how you could find the measures of sides *a* and *b*.

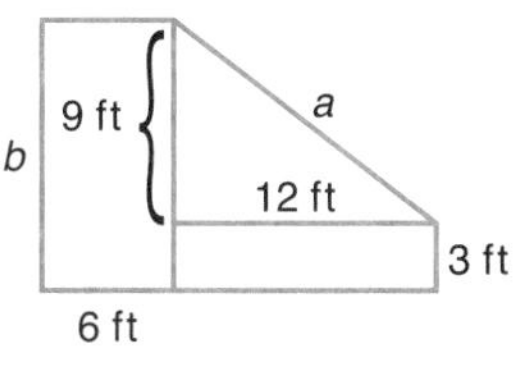

Answers start on page 203.

AREA OF SQUARES, RECTANGLES, AND PARALLELOGRAMS

Area is the measure of the surface of a flat figure. Area is measured using squares of a certain size. Imagine tiling a floor with square tiles. Area is the number of tiles that would cover the space.

The size of the tile determines the unit. If a tile is 1 foot on each side, it is a square foot. If no measurement is given, the tile is called a square unit.

How would you count the tiles in the figure to the right? The rectangle has 4 rows of 6 tiles each. The easiest way to count the tiles is to multiply: 4 × 6 = 24

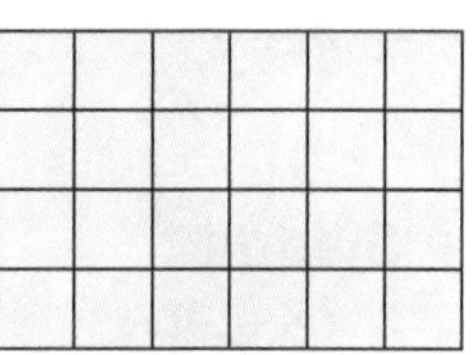
24 square units

For most two-dimensional figures, you can use this same plan. To count the squares, multiply the **base** (horizontal distance) by the **height** (vertical distance).

FINDING THE AREA OF A SQUARE

Example What is the area of the square?

Multiply the base by the height. (cm² is read "centimeters squared.")   3 × 3 = **9 cm^2**

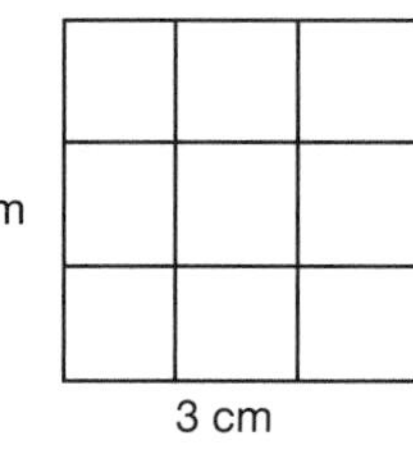

✔ **TIP**

Write square centimeters as sq cm or cm^2.

FINDING THE AREA OF A RECTANGLE

Example A high school basketball court is 84 by 50 feet. What is the area in square feet?

Multiply the base by the height.   84 × 50 = **4,200 sq ft**

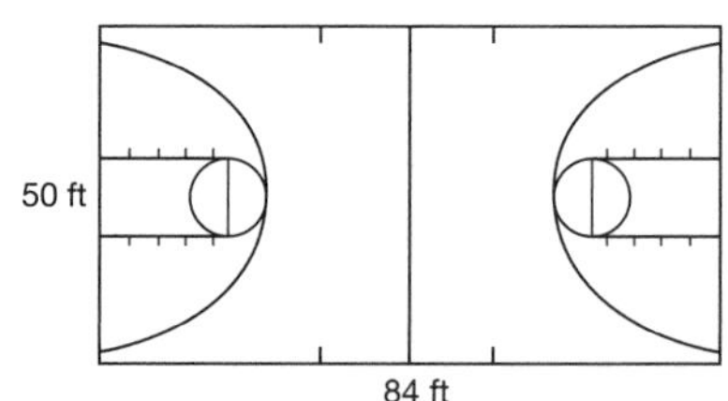

FINDING THE AREA OF A PARALLELOGRAM

Example What is the area of the parallelogram in square inches?

Multiply the base by the height. (in^2 is read "inches squared" and means square inches.)   18 × 12 = **216 in^2**

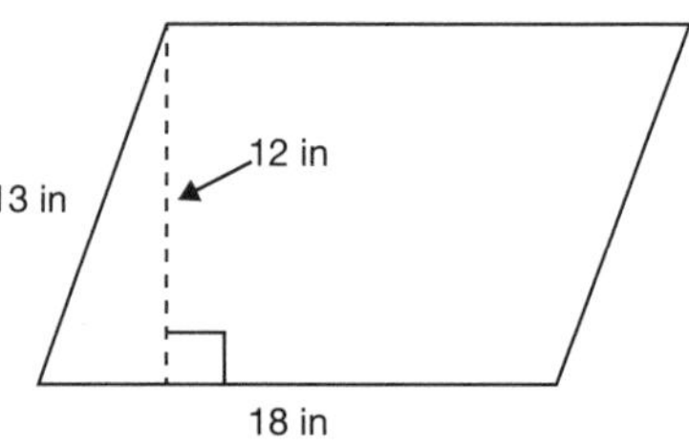

In a figure, the base and height are perpendicular. In other words, the height is at a 90° angle to the base. In the drawing of the parallelogram, the slanted sides of the parallelogram measure 13 inches, but the height is 12 inches.

To find the perimeter of a parallelogram, use the sides: 13 + 18 + 13 + 18 = 62 inches
To find its area, use the base and height: 18 × 12 = 216 square inches

Find the area of the figures. Remember to label your answer in square units.

1. 4 in, 4 in

2. 3.4 cm, 5.3 cm

3. 12 in, 9 in

4.

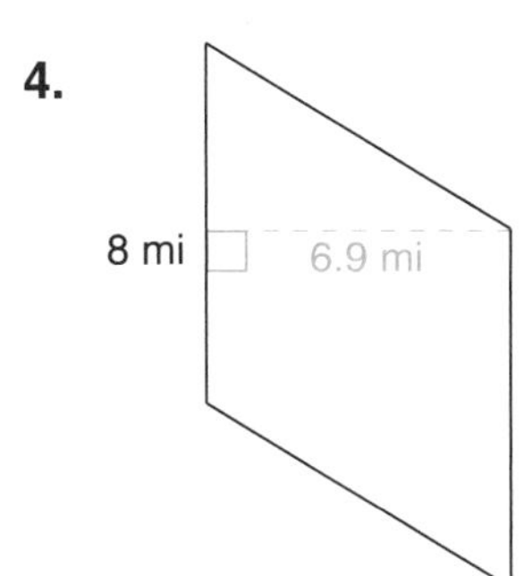

5. 0.7 cm, 0.6 cm

6.

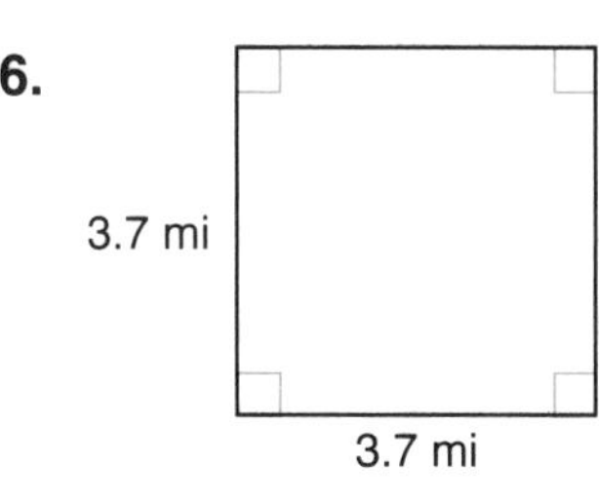

Use the diagram of a regulation tennis court for problems 7–10.

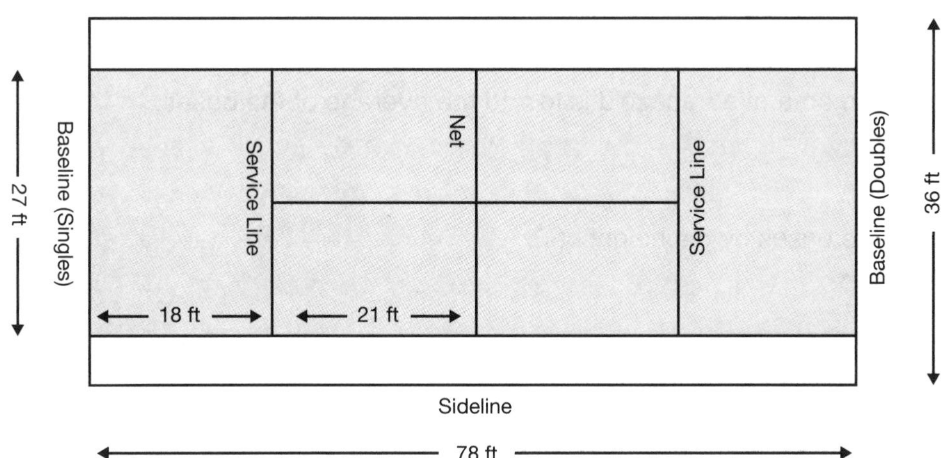

7. A singles court will be painted a contrasting color. How many square feet will be painted?

8. On a singles court, what is the area of the rectangle between the service line and the baseline?

9. A ball being served must land in the opposite small rectangle adjacent to the net. What is the area of the space where a serve must land?

10. There are 9 square feet in 1 square yard. What is the area of a regulation doubles court in *square yards*?

11. Explain Two rectangles have different dimensions but the same area. Do the rectangles have the same perimeter? Explain your thinking. Draw an example to support your reasoning.

12. Draw A figure has an area of 100 square feet. Draw and label a square, a rectangle, and a parallelogram, each with an area of 100 square feet.

Answers start on page 203.

AREA OF TRIANGLES AND TRAPEZOIDS

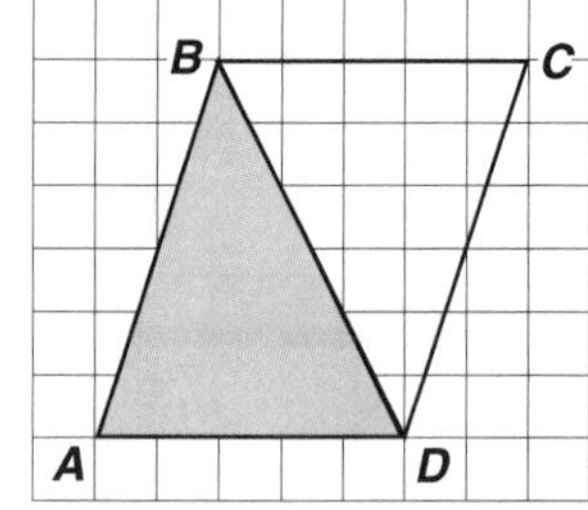

Triangles are related to parallelograms. Study the drawing to the right. Compare triangle *ABD* to parallelogram *ABCD.* What do you notice about the area of the shapes? How are they related?

The area of the triangle is one-half the area of the parallelogram. If you know one, you can solve for the other. Parallelogram *ABCD* has a base of 5 and a height of 6. Find the areas of both figures.

Area of *ABCD*:	base × height	5 × 6 = 30 square units
Area of *ABD*:	base × height ÷ 2	5 × 6 ÷ 2 = **15 square units**

You can write the following formula based on the example.

Area (*A*) of a Triangle $A = \frac{1}{2}bh$, where b = base and h = height

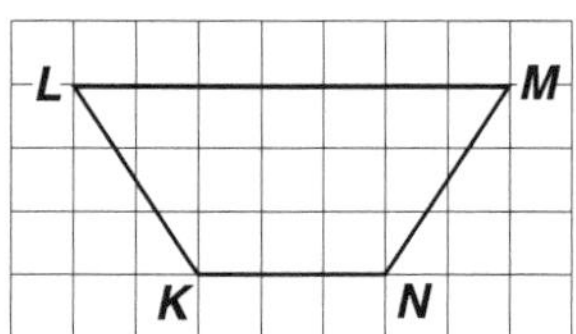

Look at trapezoid *KLMN.* To find its area, you need to multiply base by height, but a trapezoid has two bases.

The first step in finding the area of a trapezoid is to find the average of the bases.

$\frac{LM + KN}{2}$ $\frac{7+3}{2} = \frac{10}{2} = 5$

Multiply the average of the bases by the height of 3.
5 × 3 = **15 square units**

You are given the formula for finding the area of a trapezoid on the GED math formula sheet.

Area (*A*) of a Trapezoid $A = \frac{1}{2}h(b_1 + b_2)$, where h = height and b_1 and b_2 are the bases

Make sure you understand the formula. Multiplying by $\frac{1}{2}$ is the same as dividing by 2. The formula adds the bases and multiplies by $\frac{1}{2}$, which gives the average of the bases. Then it multiplies by the height. The formula puts the steps in a different order, but it accomplishes the same thing.

As you solve problems, remember that it doesn't matter how the figure is turned. In a triangle, any side can be a base. In a trapezoid, the parallel sides are bases. For all figures, the height must be at a right angle to the base.

In this figure, the base is 8 and the height is 7.4.

$A = \frac{1}{2} \times 8 \times 7.4 =$ **29.6 km²**

8 km
7.4 km

Find the area of each figure.

1. 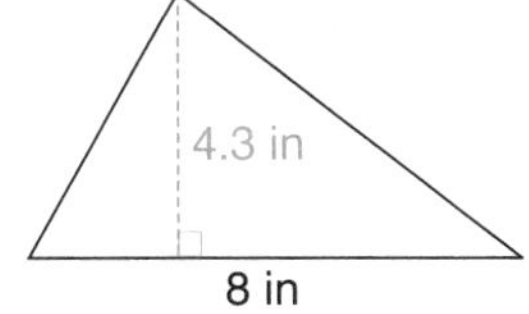

2. 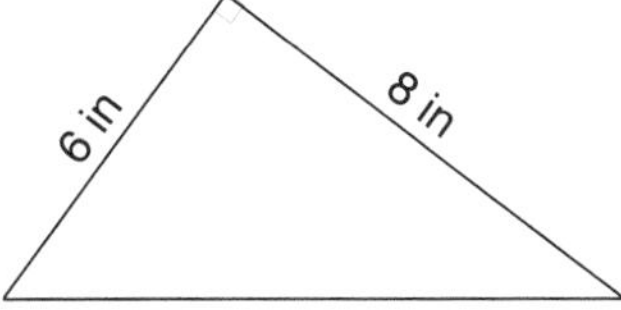

3. 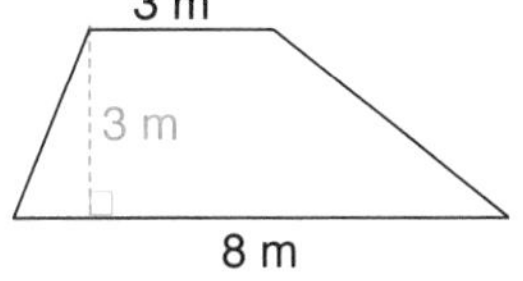

4. 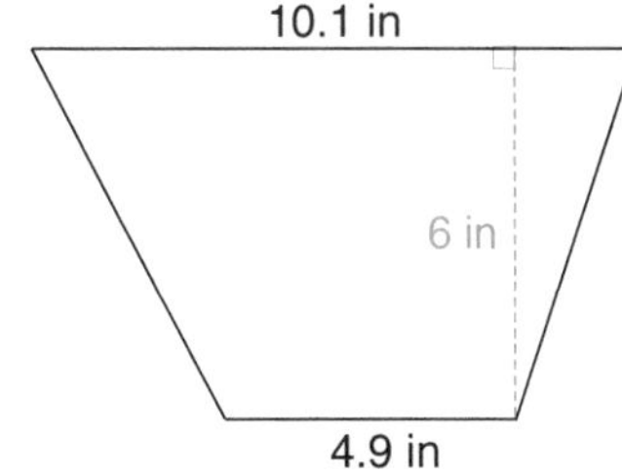

5. 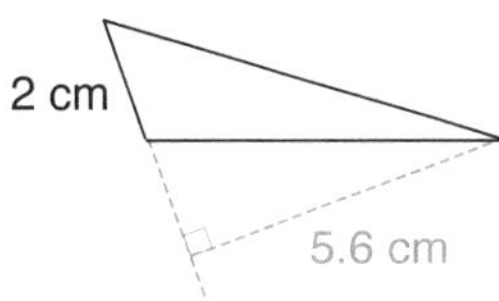

6. 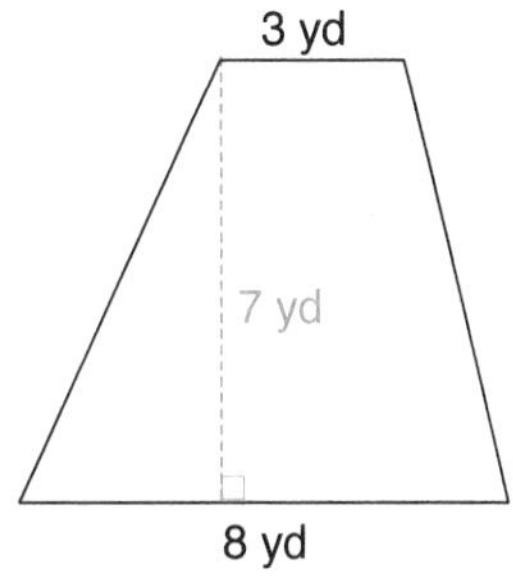

Solve as directed.

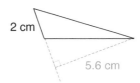

7. Karla wants to add a triangular extension to the deck shown below. How many square feet will be added to the deck?

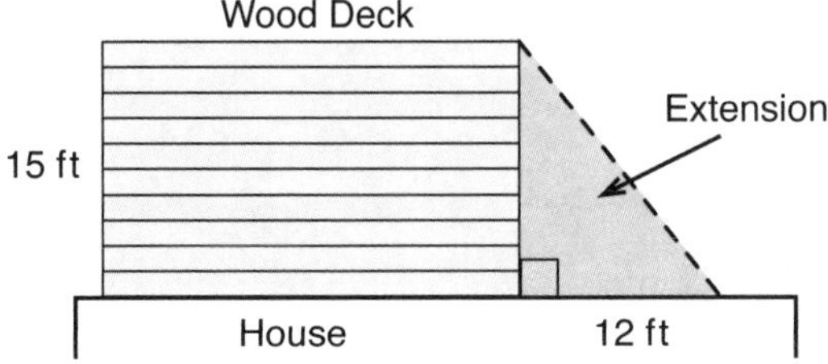

8. The two legs of a right triangle are 9 inches and 14 inches. What is the area of the triangle in square inches?

9. Explore One way to find the area of a figure is to cut it into smaller shapes.

a. Find the area of the trapezoid using the trapezoid formula.

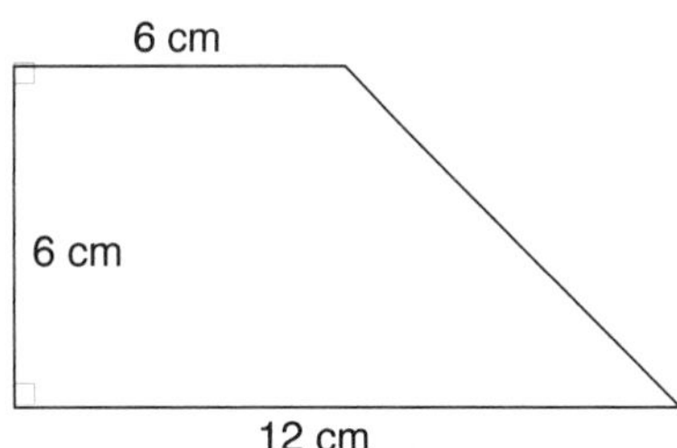

b. The trapezoid has been divided into smaller shapes in two different ways. Find the area of the individual pieces and add to find the total area.

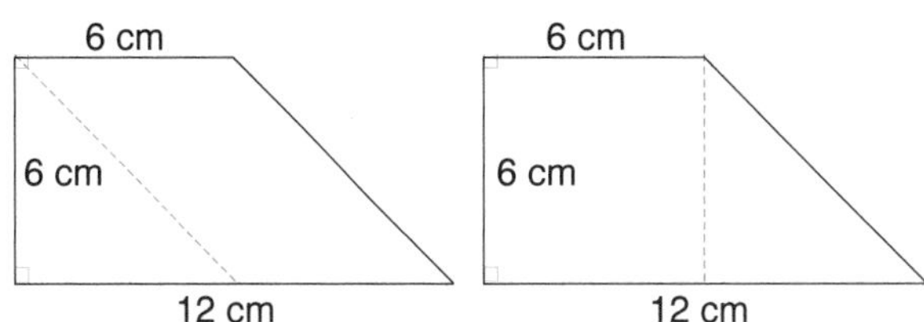

Answers start on page 203.

CIRCUMFERENCE AND AREA OF CIRCLES

A **circle** is a set of closed points in a plane. Every point on a circle is the same distance from the center.

The distance around a circle is called the **circumference.** Measuring the circumference of a circle is challenging because you can't use a ruler to measure something round. But you can measure the distance straight across.

The **diameter** is a line segment that passes through the center of a circle. Drawing a diameter cuts the circle into two equal halves.

Half of the diameter is the **radius.** The radius is the distance from the center to any point on the circle.

You can approximate circumference using a relationship that exists between the circumference of a circle and its diameter. Whatever the size of the circle, the circumference is always a little more than 3 times the diameter.

The ratio of the circumference to the diameter is called **pi,** represented by the Greek letter π. The value of π is about 3.14. Pi can be used to write formulas for finding the circumference and area of circles. You should memorize these formulas. They will not be listed on the GED math formula sheet.

Circumference (C) of a Circle	$C = \pi d$, where d = diameter
Area (A) of a Circle	$A = \pi r^2$, where r = radius

USING CIRCLE FORMULAS

Example What is the circumference and area of a circle when PQ equals 12 inches?

PQ is the diameter: $d = 12$
The radius is half the diameter: $r = 6$

Use the circumference formula:
$C = \pi d$
$\approx 3.14 \cdot 12$
≈ 37.68 inches

Use the area formula:
$A = \pi r^2$
$\approx 3.14 \cdot 6^2$
$\approx 3.14 \cdot 36$
≈ 113.04 square inches

Remember that area is measured in square units. Even though you can't fit squares into a circle, you can estimate how many would fit.

Find the circumference and area of each circle. Round to the nearest tenth.

1.

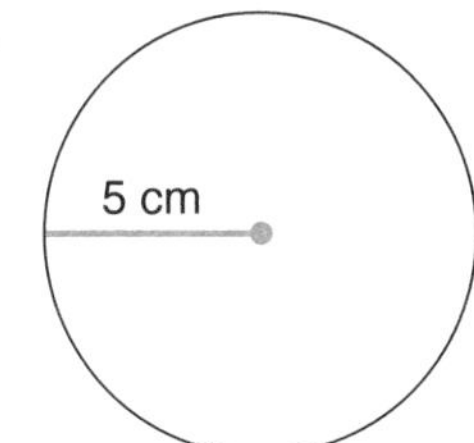

2.

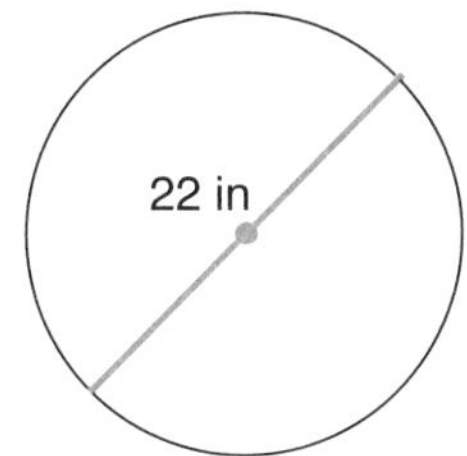

3.

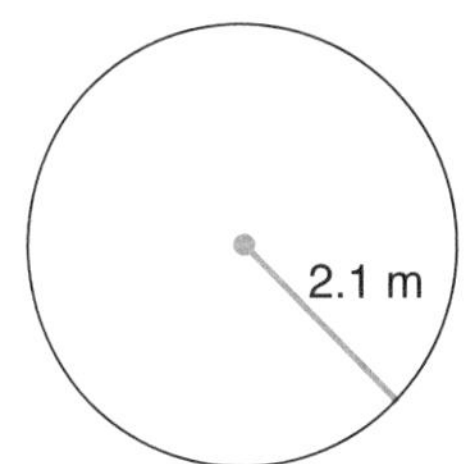

4. Sasha needs to buy one packet of seeds for every 12 square feet in her garden. If the circular garden has a diameter of 18 feet, how many packets of seeds will Sasha need?

5. Max is planting a circular flower garden in the center of a lawn. He has 30 feet of fencing to go around the garden. To the nearest tenth of a foot, what is the greatest diameter the garden can have without Max buying more fencing?

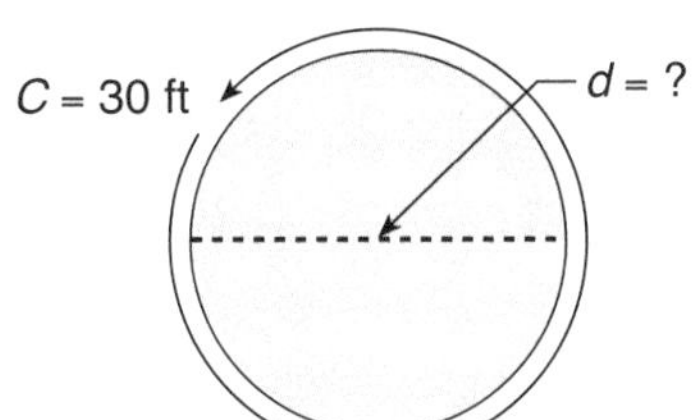

6. Cans of frozen juice concentrate often have plastic strips that you pull to remove the lid from the can. The length of the strip is the circumference of the lid plus 0.25 inch. If the radius of the lid is 1.25 inches, what is the length of the plastic strip to the nearest tenth of an inch?

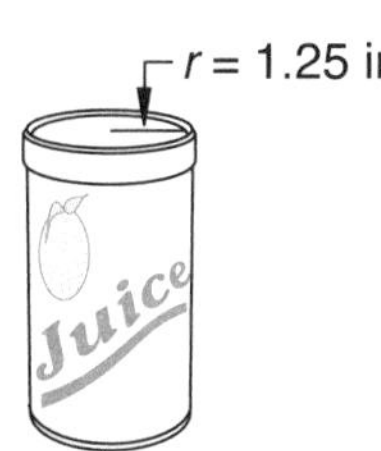

CORE CONNECTIONS: Lines of Symmetry

A figure has **symmetry** when a line can divide it into two parts that are exact mirror images of each other. Some figures have more than one line of symmetry.

A square has four lines of symmetry.

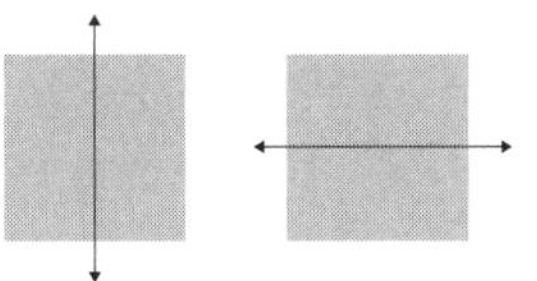
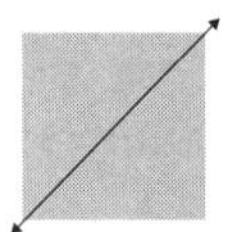
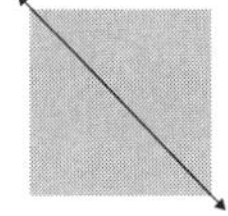

1. How many lines of symmetry can you draw for each figure?

2. What geometric shape would be symmetrical for any line drawn through its center?

Answers start on page 204.

AREA OF COMPLEX FIGURES

A complex figure is made from more than one shape. The area of a complex figure can't be found using a single formula. Instead, you have to develop a plan of your own for finding the area.

Some figures can be cut up into smaller pieces. The area is the sum of the areas of these smaller shapes.

ADDING TO FIND AREA

Example What is the area of the figure in square inches?

10, 5, 5, 9

Step 1
Divide the figure into smaller parts.

Here, the figure is divided into a rectangle and a square.

Step 2
Find the areas of the parts.

Rectangle: $A = 10 \cdot 9$
$= 90$ sq in

Square: $A = 5 \cdot 5$
$= 25$ sq in

Step 3
Find the total area.

90 + 25 = **115 sq in**

Some complex figures appear to be missing a piece. You can subtract the area of the missing piece from the area of the larger figure.

SUBTRACTING TO FIND AREA

Example What is the area of the shaded part of the figure?

20 cm, 20 cm, 9 cm, 14 cm

Step 1
Divide the figure into smaller parts.

A rectangle is cut out of a square.

Step 2
Find the areas of the parts.

Square: $A = 20 \cdot 20$
$= 400\ cm^2$

Rectangle: $A = 14 \cdot 9$
$= 126\ cm^2$

Step 3
Find the area of the shaded portion.

$400 - 126 =$ **274 cm²**

When you are working with a complex figure, there is almost always more than one way to solve the problem. Look at the measurements you are given, and choose the way that seems easiest for you.

Find the area of each figure.

1. 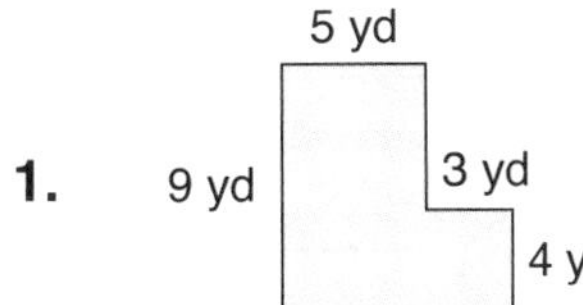

2. 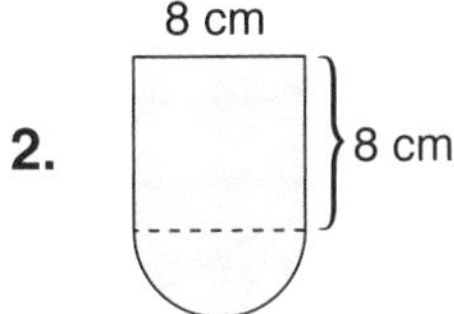

(***Hint:*** This figure contains a half-circle.)

3. 25 ft
20 ft
10 ft

4. 5 yd
9 yd
3 yd
4 yd

5. 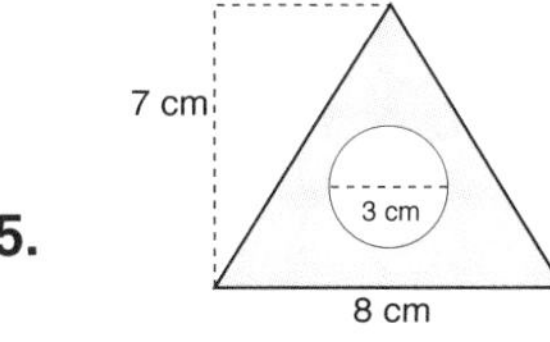

6. 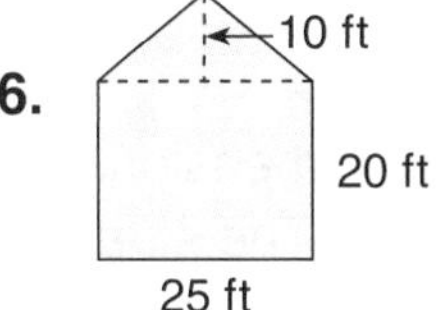

Solve.

7. A circular fountain has a 3-foot walkway surrounding it. What is the area of the walkway? Round to the nearest tenth.

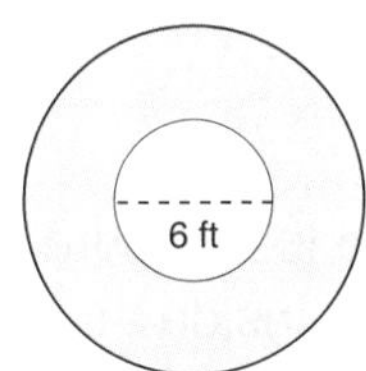

8. An X is formed by drawing one 11-by-6-inch rectangle on top of another. What is the area in square inches of the X?

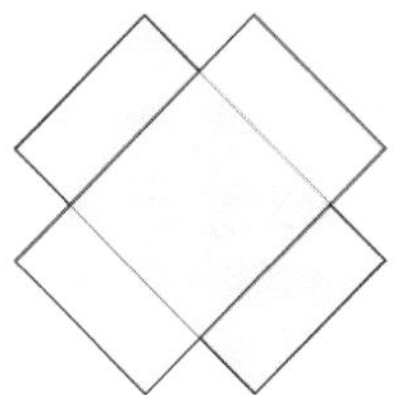

9. The shaded area represents a walkway around a triangular garden. What is the area of the walkway?

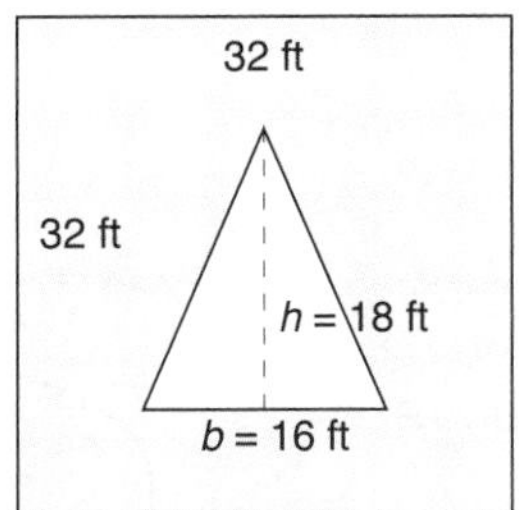

10. An event planner has the following space to create a dirt bike course. To the nearest square foot, what is the area of the space?

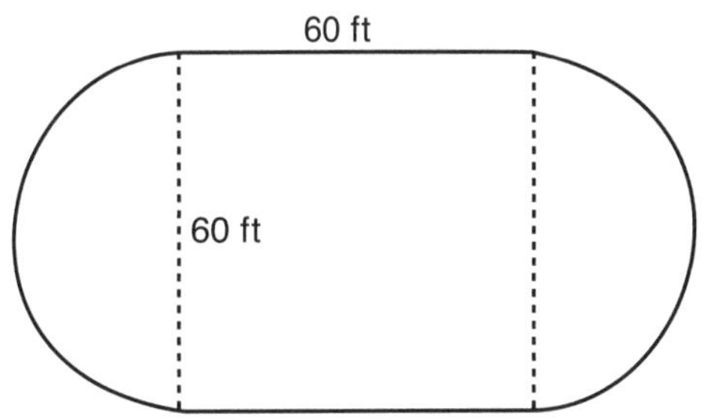

11. **Investigate** The figure below is $\frac{3}{4}$ of a circle.

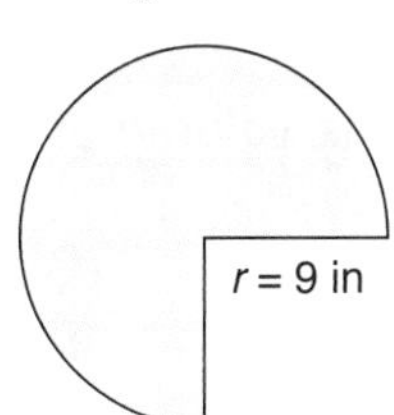

a. Find the area of the figure.

b. If a square is drawn with the same area, what would a side of the square measure to the nearest inch?

Answers start on page 204.

VOLUME OF PRISMS AND CYLINDERS

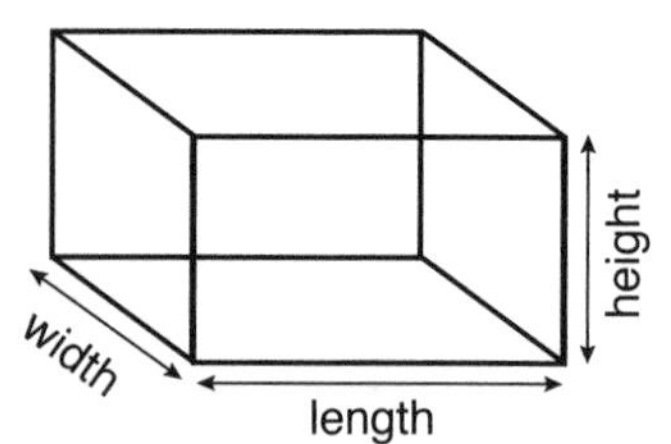

A line has only one dimension—length. A flat shape has two dimensions—length and width. Most objects in life have three dimensions—length, width, and height. Depending on the situation, one of these dimensions may be called *depth.*

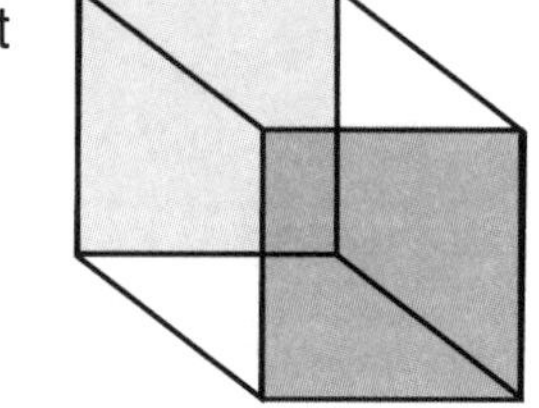
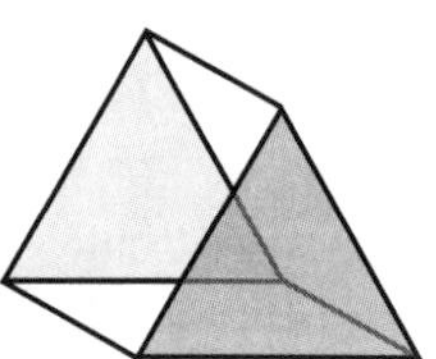

A **prism** is a three-dimensional object with parallel, identical bases that have straight edges. The sides, or faces, that connect the bases are always rectangles.

The drawing shows a rectangular prism and a triangular prism. Notice that the base determines the type of prism.

A corner of the prism is a **vertex.** The **edges** are the straight segments that define the prism's shape. The flat side of a prism is also called its **face.**

In the drawing, the prism has 8 vertices, 12 edges, and 6 faces. Take a moment to find them all.

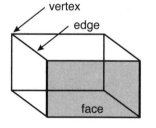

vertex

edge

face

Volume is the measure of the space inside a three-dimensional object. Volume is measured using cubic units. To find volume, you need to figure out how many cubes will fit inside the figure. Use the formula below to find the volume of any prism.

Volume (V) of a Prism	$V = Bh$, where B is the area of one base and h is the height

FINDING THE VOLUME OF A PRISM

Example Find the volume of the prism.

Step 1
Identify the bases.

Remember, bases are identical and parallel. The bases are right triangles.

Step 2
Find the area of one base.

$A = \frac{1}{2}bh$

$= \frac{1}{2} \cdot 4 \cdot 3$

$= 6$ sq in

Step 3
Multiply by the height, 8 inches.

$6 \cdot 8 =$ **48 cubic inches** or **48 in^3**

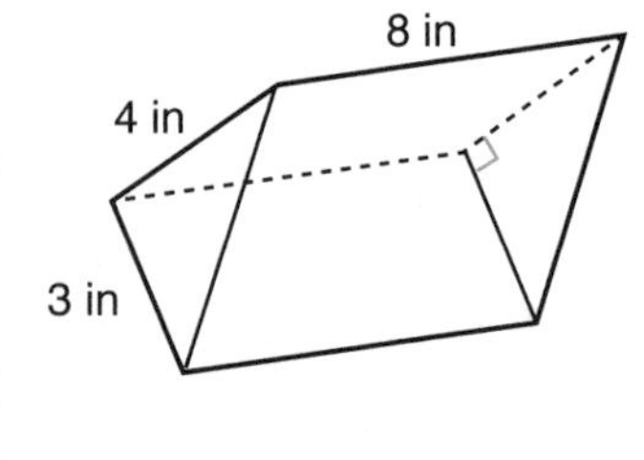

A **cylinder** is a three-dimensional shape with circular bases. The two bases are identical and parallel.

To find the volume of a cylinder, find the area of one base and multiply by the height.

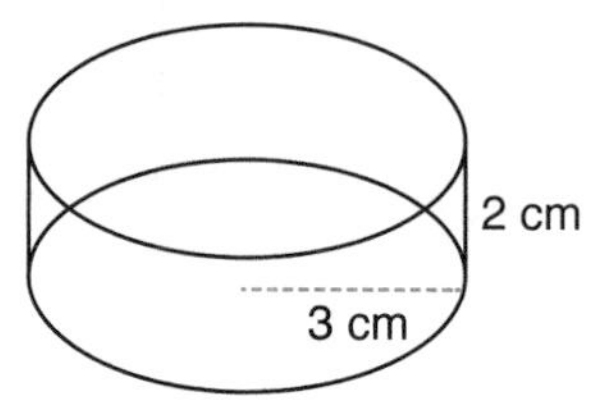

The GED math formula sheet includes the formula for volume of a cylinder, which multiplies the area of one circular base (πr^2) by the height h.

> **Volume (V) of a Cylinder** $V = \pi r^2 h$, where r = radius and h = height

Example Find the volume of a cylinder with a radius of 3 centimeters and a height of 2 centimeters.

$$V = \pi r^2 h$$
$$= 3.14 \cdot 3^2 \cdot 2$$
$$\approx 56.52 \text{ cm}^3$$

The cylinder has a volume of about **56.52 cubic centimeters** or **56.52 cm³.**

Find the volume of each figure. Use 3.14 for pi, and round your answer to the nearest tenth if necessary.

1. 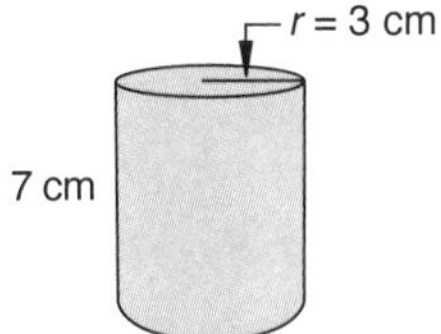

2. 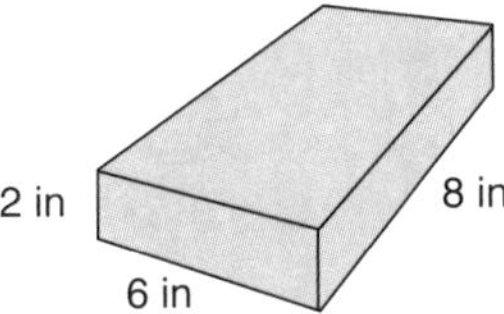

3. 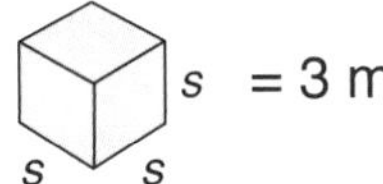

(***Hint:*** The base is a square.)

4. 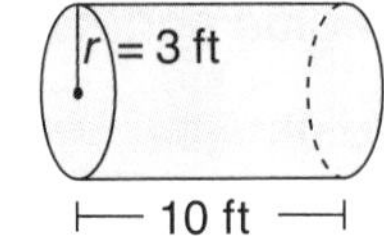

5. 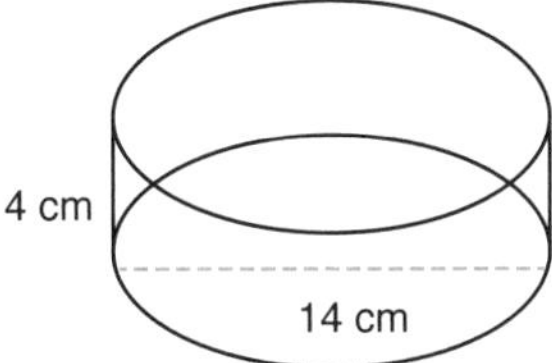

(***Hint:*** The radius is $\frac{1}{2}$ the diameter.)

6. 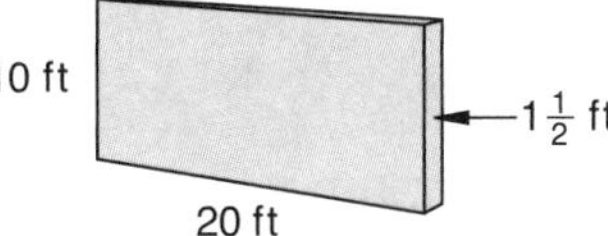

Solve.

7. How much greater is the volume of the first box than the volume of the second box?

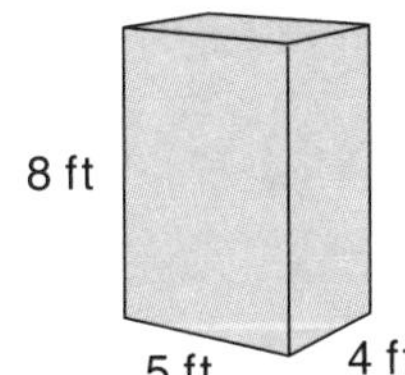

8. A plan for a concrete wall calls for it to be $\frac{1}{2}$ foot thick, 6 feet high, and 48 feet long.
   a. What is the volume of the wall in cubic feet?
   b. Concrete is sold in cubic yards. One cubic yard = 27 cubic feet. How many cubic yards of concrete are needed to build the wall?

9. A cylindrical fuel tank has a height of 20 feet and a diameter of 16 feet. What is the volume of the fuel tank in cubic feet?

10. **Explain** The illustration shows a cylindrical can and a rectangular box. If the can in the drawing is full, is it possible to pour the contents into the box without the box overflowing?

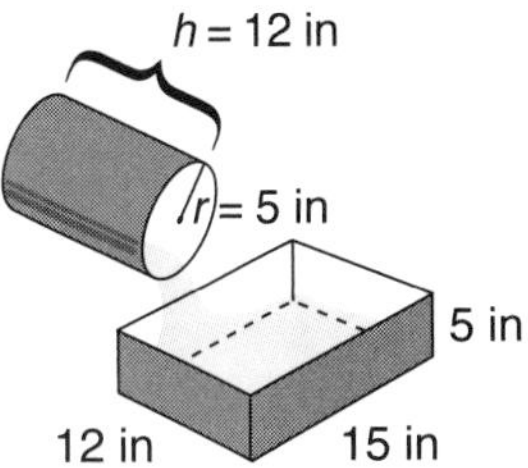

Answers start on page 204.

VOLUME OF PYRAMIDS, CONES, AND SPHERES

Every solid figure has volume. Remember, when you find volume, you are finding out how many cubes of a certain size would fit into the figure. Some shapes would be impossible to fill with cubes, so you need to use a formula to find the volume.

A **pyramid** has a base with straight sides and triangular faces that meet at a single vertex. The most common pyramid has a square base, but the base can be any polygon.

A **cone** has a circle for a base and one vertex.

A **sphere** is a three-dimensional object where each point on the surface is an equal distance from the center.

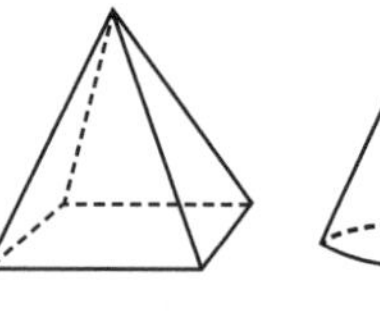
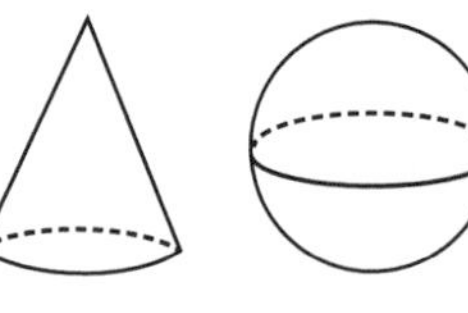

pyramid cone sphere

The GED math formula sheet has the formulas for finding the volumes of these figures. You don't need to memorize them, but take time to understand how they work.

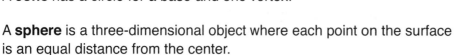

Volume (V) Formulas

Pyramid	$V = \frac{1}{3}Bh$, where B = area of the Base and h = height
Cone	$V = \frac{1}{3}\pi r^2 h$, where r = radius and h = height
Sphere	$V = \frac{4}{3}\pi r^3$, where r = radius

To solve volume problems, substitute the given values and solve. Use 3.14 for pi, or the π key on your calculator. On drawings involving height, the height is the perpendicular distance from the base to the vertex.

Find the volume. Round your answers to the nearest tenth.

1. 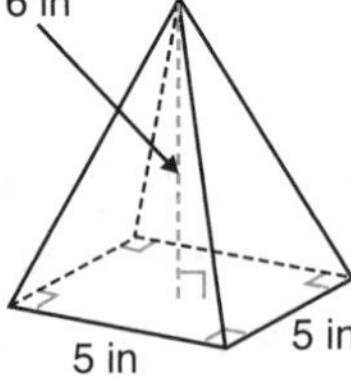

2. 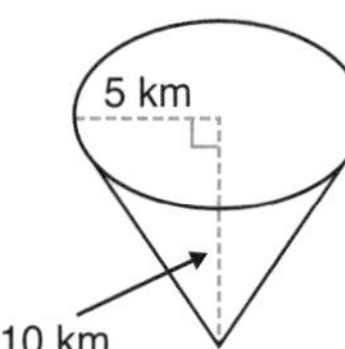

3. 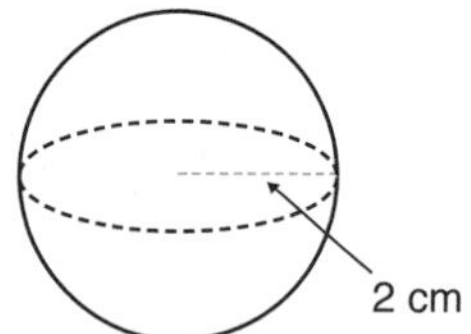

4. 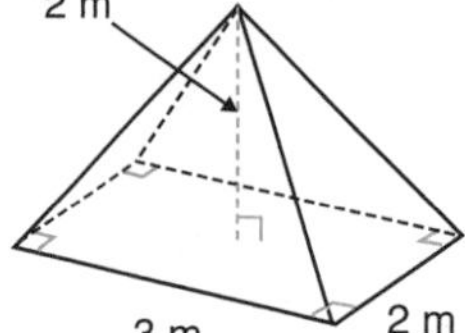

5. 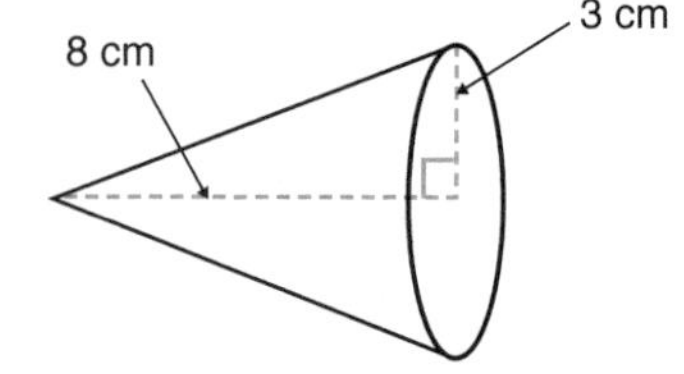

6. 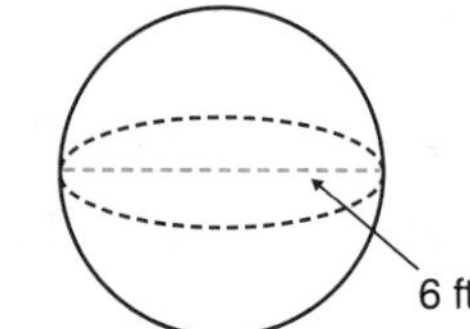

You can combine solids to form more complex figures.

FINDING THE VOLUME OF COMPLEX FIGURES

Example A cone shape is cut from a foam cylinder to create a form used to dry painted machine parts. If the height of the cylinder is 6 inches and the height of the cone is 5 inches, how many cubic inches of foam are left in the form? Round to the nearest cubic inch. (***Hint:*** The radius of the cylinder is the radius of the cone plus the 1-inch thickness of the foam.)

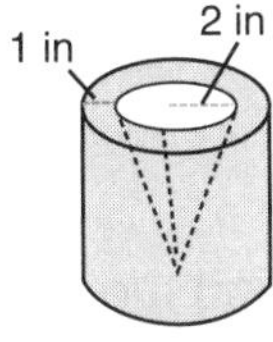

Step 1
Find the volume of both figures.

Cylinder: $V = \pi r^2 h$
$= 3.14 \cdot 3^2 \cdot 6$
$\approx 169.56 \text{ in}^3$

Cone: $V = \frac{1}{3}\pi r^2 h$
$= \frac{1}{3} \cdot 3.14 \cdot 2^2 \cdot 5$
$\approx 20.93 \text{ in}^3$

Step 2
Subtract and round to the nearest cubic inch.

$169.56 - 20.93 = 148.63$, which rounds to 149 in^3.

There are **149 in³** left in the foam.

Solve. Use 3.14 for pi. You may use the formulas on page 220 of the Tool Kit.

7. A candy company combines two identical square pyramids to make a box for its premium chocolates. The drawing shows the dimensions of the box. What is the volume to the nearest cubic inch?

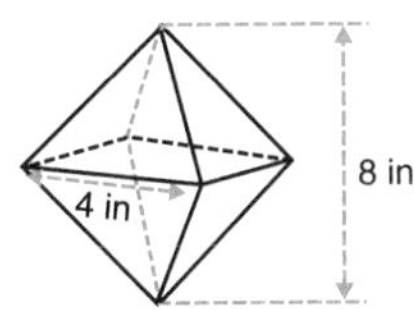

8. At a sporting goods store, basketballs are sold in boxes. Each basketball has a radius of 11.9 centimeters. Every edge of the box measures 24 centimeters. When the basketball is in the box, how much space is left in the box? Round to the nearest cubic centimeter.

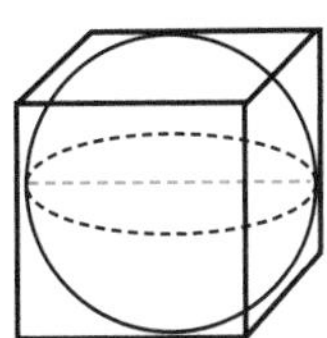

9. A model rocket has the dimensions shown in the drawing. If the rocket has a diameter of 2 inches, what is the volume in cubic inches?

Round to the nearest cubic inch.

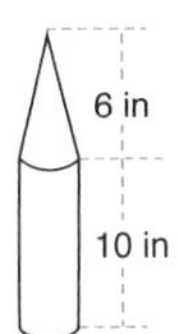

10. Max plans to build a storage shed with the dimensions shown in the drawing. What is the volume of the shed in cubit feet?

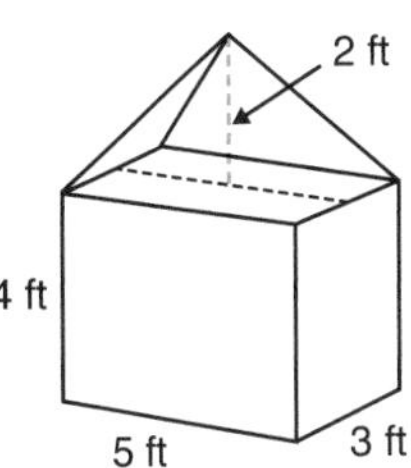

Answers start on page 205.

SURFACE AREA

Surface area is the sum of the areas of the faces of a three-dimensional figure. You already know how to find the area of a complex figure. You can use this knowledge to find surface area.

FINDING SURFACE AREA BY ADDING AREAS

Example Find the surface area of the box.

The box, a rectangular prism, has 6 faces. Each face is a rectangle that has its own length and width.

Imagine unfolding the box so that the cardboard lies flat. Make sure you understand how the second drawing can be folded to make the box in the first drawing.

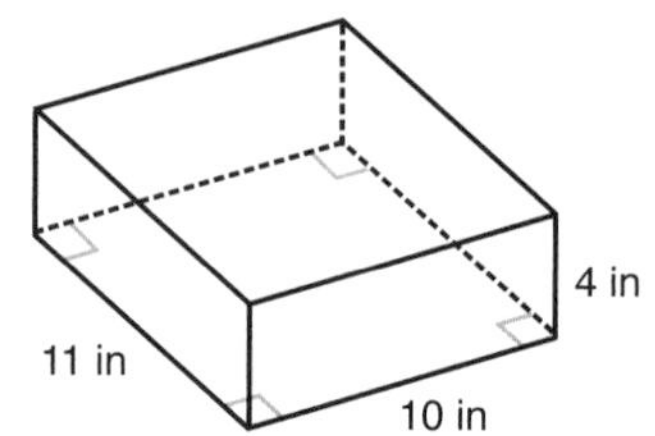

Step 1
Find the area of each rectangle.

Top:	10 × 4 = 40
Bottom:	10 × 4 = 40
Left side:	11 × 4 = 44
Right side:	11 × 4 = 44
Front:	11 × 10 = 110
Back:	11 × 10 = 110

Step 2
Add the areas of the faces.

40
40
44
44
110
+ 110
388

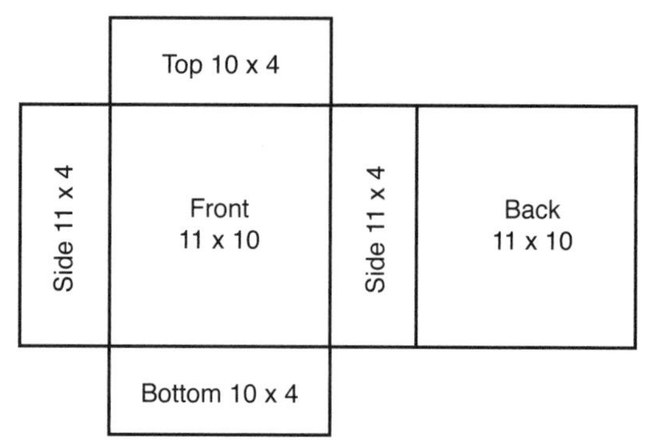

The surface area of the box is **388 square inches.**

You will be expected to find the surface areas of rectangular prisms, pyramids, cylinders, cones, and spheres. To make your work easier, the GED math formula sheet includes formulas for finding the surface areas of these figures.

Surface Area (*SA*) Formulas

(p = perimeter of base, B = area of the base, h = height, r = radius, s = slant height)

Rectangular/Right Prism	$SA = ph + 2B$
Cylinder	$SA = 2\pi rh + 2\pi r^2$
Square Pyramid	$SA = \frac{1}{2}ps + B$
Cone	$SA = \pi rs + \pi r^2$
Sphere	$SA = 4\pi r^2$

Remember, a formula uses algebra to write a procedure for doing something. These formulas add the areas of the faces of a figure. You don't have to use formulas, but they may save you time.

USING A FORMULA TO FIND SURFACE AREA

Example Find the surface area of the pyramid.

Use the formula: $SA = \frac{1}{2}ps + B$

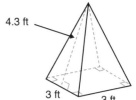

Step 1
Find the facts you need to use the formula.

The slant height s is 4.3 feet.

Find p, the perimeter of the base:
$3 + 3 + 3 + 3 = 12$

Find B, the area of the base: $3^2 = 9$

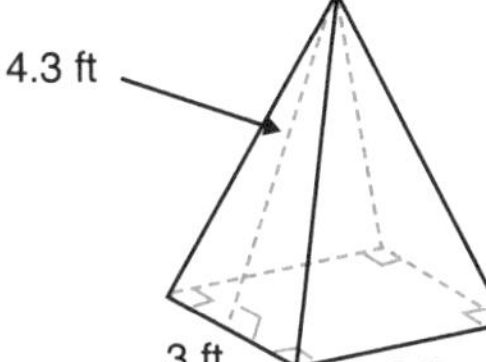

Step 2
Evaluate the formula.

$SA = \frac{1}{2}ps + B$

$= \frac{1}{2} \cdot 12 \cdot 4.3 + 9$

$=$ **34.8 sq ft**

The surface area is **34.8 sq ft.**

Find the surface area of each figure. If necessary, round your answer to the nearest tenth square unit.

1. 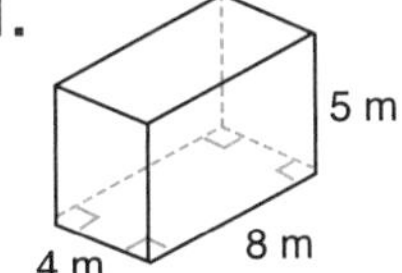

2. 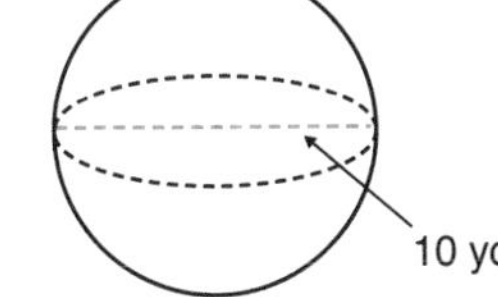

3. 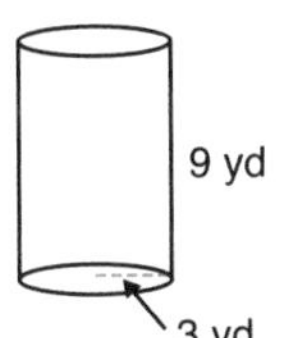

4. 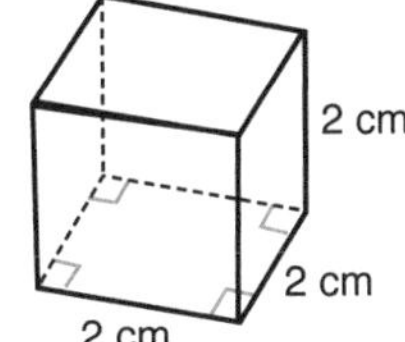

5. 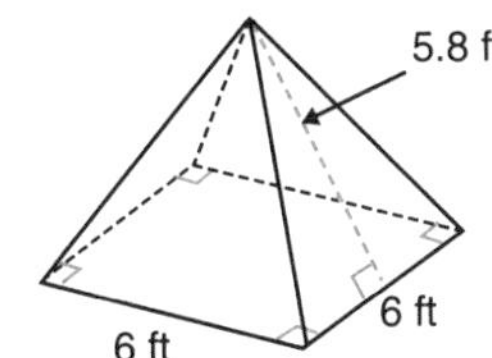

6. 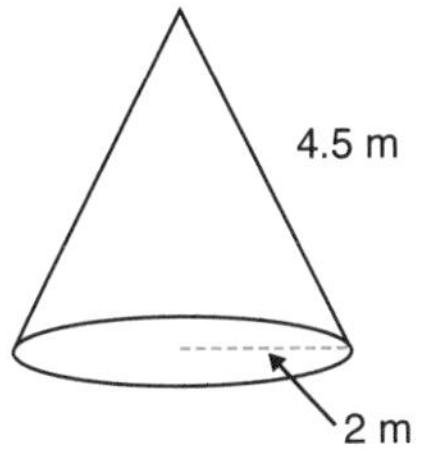

Solve as directed.

7. The illustration shows a truck bed with no top. What is the surface area of the inside of the truck bed?

8. Crunchy Oats cereal comes in a box that measures 8 by 11 by 2 inches. Bran Crisps cereal comes in a box that measures 7 by 10 by 3 inches. (***Hint:*** Make a drawing with labels.)
   a. Which box has a larger surface area?
   b. Which box has a greater volume?

Answers start on page 205.

CHOOSING AREA, PERIMETER, VOLUME, OR SURFACE AREA

You know how to find the perimeter, area, volume, and surface area of various figures. But knowing which to solve for takes practice.

Remember: **Perimeter** is the distance around a flat figure. **Area** is the space inside a flat figure. **Volume** is the space inside a three-dimensional figure. **Surface area** is the sum of the areas of the faces of a three-dimensional figure.

Some area and volume formulas are given on the GED math formula sheet. You can see these formulas and others on pages 220 and 221 of the Tool Kit.

For each problem, select whether to solve for perimeter, area, volume, or surface area. Then solve the problem. Round to the nearest whole unit if necessary.

1. How many cubic feet does the moving truck shown in the ad hold?

15 ft long
7 ft high
7 ft wide
MOVE IT
Local and One Way!
CALL NOW!

Solve for:

perimeter
area
volume
surface area

Solution: ____________________

2. A revolving sprinkler sprays a lawn for a distance of 18 feet. How much ground is covered by the sprinkler as it makes 1 complete revolution?

18 ft

Solve for:

perimeter
area
volume
surface area

Solution: ____________________

3. How many feet of chrome edging are needed to finish a rectangular kitchen table?

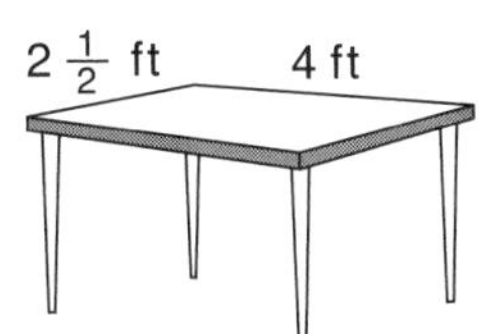

Solve for:

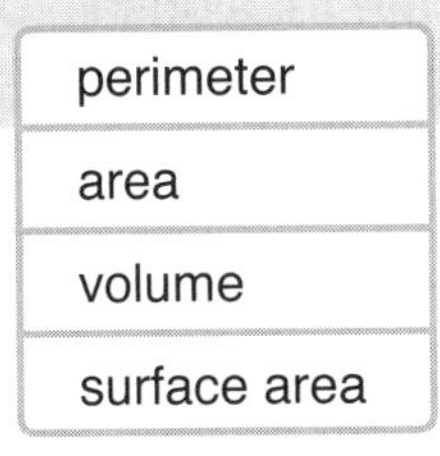

Solution: ____________________

4. To prevent leakage, an oil storage tank is coated with a sealant. How many square meters will need to be coated to cover the container?

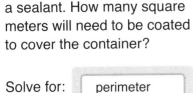

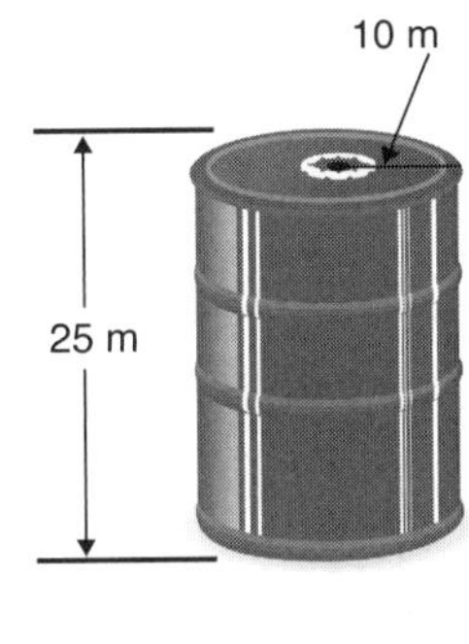

Solve for:

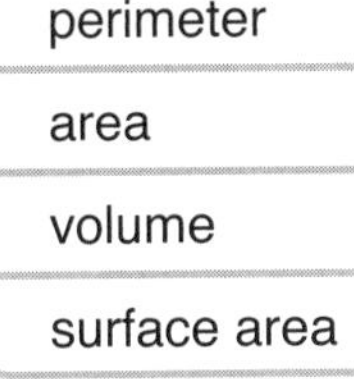

Solution: ____________________

5. Marisol wants to put a satin border on a quilt she made. The drawing shows the dimensions of the quilt. How many inches long is the border?

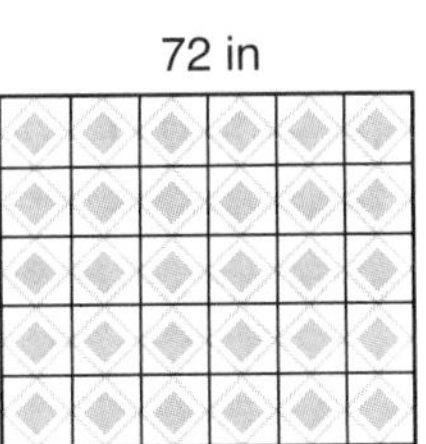

Solve for:

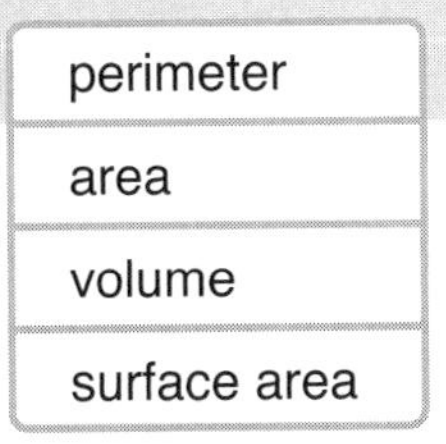

Solution: ____________________

6. A public school wants to install rubber padding over a rectangular playground space that measures 22 feet by 15 feet. The padding comes in square tiles that measure 1 foot by 1 foot. How many tiles are needed?

Solve for:

- perimeter
- area
- volume
- surface area

Solution: ____________________

7. A storage unit has the dimensions shown in the drawing. If the top and four sides of the unit are repainted, how many square yards will be painted?

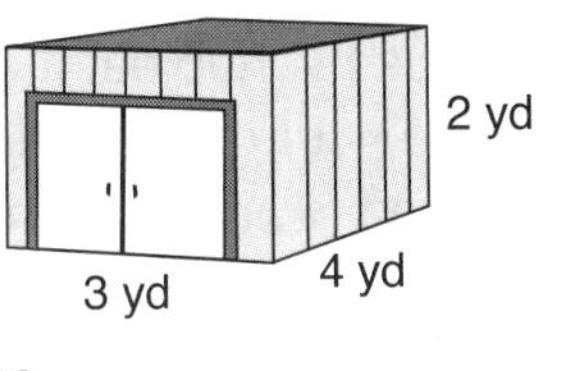

Solve for:

- perimeter
- area
- volume
- surface area

Solution: ____________________

8. How many cubic feet of water will the circular wading pool hold?

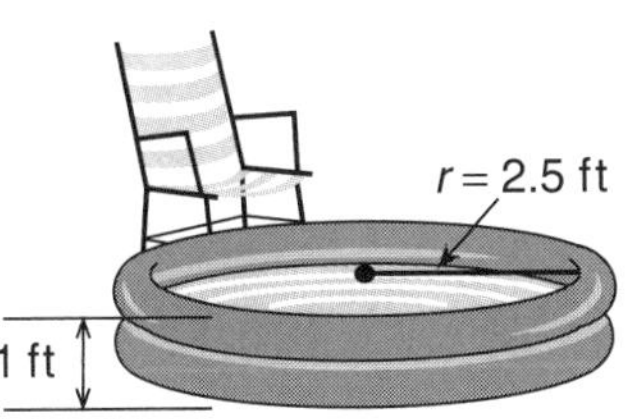

Solve for:

- perimeter
- area
- volume
- surface area

Solution: ____________________

Answers start on page 205.

USING ALGEBRA IN GEOMETRY PROBLEMS

You already know that algebra makes it easy to express the relationship between the numbers in a problem. It can also be used to express the relationships found in geometry problems.

In the first example, you are given clues about the relationship between the length and width of a rectangle, but you aren't given either value. To assign a value, think: "Which measure do I know the least about?" The clue describes the length. You don't have any clues about the width. Represent the width as a variable.

Example The length of a rectangle is 3 times its width. If the perimeter of the rectangle is 32 inches, what is the width of the rectangle?

Step 1
Choose variables. If you aren't given a drawing, make your own and label it. Here, the width is labeled w and the length is $3w$ (3 times the width).

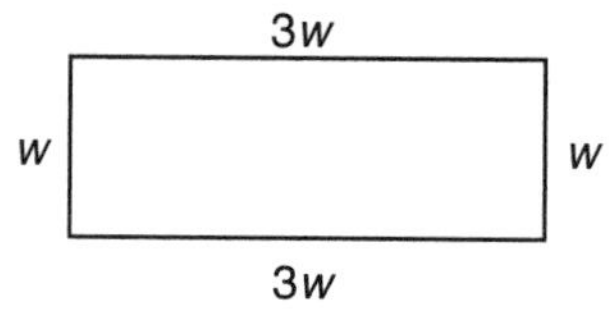

Step 2
Write and solve an equation. Since perimeter is the distance around a figure, write an equation that adds the sides.

$$w + 3w + w + 3w = 32$$
$$8w = 32$$
$$w = 4$$

The width is **4 inches.**

Formulas can help you write an equation.

Example: Dylan is adding a metal frame to a round mirror. If the strip of metal is 12.56 feet long, what is the radius of the mirror?

Step 1
Make a sketch and label it.

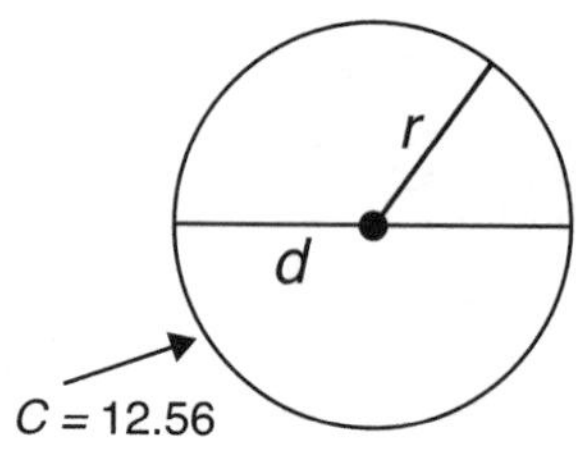

Step 2
Write and solve an equation. The distance around a circle is the circumference. Use the formula $C = \pi d$, where d = diameter. The radius r is half of the diameter.

Solve for d.

$$C = \pi d$$
$$12.56 = 3.14d$$
$$\frac{12.56}{3.14} = \frac{3.14d}{3.14}$$
$$4 = d$$

Solve for r.

$$r = \frac{1}{2}d$$
$$r = \frac{1}{2} \cdot 4$$
$$r = 2$$

The radius is **2 feet.**

Solve as directed. You may refer to the formulas on page 220 of the Tool Kit.

1. In triangle DEF, what is the measure of $\angle F$?

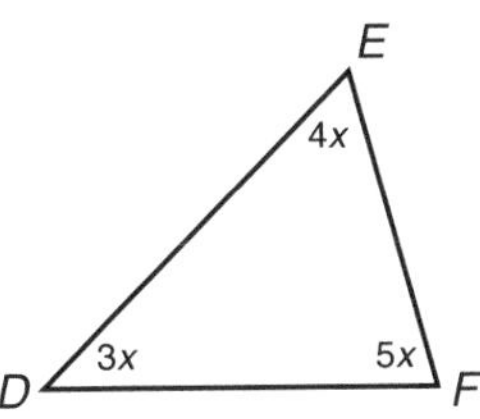

2. In the trapezoid, base SV is one-third the length of base TU. The other sides, ST and VU, are both 10 cm.

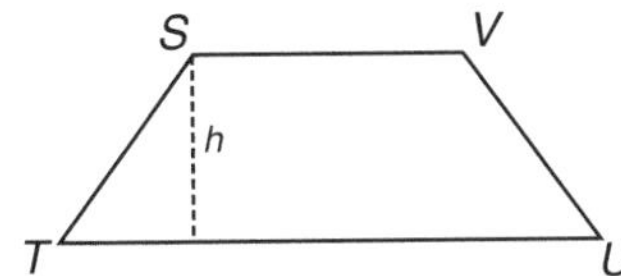

If the height of the trapezoid is 8 cm and the perimeter of the trapezoid is 68 cm, what is the area of the trapezoid in square centimeters?

3. What is the measure of $\angle A$ in the figure below?

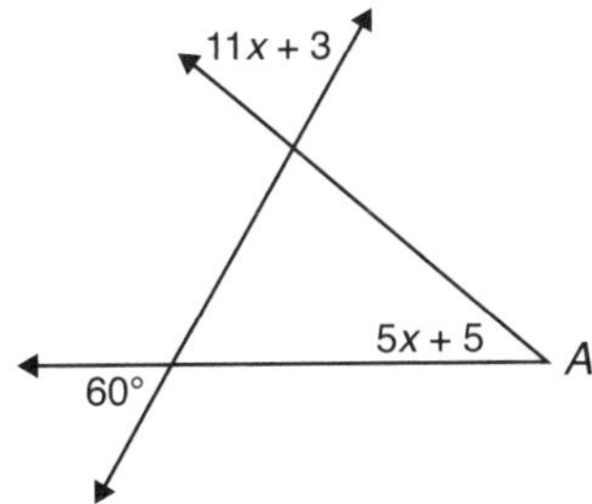

4. Alfonso has to create a base for a statue. The base will be in the shape of a rectangular prism.

   The requirements for the base are:
   1. The volume must be 400 cubic feet.
   2. The longest measurement must not exceed 12 feet.

   The dimensions of three possible bases are given below. Which base meets the stated requirements?

   A. length = 8 ft
   width = 5 ft
   height = 9 ft

   B. length = 10 ft
   height = 10 ft
   volume = 400 ft^3

   C. length = 5 ft
   height = 4 ft
   volume = 400 ft^3

5. The cone has a volume of about 151 cubic inches. To the nearest inch, what is the height of the cone?

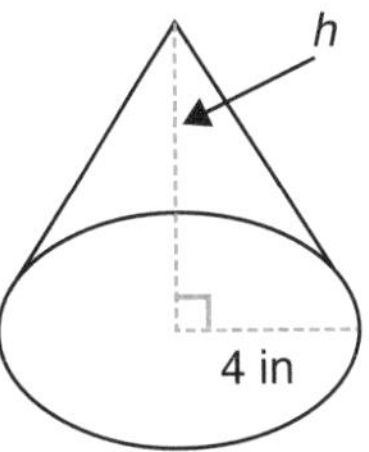

6. **Explain** The three sides of a triangle are labeled x, $2x + 2$, and $3x - 2$. Find two possible values for x that will make the triangle isosceles. Explain how you know your answers are correct.

Answers start on page 206.

Unit 4 Review

Solve as directed.

Problems 1 and 2 refer to the drawing below.

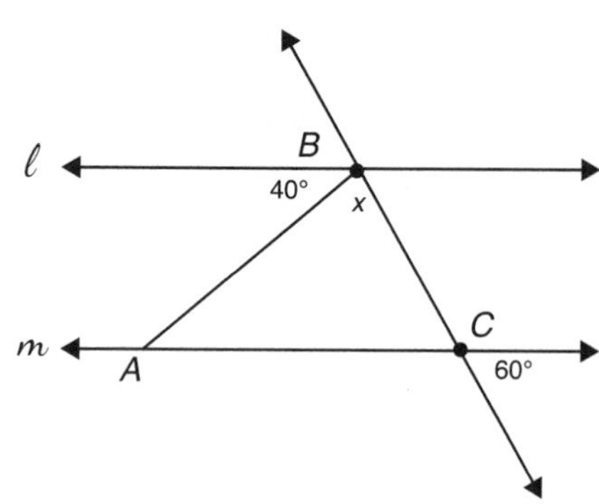

1. In the drawing, lines l and m are parallel. What is measure of the angle marked x?

   $m\angle x =$ ☐ degrees

2. What kind of triangle is $\triangle ABC$?
   A. isosceles
   B. right
   C. scalene
   D. equilateral

3. In the drawing below, the curved portion is $\frac{3}{4}$ of a circle. What is the perimeter of the figure to the nearest tenth centimeter?

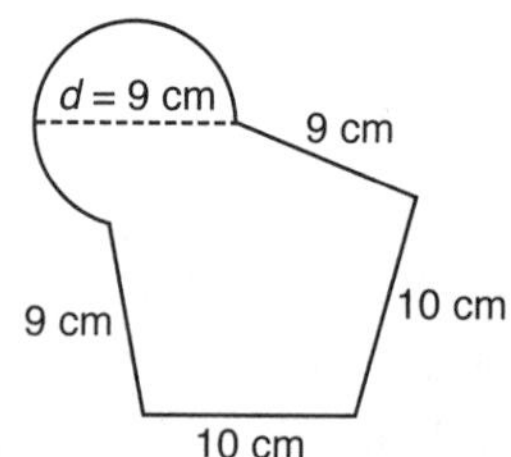

☐ centimeters

4. For a banner, the letter W is formed from five equal squares. What is the area of the W to the nearest square inch?

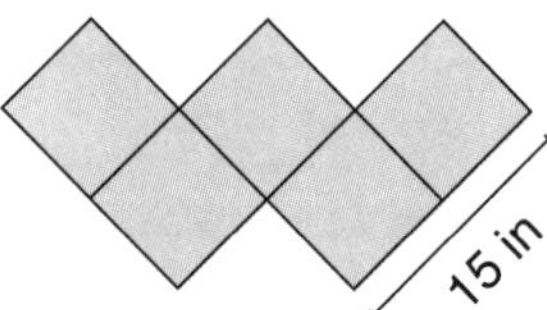

   A. 75
   B. 90
   C. 281
   D. 1,125

5. An Explorer 3-person tent has the measurements shown in the drawing. What is the volume of the tent to the nearest cubic foot?

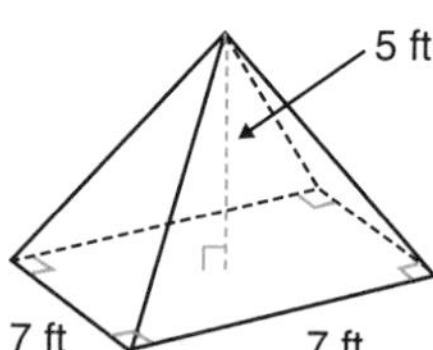

☐ cubic feet

6. Find the perimeter of the figure in centimeters.

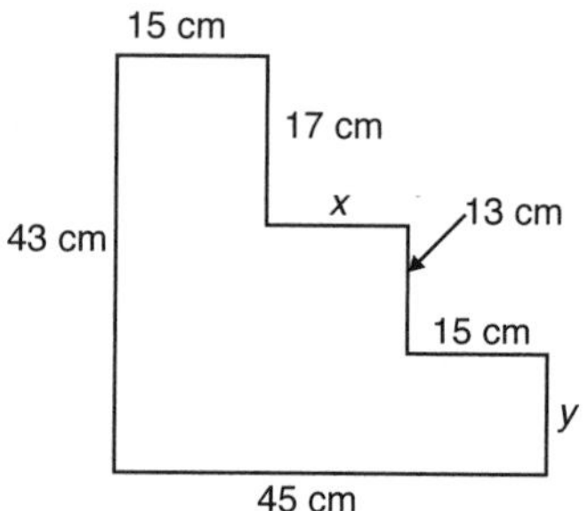

☐ centimeters

7. To make apple cider, the owner of an apple orchard uses rectangular metal containers like the one shown in the drawing.

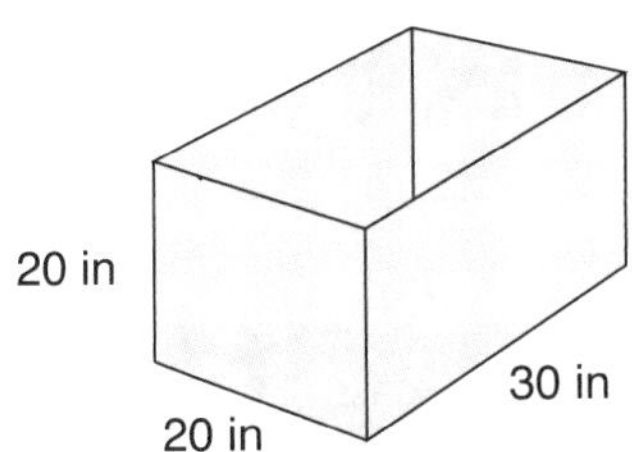

One gallon of cider fills about 230 cubic inches. What is the best estimate for how many gallons of cider the container will hold?

A. 20
B. 30
C. 40
D. 50

8. A farmer plans to paint an aboveground storage tank. The bottom of the tank will not be painted. To the nearest square foot, how many square feet will the farmer paint?

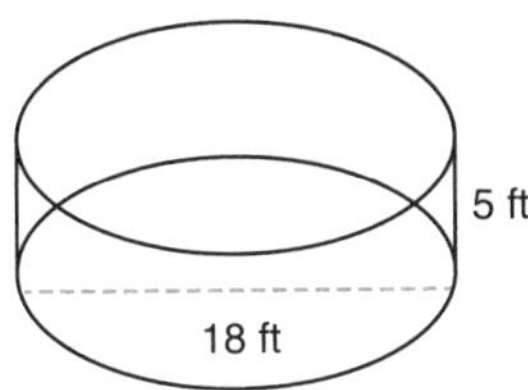

[ ] square feet

9. What is the measure of side *EF*?

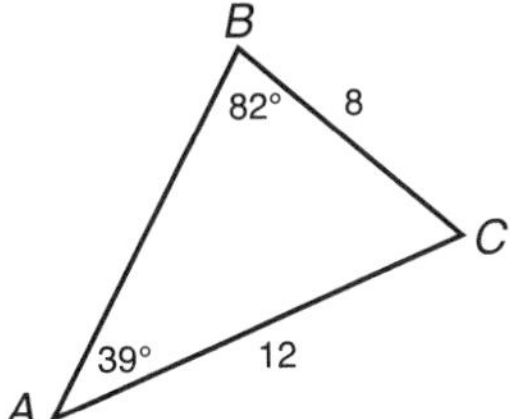

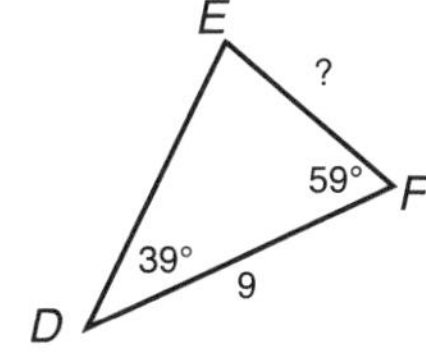

A. 6
B. 8
C. 9.3
D. 13

Use the information to answer problems 10 and 11.

A store owner wants to advertise the number of calories in a large chocolate ice cream cone, shown below.

The sugar cone by itself has 70 calories.

Chocolate ice cream has 20 calories per cubic inch.

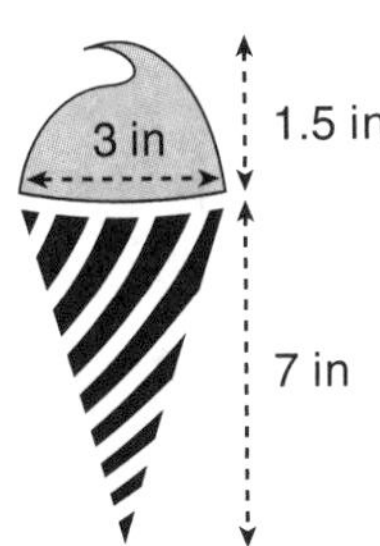

10. Explain how you could use solid figures to estimate the volume of ice cream in the ice cream cone.

11. What is the best estimate for the number of calories in a large sugar cone filled with chocolate ice cream?

A. 135
B. 290
C. 470
D. 540

12. Mark has a job 8 miles north of his home. He goes to school 15 miles east of his home. To the nearest tenth mile, what is the distance from where he works to his school?

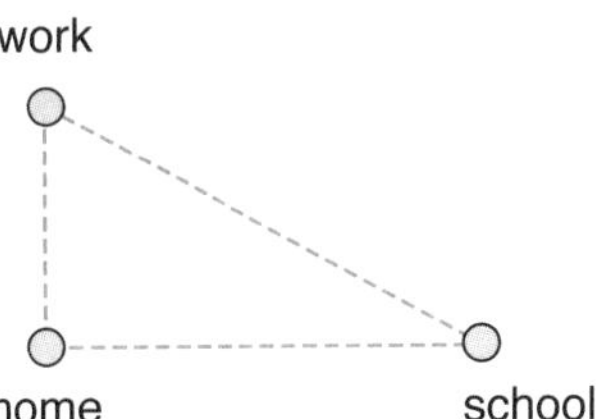

[ ] miles

Answers start on page 206.

CONNECTING ALGEBRA AND GEOMETRY

SKILLS

- Plotting points on a coordinate grid
- Graphing lines
- Finding slope
- Writing the equation of a line
- Finding the distance between two points

TOOLS AND STRATEGIES

- Using a table to graph an equation
- Solving problems with slope
- Working with geometric figures on a coordinate plane

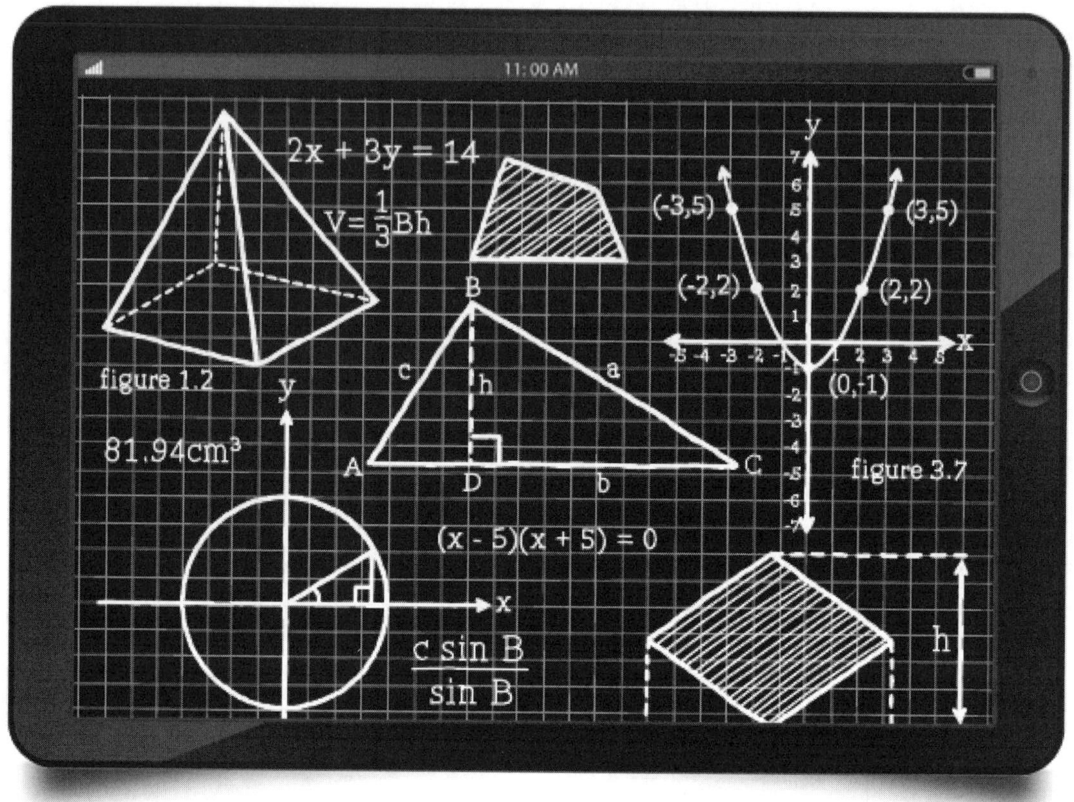

HOW DO YOU CONNECT algebra and geometry? You can use the principles of algebra to translate words into equations. You can use the principles of geometry to describe figures and shapes. Connecting the two will let you write equations that represent figures.

Points and lines in algebra are drawn on a grid called a **rectangular coordinate plane.** In this unit, you'll learn how to locate and plot points on a coordinate grid. You'll also learn some key properties of **linear equations,** such as **slope,** that will help you write and graph linear equations. You can use these properties to solve many types of problems.

USING ALGEBRA AND GEOMETRY

You connect algebra and geometry when you:

- Give directions from one location to another
- Plot data on a line graph
- Measure the steepness of a staircase or a ramp
- Find the correct seat at a movie theater or a stadium
- Draw a geometric shape on a grid

Read the following items. Describe some of your experiences in writing or discuss them with a partner.

1. Think of a time when you used graph paper. Why did you decide to use it? How was it useful?

2. Describe the location of your school or workplace. What streets is it near? How would you give directions to get there from your home?

3. Have you ever seen a TV show where a team needs to search a large area? Did you know that search and rescue teams first mark an area with a grid? How do you think this helps them search?

4. Have you ever seen a line graph in a news article? What did the graph show? How did you read the information in the graph?

MATH TALK

In real life, some things are meant to be steep. A roller coaster wouldn't be very fun if it were flat. On the other hand, you wouldn't want a wheelchair ramp or a beginner ski slope to be too steep.

Discuss with a partner how you could measure the steepness of a ramp. What would make a wheelchair ramp too steep? What about a staircase?

How could you measure the steepness of something larger, like a hiking trail or a ski slope?

THE COORDINATE PLANE

How do you give directions? One way is to describe the path the person should take. "Drive three blocks north and six blocks west." Another way is to name major cross streets. "City Hall is near the corner of Fifth Street and Lincoln Avenue." Both methods work because cities are often organized using a grid of intersecting streets.

A **rectangular coordinate plane** works the same way. A coordinate plane, or grid, is made up of two perpendicular number lines that intersect at zero. The horizontal line is the ***x*-axis,** and the vertical line is the ***y*-axis.** The point where the lines intersect is called the **origin.** Markings at even intervals measure the distance from the origin.

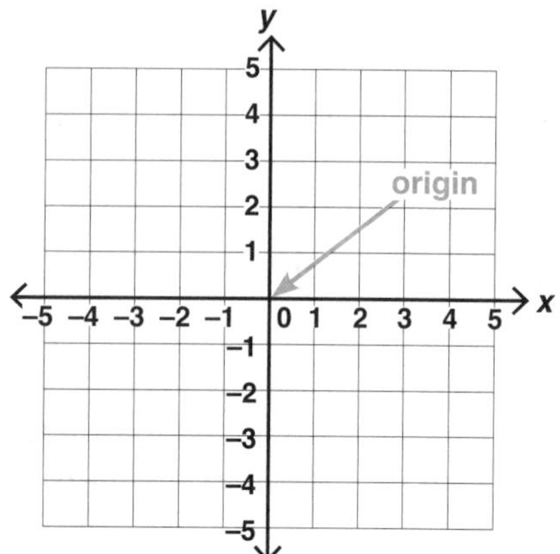

You can describe a point by using the numbers along the *x*-axis and *y*-axis.

First, line the point up with a value on the *x*-axis. This is called the ***x*-coordinate.** Points to the right of the origin have a positive *x*-coordinate. Points to the left of the origin have a negative *x*-coordinate.

Then, line the point up with a value on the *y*-axis. This is called the ***y*-coordinate.** Points above the origin have a positive *y*-coordinate. Points below the origin have a negative *y*-coordinate.

Together, these two coordinates form an **ordered pair.** Ordered pairs are always written in the order (*x, y*). The origin is written as (0, 0).

IDENTIFYING POINTS ON THE COORDINATE PLANE

Example What are the coordinates of point *A*?

Step 1
Find the *x*-value.
Line up the point with the *x*-axis. Point *A* lines up with 3. The *x*-coordinate is 3.

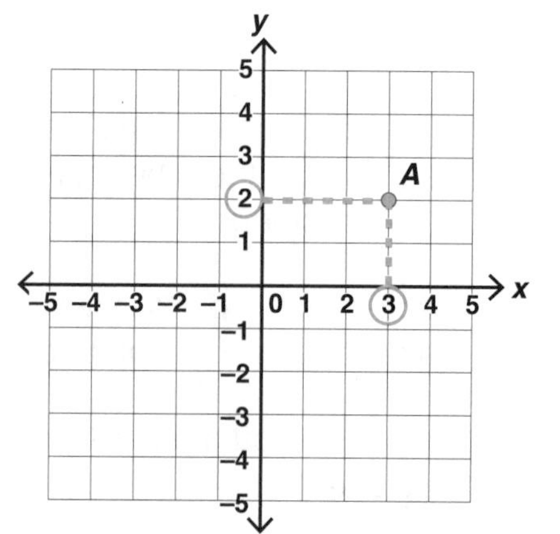

Step 2
Now line up the point with the *y*-axis. Point *A* lines up with 2. The *y*-coordinate is 2.

Step 3
Write the ordered pair. The coordinates of point *A* are (3, 2).

Write the coordinates of the points on this coordinate grid.

1. A =

2. B =

3. C =

4. D =

5. E =

6. F =

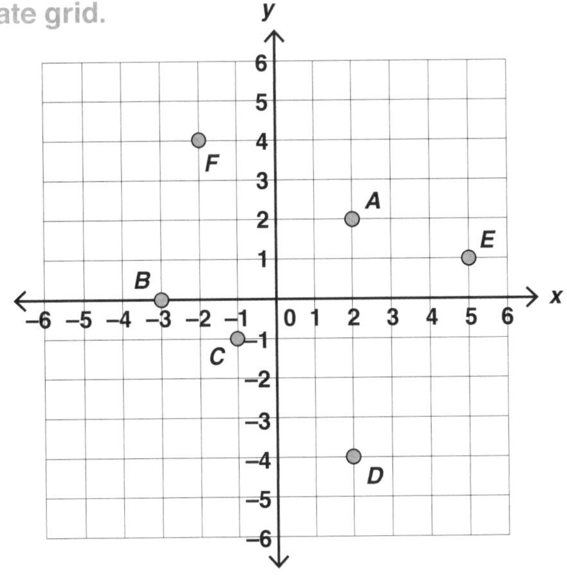

Plot the points below on the coordinate grid. Be sure to label each point with the appropriate letter.

7. G = (4, –1)

8. H = (–1, 5)

9. I = (0, 3)

10. J = (–4, 0)

11. K = (2, 3)

12. L = (–2, –5)

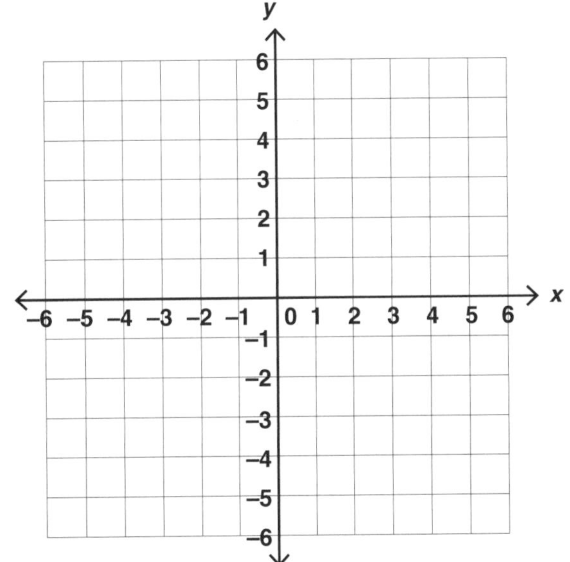

The *x*-axis and the *y*-axis divide the coordinate plane into four quadrants. You can determine which quadrant a point is in by looking at the signs of the coordinates.

Points with a positive *x*-coordinate and a positive *y*-coordinate are in Quadrant I.
Points with a negative *x*-coordinate and a positive *y*-coordinate are in Quadrant II.
Points with a negative *x*-coordinate and a negative *y*-coordinate are in Quadrant III.
Points with a positive *x*-coordinate and a negative *y*-coordinate are in Quadrant IV.

Points that lie on an axis line are not in a quadrant.

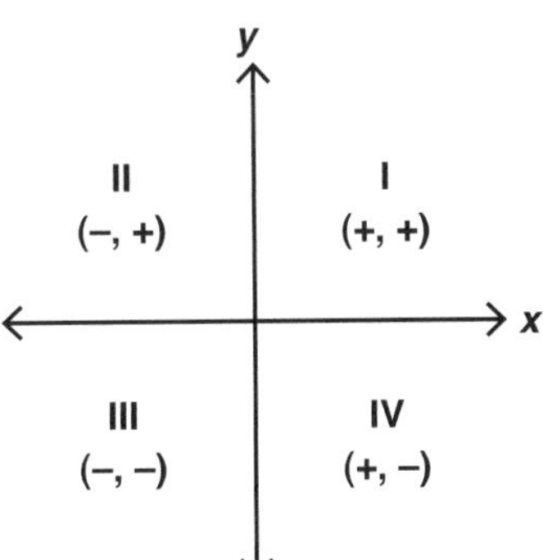

Name the quadrant of each point.

13. (–2, 7)

14. (5, –2)

15. (4, 4)

16. (–1, –4)

17. (–3, 2)

18. (1, 6)

Answers start on page 207.

MAKING A TABLE TO GRAPH AN EQUATION

Equations with two variables have an infinite number of solutions. Think about the equation $y = x - 1$. For every value of x, there is a value of y that makes the equation true. For example, if $x = 5$, then $y = 4$. If $x = 3$, then $y = 2$.

You can use a table to organize the solutions to an equation. Then, the solutions can be used to plot points on a graph. When a line is drawn through the points, the line represents all the possible solutions to the equation.

MAKING A TABLE TO GRAPH AN EQUATION

Example Graph the equation $y = x - 2$.

Step 1
Make a table of values. Choose values for x, substitute, and solve for y.

If $x = -1$, then $y = -3$.
If $x = 0$, then $y = -2$.
If $x = 1$, then $y = -1$.

You can organize the work using a table. Notice how the values on the table become coordinates for points.

x	y	
–1	–3	(–1, –3)
0	–2	(0, –2)
1	–1	(1, –1)

Step 2
Plot the points on the coordinate grid. Then draw a line through the points.

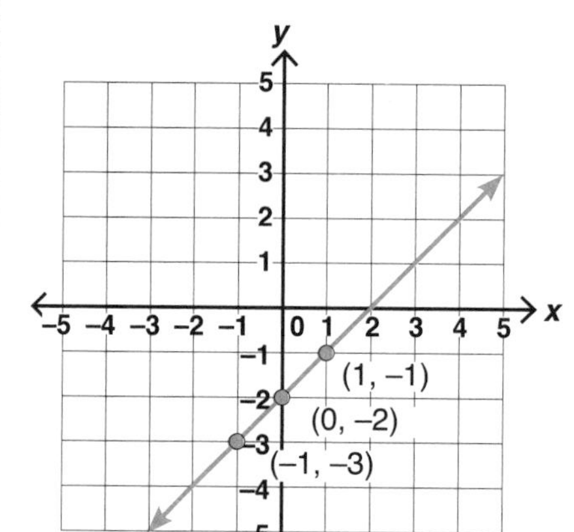

TIP
Always plot at least 3 points. You will know you made a mistake if the points don't line up.

You could choose other x-values to graph more points on the line. There are an infinite number of points that will make the equation true. The line shows that the solutions go on and on. This kind of equation is called a **linear equation** because its solutions can be represented by a straight line.

Complete the table for each equation.

1. $y = 3x - 5$

x	y
–2	
0	
2	

2. $y = 2x + 3$

x	y
2	
4	
5	

3. $y = -x + 5$

x	y
1	
3	
5	

Make a table of values for each equation. Choose at least three points to plot on the coordinate grid. Then graph the line for the equation.

4. $y = x + 1$

(***Hint:*** Choose small values for x that will give small values to y. The numbers –1, 0, and 1 are usually good choices.)

x	y

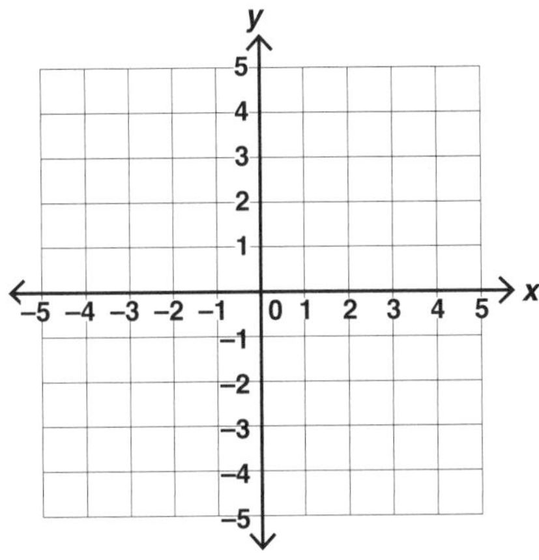

5. $y = 3x - 4$

x	y

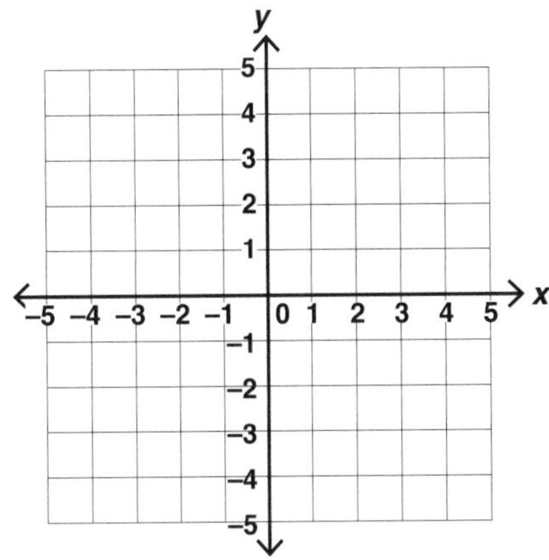

6. $y = -2x + 5$

x	y

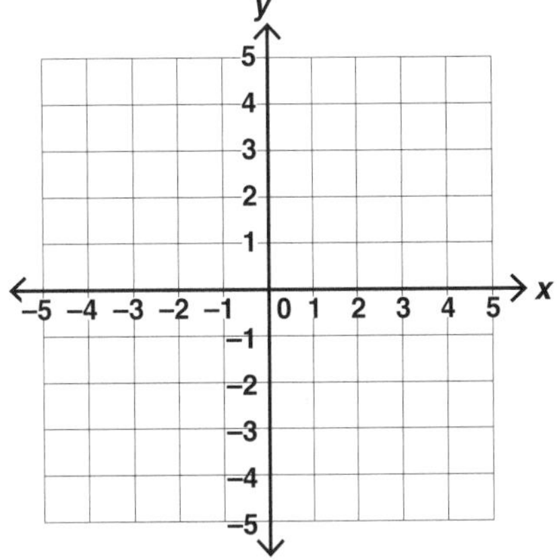

7. $y = \frac{x}{2} + 3$

(***Hint:*** To avoid fractions, choose multiples of 2 for the x-values.)

x	y

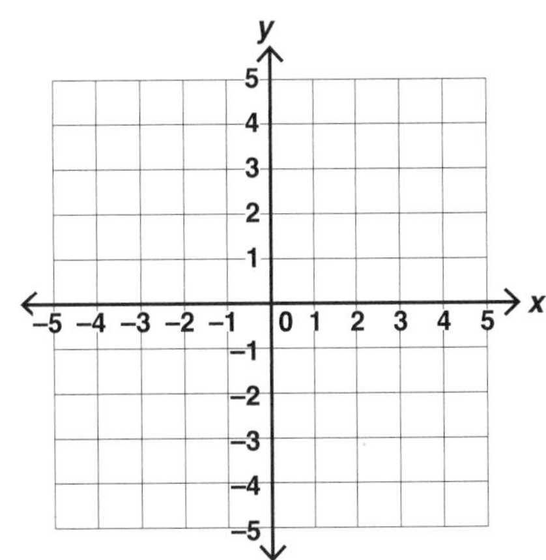

Answers start on page 207.

USING INTERCEPTS TO GRAPH A LINE

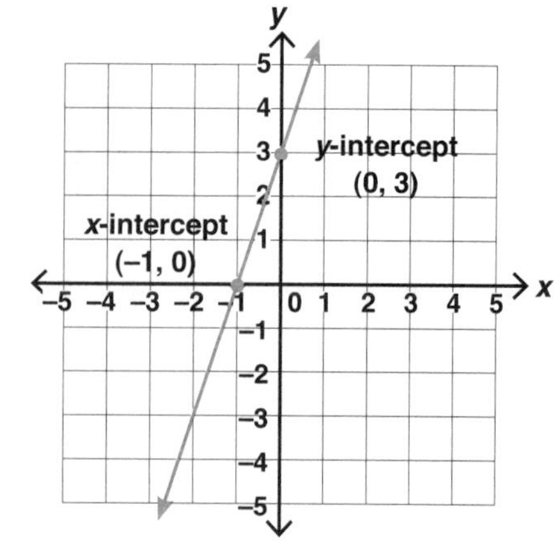

When a line crosses an axis, the points of intersection are called *intercepts.*

Look at the graph of $y = 3x + 3$ to the right.

When the line crosses the y-axis, the x-value is 0 and the y-value is 3.
The ***y*-intercept** is (0, 3).

When the line crosses the x-axis, the x-value is –1 and the y-value is 0.
The ***x*-intercept** is (–1, 0).

You can find the intercepts of any linear equation by substituting 0 into the equation. To find the y-intercept, substitute 0 for x. To find the x-intercept, substitute 0 for y.

FINDING THE INTERCEPTS OF A LINEAR EQUATION

Example Find the x- and y-intercepts of the equation $3x - 5y = 15$.

Step 1
Find the y-intercept by substituting 0 for x.

$$3(0) - 5y = 15$$
$$-5y = 15$$
$$y = -3$$

Step 2
Find the x-intercept by substituting 0 for y.

$$3x - 5(0) = 15$$
$$3x = 15$$
$$x = 5$$

The y-intercept is **(0, –3)**. The x-intercept is **(5, 0)**.

Intercepts make it easy to graph an equation. After you find the intercepts, plot the points on a graph and draw a line to connect them.

USING INTERCEPTS TO GRAPH A LINE

Example Graph the equation $3x - 5y = 15$.

The y-intercept is (0, –3).
The x-intercept is (5, 0).

Plot the points and draw a line.

 TIP

Intercepts are a good way to graph a line when both the x- *and* y-*variables are preceded by numbers.*

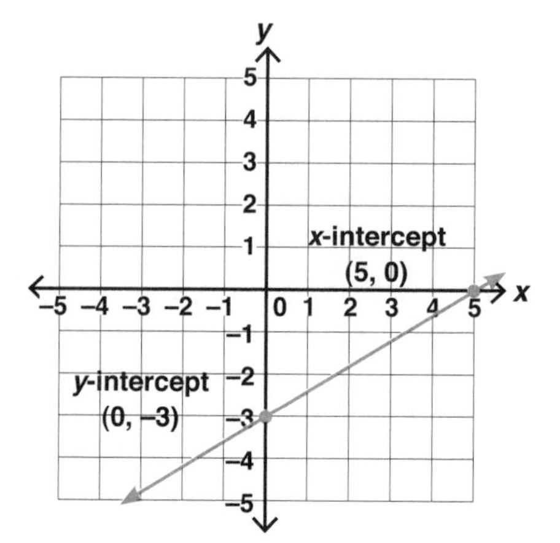

Calculate the coordinates of the x-intercept and the y-intercept.

1. $y = 3x - 3$
2. $x + 5y = -10$
3. $4x - 3y = 12$
4. $-2x + 4y = 8$

Use the graph to answer question 5.

5. Which of the following is the equation of the line shown on the graph?
   A. $2x + y = -4$
   B. $-2x + y = 4$
   C. $2x + y = 4$
   D. $2x - y = 4$

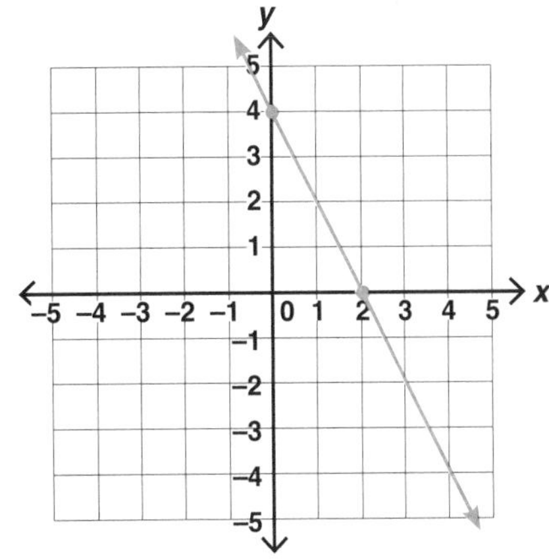

For each problem, calculate the coordinates of the x-intercept and the y-intercept. Then graph the line on the coordinate grid.

6. $2x + 3y = 6$

   y-intercept:

   x-intercept:

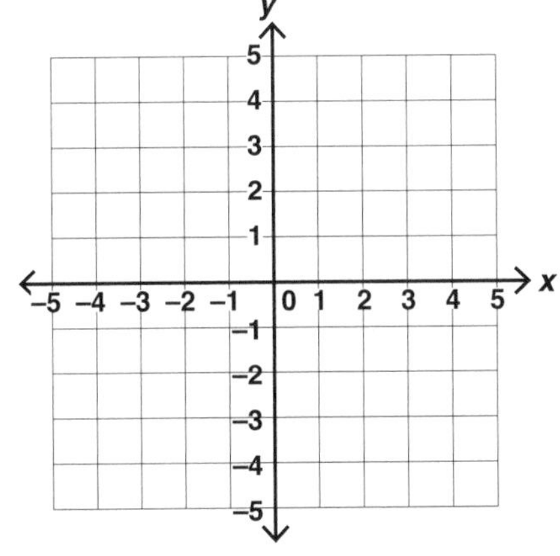

7. $x - y = 4$

   y-intercept:

   x-intercept:

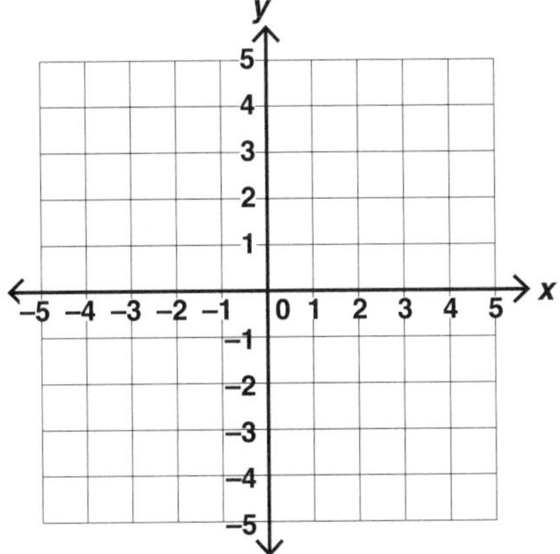

8. $3x + y = 3$

   y-intercept:

   x-intercept:

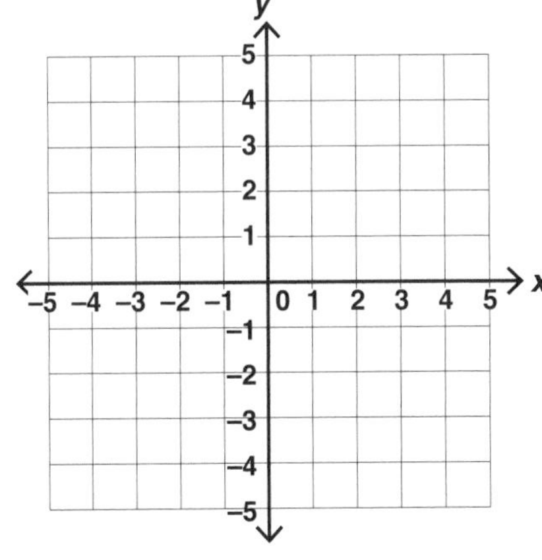

9. $y = -x + 2$

   y-intercept:

   x-intercept:

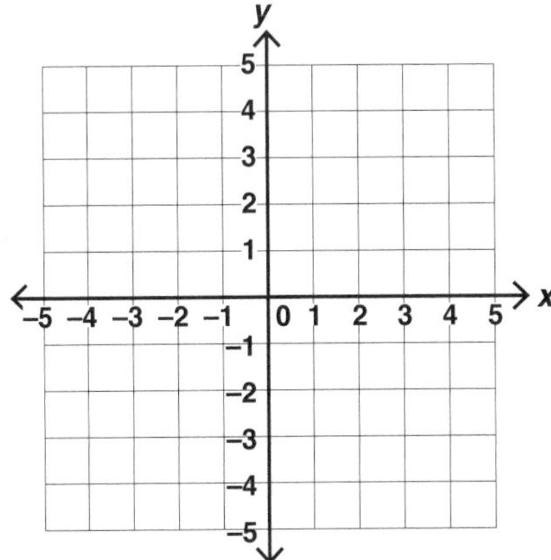

10. **Explain** Is it possible for the x- and y-intercepts to have the same coordinates? Explain your reasoning.

Answers start on page 208.

SLOPE: RISE OVER RUN

Slope refers to the amount of incline, slant, or steepness. Ski runs, most roofs, and the graphs of linear equations have slope.

Slope is a ratio that compares the **rise** of an incline to the **run.**

Look at the ramp. The rise is 1 foot, the vertical distance. The run is 3 feet, the horizontal distance. The slope of the ramp is 1:3. This means that for every foot of vertical distance (rise), there are 3 feet of horizontal distance (run).

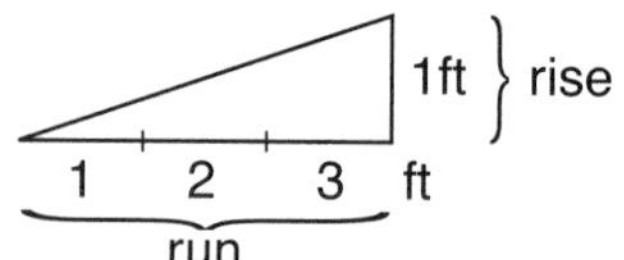

FINDING SLOPE ON A COORDINATE GRID

Example Find the slope of the line shown on the graph.

Choose any two points on the line. Points *A* and *B* are used here.

Step 1
Count the rise and the run.

To get from *A* to *B,* you would go up 4 units and go right 2 units. The rise is 4, and the run is 2.

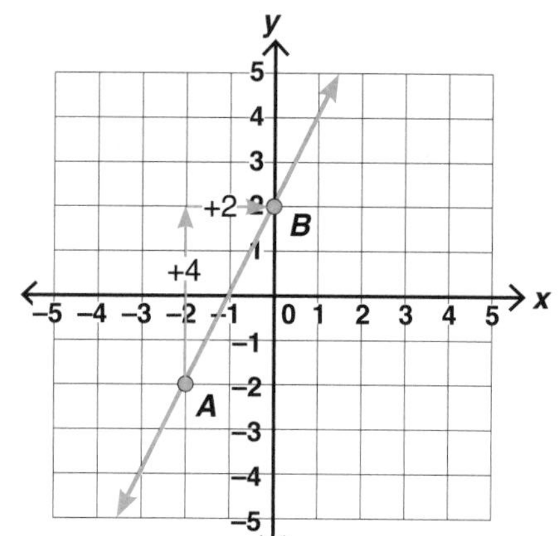

Step 2
Write the slope ratio.

The slope of the line is $\frac{4}{2}$, which equals **2.**

You can also find slope without a graph if you know the coordinates of two points. To find rise, subtract the *y*-coordinates. To find run, subtract the *x*-coordinates. Then write the rise over the run. This formula from the GED math formula sheet uses subtraction to find slope.

slope (m) = $\frac{y_2 - y_1}{x_2 - x_1}$, where (x_1, y_1) and (x_2, y_2) are two points on the coordinate plane

CALCULATING SLOPE

Example What is the slope of the line that passes through the points (1, 1) and (–2, 3)?

Step 1
Decide which point will be (x_1, y_1).

Let (1, 1) be (x_1, y_1) and (–2, 3) be (x_2, y_2).

Step 2
Substitute these values into the formula and simplify.

$m = \frac{y_2 - y_1}{x_2 - x_1} = \frac{3-1}{-2-1} = \frac{2}{-3} = -\frac{2}{3}$

The slope is $-\frac{2}{3}$.

There are two kinds of lines with special slopes.

Look at line *l*. It doesn't rise at all. For every unit of run, the line rises 0 units. The slope is $\frac{0}{1}$, or 0.

Look at line *m*. It only rises; it never runs. For every unit of rise, the line runs 0 units. You could write the slope as $\frac{1}{0}$, but division by 0 has no meaning in math. The slope of a vertical line is **undefined.**

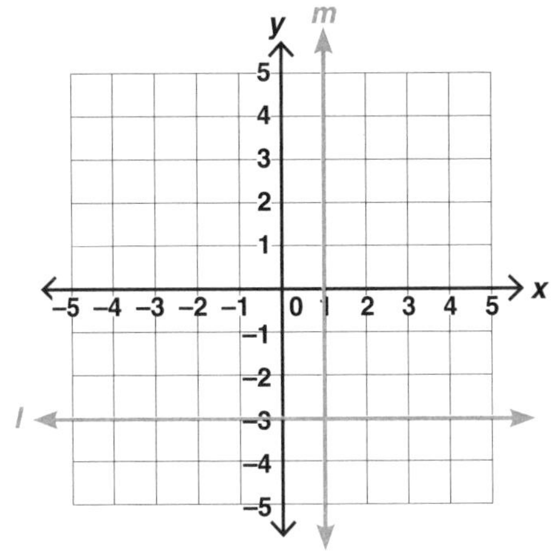

Choose two points and calculate the slope for each line.

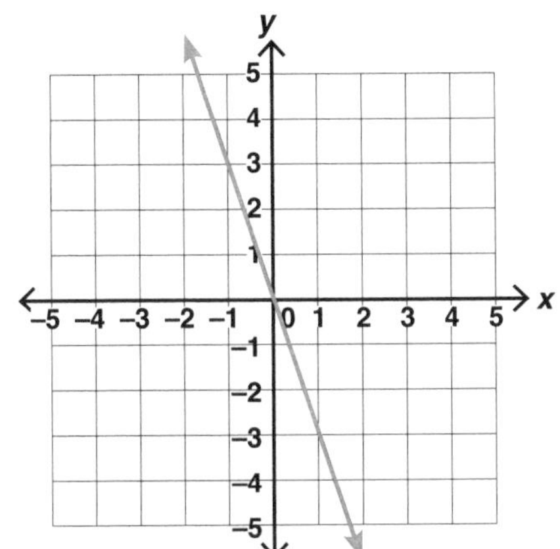

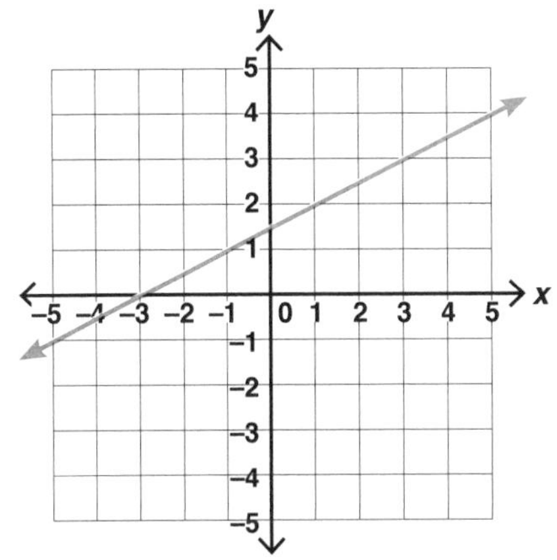

1. 1st point ____________

   2nd point ____________

   Slope ____________

2. 1st point ____________

   2nd point ____________

   Slope ____________

Calculate the slope of the line that passes through each pair of points.

3. (–2, 4) and (2, 5)

4. (6, –7) and (5, –2)

5. (–5, 3) and (–1, 6)

6. (0, 8) and (–1, 3)

7. (4, 2) and (4, 7)

8. (–4, –5) and (–9, –6)

9. (–3, 0) and (0, 3)

10. (–1, 9) and (5, 9)

11. (5, 2) and (1, 2)

12. (6, 1) and (8, 3)

Answers start on page 209.

PARALLEL AND PERPENDICULAR LINES

You have already learned the definitions of **parallel** and **perpendicular.** Parallel lines will never intersect. Perpendicular lines intersect at right angles. You can recognize these types of lines on a coordinate plane by looking at their slopes.

Parallel lines have the same slope.

FINDING PARALLEL LINES ON A COORDINATE PLANE

Example On the coordinate grid below, which two lines are parallel?

Find the slopes of all three lines.

Line *AB*: $m = \frac{3-(-1)}{-1-(-3)} = \frac{4}{2} = 2$

Line *CD*: $m = \frac{5-2}{2-1} = \frac{3}{1} = 3$

Line *EF*: $m = \frac{-2-(-4)}{3-2} = \frac{2}{1} = 2$

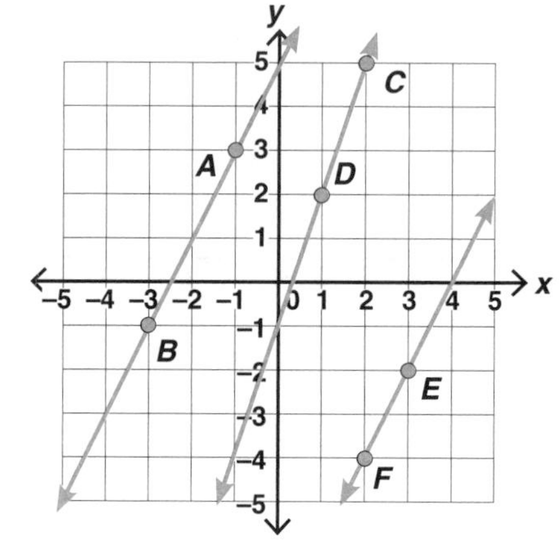

Line *AB* and **line *EF*** have the same slope. They are parallel.

Look at the perpendicular lines graphed on the coordinate grid. Can you see that they go in opposite directions?

A line that *rises* from left to right has a **positive slope.**
A line that *falls* from left to right has a **negative slope.**

Find the slopes of these two perpendicular lines.

Line *GH*: $m = \frac{4-1}{4-2} = \frac{3}{2}$ Line *JK*: $m = \frac{4-2}{1-4} = -\frac{2}{3}$

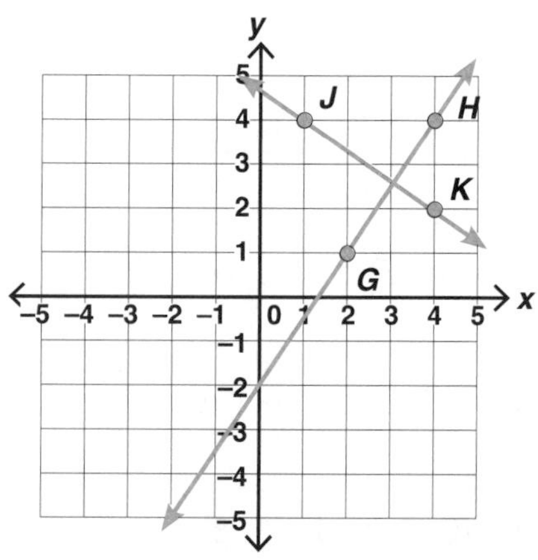

Because the lines go in opposite directions, one slope is positive and the other slope is negative. The fractions are also inverted. This type of opposite is called a **negative reciprocal.** $-\frac{2}{3}$ is the negative reciprocal of $\frac{3}{2}$.

For perpendicular lines, the slope of one line is the negative reciprocal of the slope of the other line.

Solve as directed.

Problems 1 and 2 refer to the graph below.

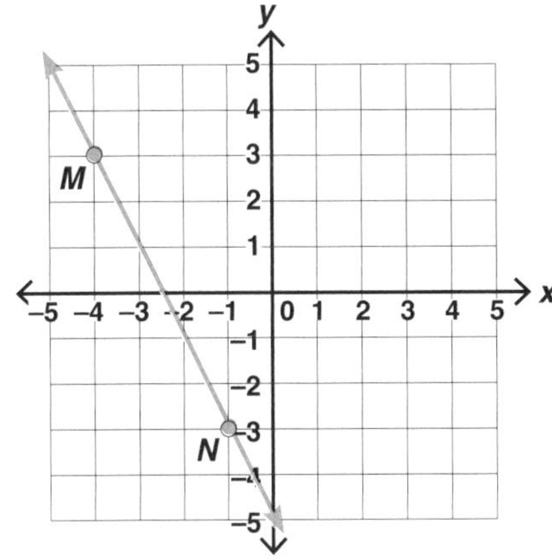

1. What is the slope of a line parallel to line *MN*?

2. What is the slope of a line perpendicular to line *MN*?

Problems 3 and 4 refer to the graph below.

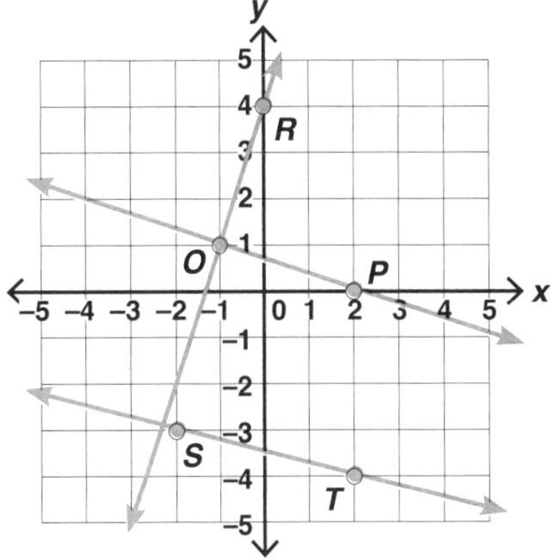

3. Are lines *OP* and *ST* parallel? How do you know?

4. Are lines *OP* and *OR* perpendicular? Explain your reasoning.

CORE CONNECTIONS: Slope and Line Graphs

Slope tells how quickly a line changes. You can use slope to analyze data in a line graph. Portions of the graph with a greater slope show a faster increase. Portions of the graph with a negative slope show a decrease.

Example Between which two months did sales decrease in Year 2?

Refer to the line for Year 2. Look for a section with a negative slope. Remember, slope is negative when the line falls from left to right.

The line falls from May to June, so sales in Year 2 decreased from May to June.

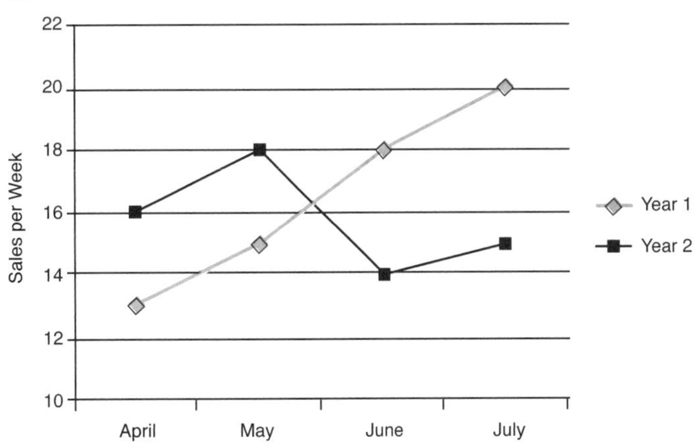

Use the chart above to solve.

1. In the period from June to July, did sales increase more in Year 1 or Year 2?

2. In Year 1, during which period did sales increase the most?

Answers start on page 209.

PROBLEM SOLVING WITH SLOPE

Slope is the ratio that is used to measure steepness. Without realizing it, you encounter situations that involve slope every day.

Think about the simple experience of walking up or down a staircase. If the steps are built according to established building codes, you hardly need to think as you climb the stairs. If the building codes aren't followed, you may very well trip or fall.

tread

rise

A stair has two parts: the *rise* and the *tread.* The minimum rise is 5 inches, and the minimum tread is 9 inches. Builders use this formula: 2 × Rise + Tread = 24.6 inches

Example A builder wants to use a rise of 5.75 inches. Find the length of the tread. Find the slope of the staircase.

Step 1
Use the formula 2 × Rise + Tread = 24.6 in.

2 × Rise + Tread = 24.6 in
$2 \times 5.75 + T = 24.6$ in
$11.5 + T = 24.6$ in
$T = 13.1$ in

Step 2
Find the slope. Substitute tread for run in the slope ratio.

$\frac{\text{rise}}{\text{run}} \quad \frac{5.75}{13.1} \approx 0.44$

For a rise of 5.75 inches, the tread should be **13.1 inches.**
The slope is about **0.44.**

Finding the steepness of a ramp is another common application of slope. Disability access codes state that the maximum slope for a ramp is 1:12 (or $\frac{1}{12}$). However, slopes between 1:16 and 1:20 are preferred.

Example One Stop Office Supplies needs to build an access ramp to get to the store's entrance. The ramp needs to rise a distance of 3 feet. If the owner wants to use a 1:16 slope for the ramp, how many feet long will the ramp need to be?

Write and solve a proposition: $\frac{\text{rise}}{\text{run}} \quad \frac{1}{16} = \frac{3}{x}$

$x = 3 \cdot 16$
$x = 48$ ft

The ramp needs to be **48 feet** long.

Slope is a ratio. Besides using a colon, you can also write slope as a fraction or a decimal. You can easily compare slopes as decimals on a calculator.

Example A ramp rises 3 inches for every 20 inches of length. Does the ramp exceed the building limit of a 1:12 slope?

Turn the slopes into decimals: $\frac{1}{12} = 0.0833$ $\frac{3}{20} = 0.15$

Yes, 0.15 is greater than 0.08, so the slope of the ramp exceeds the building limit.

Solve as directed.

Problems 1 and 2 refer to the drawing to the right.

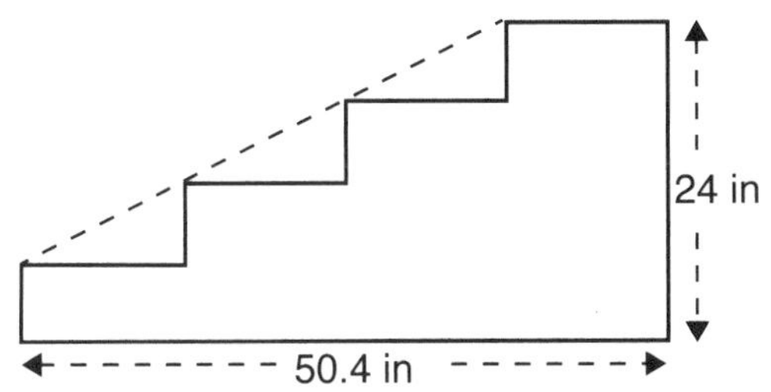

1. What is the slope of the staircase in the drawing? Express your answer as a decimal to the nearest hundredth.

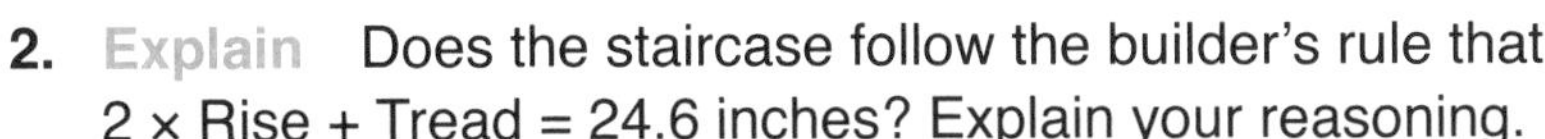

2. Explain Does the staircase follow the builder's rule that $2 \times \text{Rise} + \text{Tread} = 24.6$ inches? Explain your reasoning.

3. On a steep hill, the road rises 4 feet for every 25 feet it moves forward.

    a. What is the slope of the hill?

    b. The city posts a warning sign if the grade, or slope, of a road is 15% or greater. Will the city post a warning sign on this hill?

4. A moving truck comes with a ramp that is 8.5 feet long.

    a. How far is the end of the ramp from the back of the truck? In other words, what is the length of the dotted line in the drawing? (***Hint:*** The ramp forms a right triangle.)

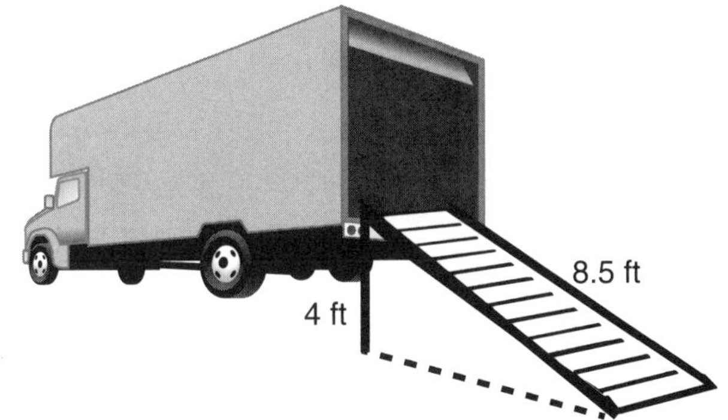

    b. What is the slope of the ramp? Express your answer as a decimal to the nearest hundredth.

Use the information to answer problems 5–8.

Ski trail difficulty ratings are determined by slope. A beginner's slope is less than 25%. An intermediate slope is from 25% to 40%, and an advanced slope has a greater than 40% slope.

Determine the appropriate rating for each slope.

5. A trail drops 5 feet vertically for every 12 feet of horizontal distance.

6. A trail drops 9 feet vertically for every 20 feet of horizontal distance.

7. A trail drops 25 feet vertically for every 90 feet of horizontal distance.

8. A trail drops 60 feet vertically for every 140 feet of horizontal distance.

Answers start on page 209.

WRITING THE EQUATION OF A LINE

By looking at a line or its points, you can write the equation that corresponds with the line. All you need are the slope of the line and the *y*-intercept.

The **slope-intercept** form of an equation is $y = mx + b$, where m is the slope and b is the *y*-value of the *y*-intercept. Find the slope and the *y*-intercept, and then substitute those values into the slope-intercept equation.

WRITING THE EQUATION OF A LINE

Example Write the equation of line *l*.

Step 1
Pick two points such as (3, –1) as (x_1, y_1) and (2, –2) as (x_2, y_2) and find the slope.

$m = \frac{-2-(-1)}{2-3} = \frac{-1}{-1} = 1$

Step 2
Find the *y*-intercept.
The line crosses the *y*-axis at (0, –4).

$b = -4$

Step 3
Substitute both values into the equation.

$y = mx + b$
$y = 1x + (-4)$
$y = x - 4$

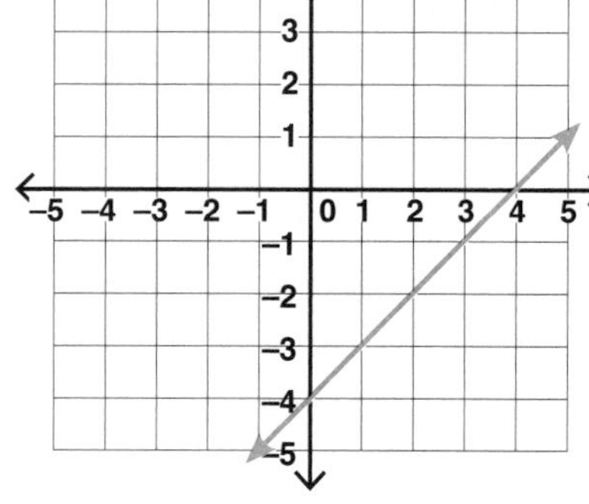

The equation of the line is $\boldsymbol{y = x - 4}$.

You can use slope-intercept form to graph an equation. Plot the *y*-intercept on the graph. Then use the slope to count rise and run.

USING THE SLOPE-INTERCEPT FORM TO GRAPH A LINE

Example Graph the line $y = \frac{1}{2}x - 3$

Step 1
Identify the slope and the *y*-intercept: $m = \frac{1}{2}$ and $b = -3$

Step 2
Plot the *y*-intercept at (0, –3).

Step 3
Count out the slope.
The line rises 1 and runs 2. Count up 1 unit and to the right 2 units and plot a point. Good test-takers plot 3 points before drawing the line.

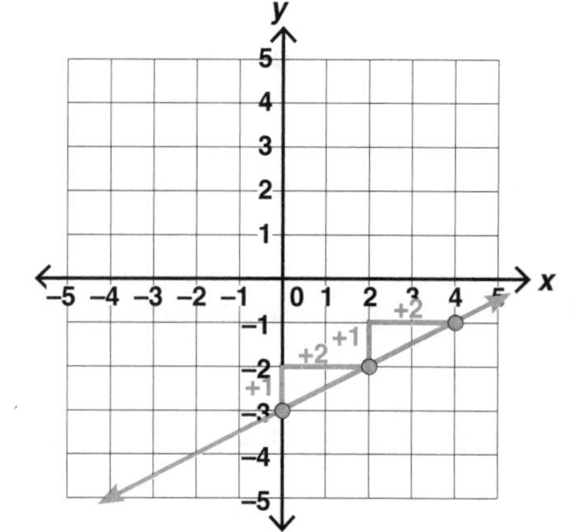

Write the equation of each line in slope-intercept form.

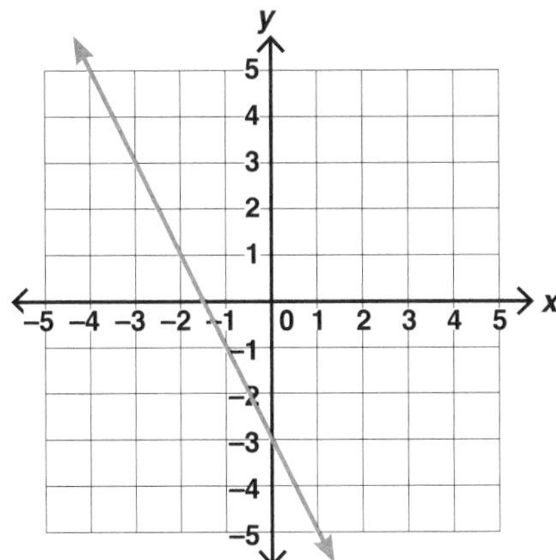

1. Slope (m): ____________________

   y-intercept: ____________________

   Equation: ____________________

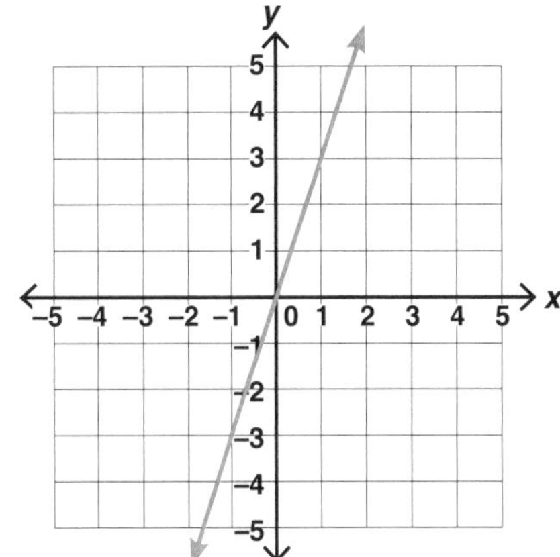

3. Slope (m): ____________________

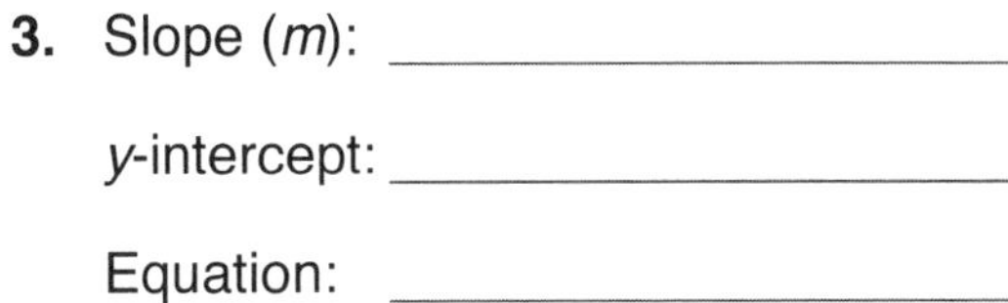

   y-intercept: ____________________

   Equation: ____________________

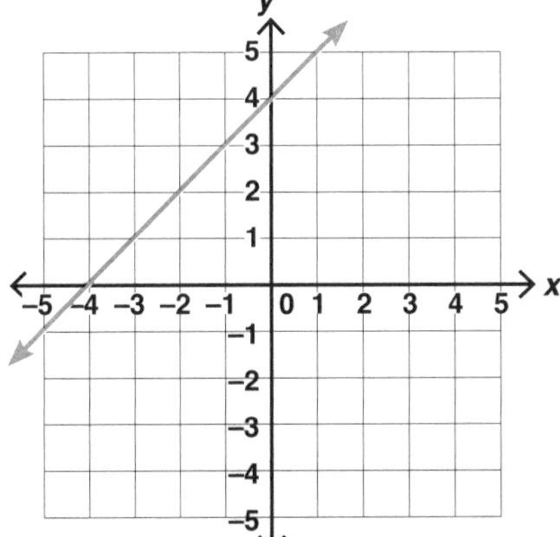

2. Slope (m): ____________________

   y-intercept: ____________________

   Equation: ____________________

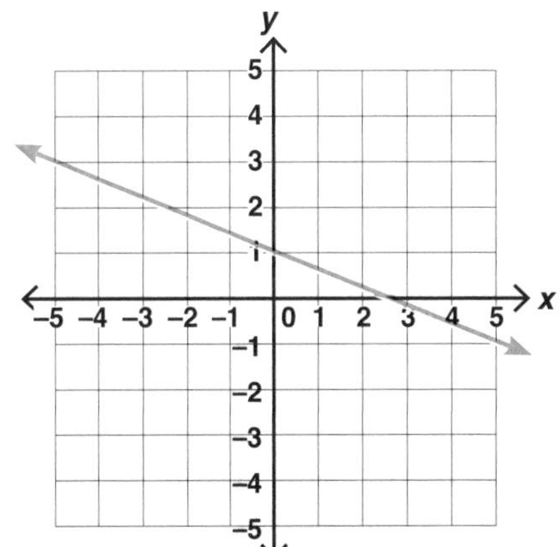

4. Slope (m): ____________________

   y-intercept: ____________________

   Equation: ____________________

Graph each equation by finding the y-intercept and counting out the slope.

5. $y = 3x + 1$

6. $y = \frac{2}{3}x - 4$

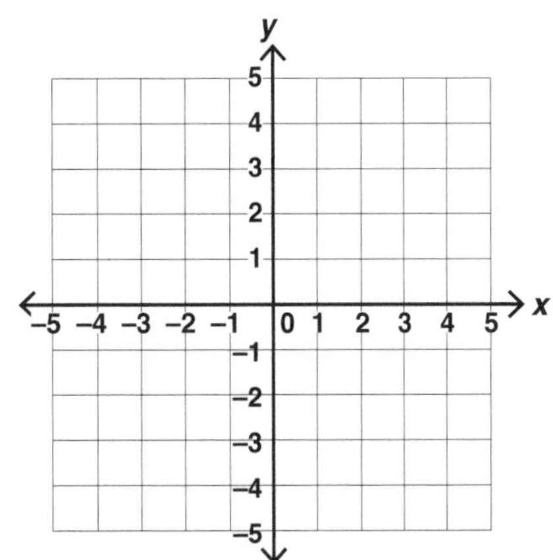

Answers start on page 210.

USING POINT-SLOPE FORM

Sometimes you can't find the y-intercept by looking at the graph. The y-intercept may be a fraction, or it may intersect at a point not shown on the graph. In this lesson, you will learn to use the **point-slope form.** Use this form when you don't know the y-intercept.

The point-slope form appears on the GED math formula sheet.

> **point-slope form** $y - y_1 = m(x - x_1)$, where m = slope and (x_1, y_1) is a point on the line

USING POINT-SLOPE FORM

Example Write the equation of the line passing through (5, 2) and (7, –2).

Step 1
Use the slope formula to find the slope. Let (5, 2) be (x_1, y_1) and (7, –2) be (x_2, y_2).

$$m = \frac{-2-2}{7-5} = \frac{-4}{2} = -2$$

Step 2
Substitute the values into point-slope form. You may use either point.

$$y - y_1 = m(x - x_1)$$
$$y - 2 = -2(x - 5)$$

Step 3
Rewrite the equation in slope-intercept form.

$$y - 2 = -2(x - 5)$$
$$y - 2 = -2x + 10$$
$$y = -2x + 12$$

The equation of the line is $\boldsymbol{y = -2x + 12}$.

You will also see linear equations written in **standard form.** The standard form of an equation is $Ax + By = C$, where A, B, and C are numbers. Standard form can be useful for finding the x- and y-intercepts, but it isn't always the most helpful way to graph an equation. Use algebra to change standard form into slope-intercept form.

CHANGING FROM STANDARD FORM TO SLOPE-INTERCEPT FORM

Example Graph the equation $2x - 3y = 9$.

Step 1
Write the equation in slope-intercept form by isolating y.

$$2x - 3y = 9$$
$$-3y = -2x + 9$$
$$y = \frac{2}{3}x - 3$$

Step 2
Graph the equation using the slope and y-intercept.

$y = \frac{2}{3}x - 3$
The slope is $\frac{2}{3}$.
The y-intercept is (0, –3).

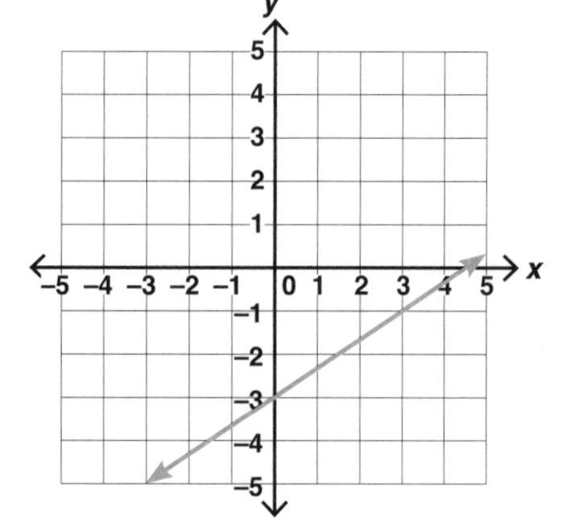

Change from standard form to slope-intercept form: $y = mx + b$

1. $3x - y = 4$
2. $5x + 5y = 15$
3. $-2x + y = 1$
4. $-2x + 6y = -12$
5. $5x + 4y = 28$
6. $3x + 8y = 40$

When you write the equation for a horizontal or vertical line, you don't need to use a specific form. All the information you need can be found from the graph or its points.

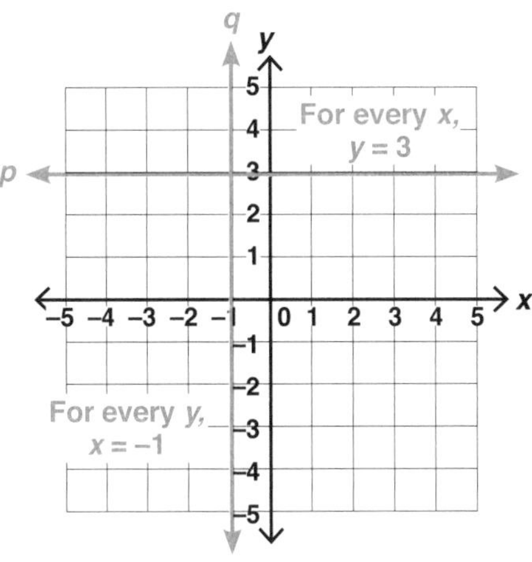

Example Write the equations of lines *p* and *q*.

Line *p* is horizontal, so it has a slope of 0. The *y*-intercept is (0, 3). Use the slope-intercept form.

$y = 0x + 3$
$y = 3$

Line *q* is vertical, so its slope is undefined. No matter what the *y*-value is, the *x*-value will always be –1.

$x = -1$

Write the equation of each line in slope-intercept form using the given information.

7. The slope of the line is 3. The line passes through (1, 3).

8. The slope of the line is –2. The line passes through (–1, –1).

9. The line passes through (–1, –8) and (3, 4).

10. The line passes through (–3, –1) and (–1, –5).

11. The line passes through (5, –4) and (0, –4).

12. The slope of the line is $-\frac{1}{2}$. The line passes through (–2, 1).

13. The slope of the line is undefined. The line passes through (5, –4).

14. The slope of the line is –7. The line passes through (3, 5).

15. The line passes through (1, –4) and (0, 0).

16. The line passes through (4, –4) and (4, 5).

17. The slope of the line is 4. The line passes through (–2, –5).

18. The line passes through (0, 2) and (5, 3).

Answers start on page 210.

DISTANCE BETWEEN POINTS

You can use a coordinate grid to find the distance between two points. The *x*-coordinate will help you find horizontal distance. The *y*-coordinate will help you find vertical distance.

FINDING HORIZONTAL OR VERTICAL DISTANCE

Example 1 What is the distance from *A* to *B*?

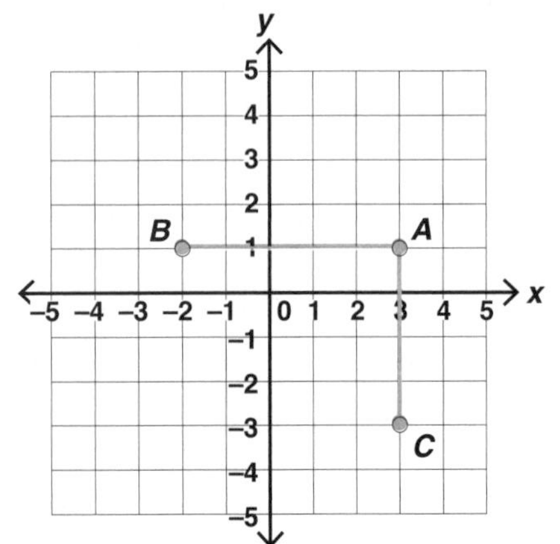

Point *A* is 3 units from the *y*-axis. Point *B* is 2 units from the *y*-axis. The total distance is 3 + 2 = **5.**

Example 2 What is the distance from *A* to *C*?

Point *A* is 1 unit from the *x*-axis. Point *C* is 3 units from the *x*-axis. The total distance is 1 + 3 = **4.**

You can also subtract the coordinates and take the absolute value.

In the first example, subtract the *x*-coordinates. $|-2-3| = |-5| = 5$

In the second example, subtract the y-coordinates. $|1 - -3| = |1+3| = |4| = 4$

Once you find the horizontal and vertical distances, you can use the Pythagorean theorem to find any distance on a coordinate plane.

USE THE PYTHAGOREAN THEOREM WITH THE COORDINATE PLANE

Example What is the distance from *D* to *E*?

Step 1
By drawing horizontal and vertical lines, you can create a right triangle where *DE* is the hypotenuse. Find the lengths of *DF* and *EF.*

$DF = |-3-1| = |-4| = 4$

$EF = |0-3| = |-3| = 3$

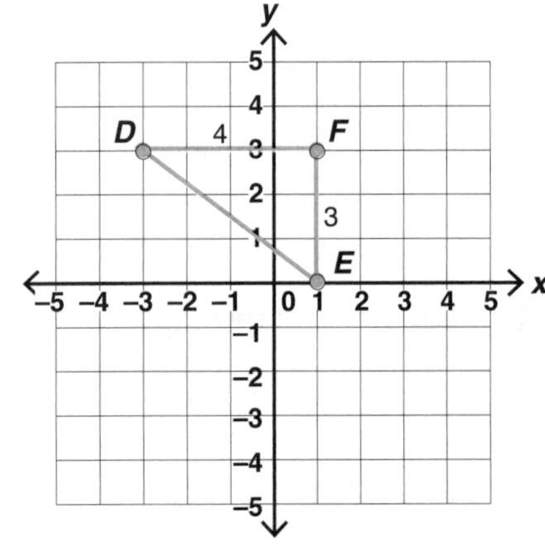

Step 2
Use the Pythagorean theorem.

$$a^2 + b^2 = c^2$$
$$3^2 + 4^2 = c^2$$
$$\sqrt{9+16} = c$$
$$\sqrt{25} = c$$
$$5 = c$$

The distance from *D* to *E* is **5 units.**

There is a formula for finding the distance between two points that combines the process of subtracting the coordinates and the Pythagorean theorem. You don't have to memorize it because you already know the Pythagorean theorem. Take a moment to investigate the formula. How is it like the Pythagorean theorem?

> Distance (d) = $\sqrt{(x_2 - x_1)^2 + (y_2 - y_1)^2}$, where (x_1, y_1) and (x_2, y_2) are points

Find the distance between each pair of points.

1. R and S

2. R and U

3. U and S

4. T and U

5. What is the best estimate for the distance between points S and T?
   A. between 3 and 4
   B. between 4 and 5
   C. between 5 and 6
   D. between 6 and 7

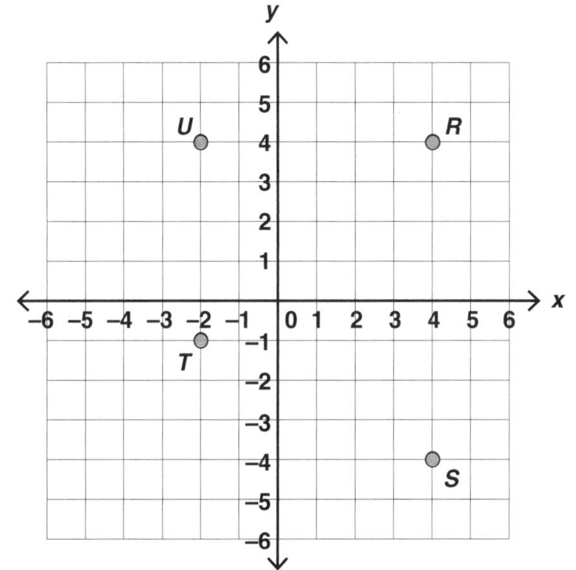

6. P and N

7. N and O

8. P and O

9. L and M

10. What is the best estimate for the distance between points L and O?

   A. between 9 and 10
   B. between 10 and 11
   C. between 11 and 12
   D. between 12 and 13

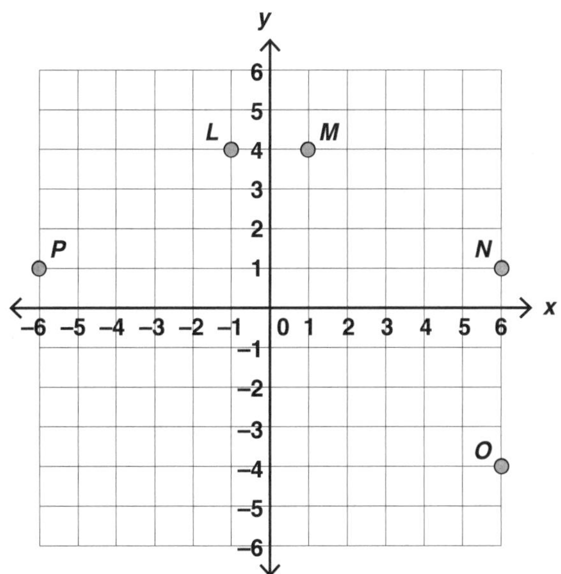

Answers start on page 211.

GEOMETRIC FIGURES ON THE COORDINATE PLANE

In this unit, you have gained many skills. You can plot points, draw lines, and write equations for lines drawn on a coordinate plane. You can find slope and use slope to draw parallel and perpendicular lines. You can also work with similar figures, use the Pythagorean theorem to measure distance, and find perimeter and area of flat figures.

On the GED and other math tests, you will be asked to apply several skills at once to solve a problem.

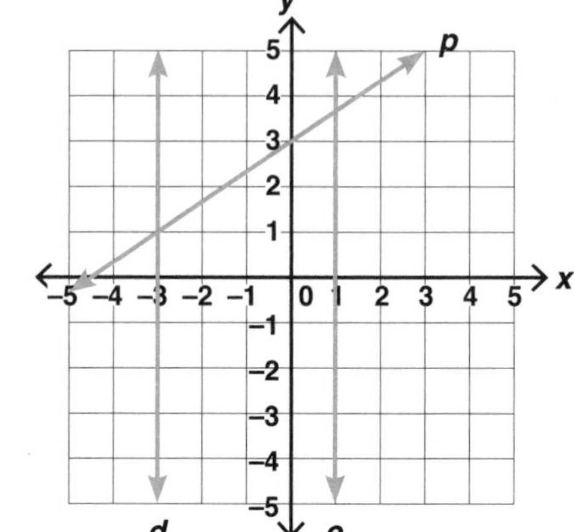

Example 1 On the coordinate plane, lines *d* and *e* are parallel. Line *p* passes through points (–3, 1) and (0, 3). Line *q* is to be drawn through point (0, –2) to complete a parallelogram. Find the equation of line *q*.

Step 1
Apply your knowledge of polygons.

A parallelogram has two pairs of parallel lines. The new line *q* must be parallel to line *p*, so *p* and *q* must have the same slope.

Step 2
Find the slope of line *p*.

The slope of *p* is $\frac{2}{3}$ because the line rises 2 spaces as it runs 3 spaces.

Step 3
Find the equation of line *q*.

You know the slope and one point (0, –2).

Use the point-slope form: $y - y_1 = m(x - x_1)$

The equation of line *q* is $\mathbf{y = \frac{2}{3}x - 2}$.

$$y - y_1 = m(x - x_1)$$
$$y - -2 = \frac{2}{3}(x - 0)$$
$$y + 2 = \frac{2}{3}x - 0$$
$$y = \frac{2}{3}x - 2$$

The grid marks on the coordinate plane also make it possible to solve area and perimeter problems by counting units.

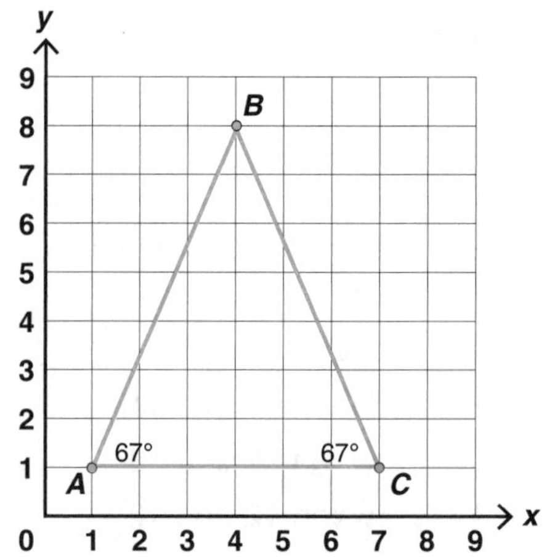

Example 2 Find the perimeter of isosceles triangle *ABC* to the nearest whole unit.

Since the triangle is isosceles, *AB* is equal in measure to *BC*.

Find the distance between the points for each segment. Notice that *AB* is the hypotenuse for a triangle with a base of 3 and a height of 7.

$AB \approx 7.6$ $\quad BC \approx 7.6$ $\quad AC = 6$

Add to find the perimeter: 7.6 + 7.6 + 6 = 21.2, which rounds to **21 units.**

Solve as directed.

1. A square is drawn on a coordinate plane.

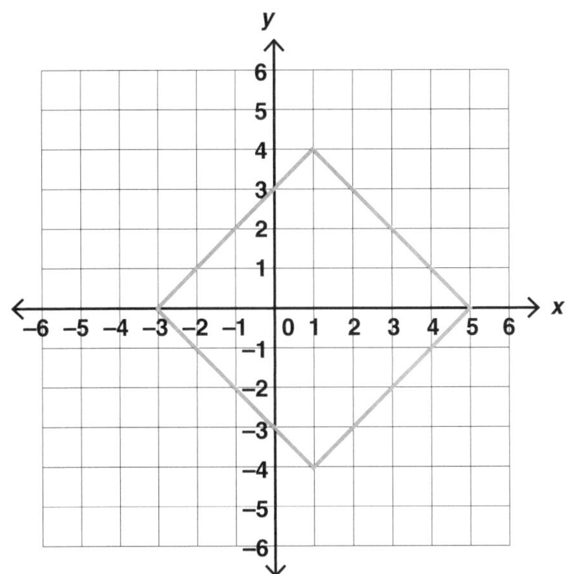

What is the area of the square in square units?

A. 8

B. 11.3

C. 16

D. 32

2. Explain If $\overline{FE}$ is extended, will it intersect $\overline{CD}$ at a right angle? Explain your reasoning.

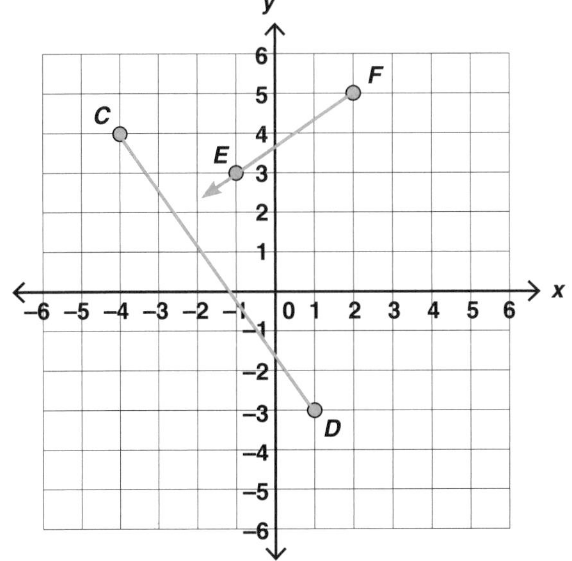

3. Explain Is triangle PQR a right triangle? Explain how you know your answer is correct.

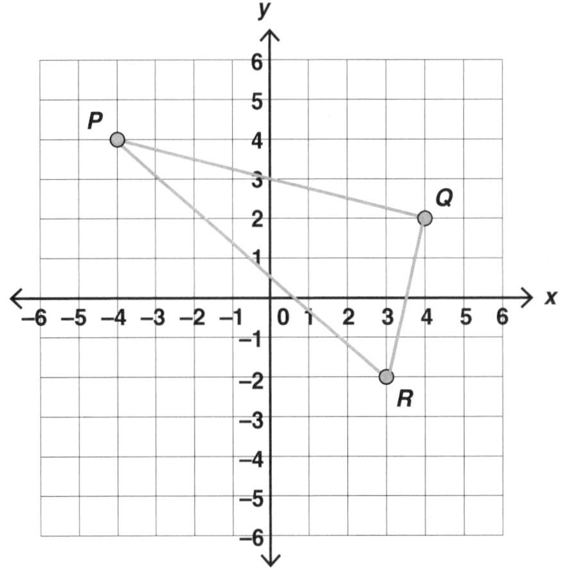

4. Emma is drawing a parallelogram on the grid below. She has plotted three points as shown. Where should she plot point F to complete the parallelogram?

Write the coordinates of the point.

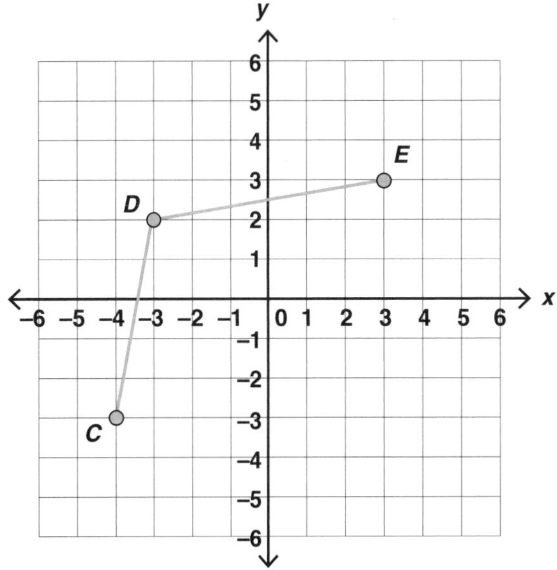

Answers start on page 211.

Unit 5 Review

Solve as directed.

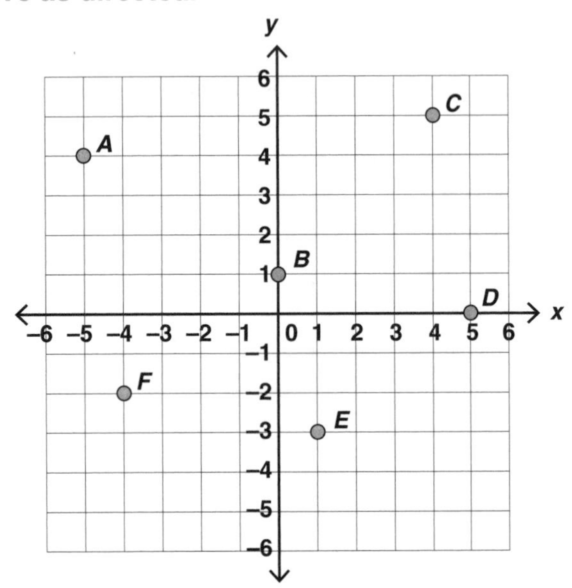

1. Write the coordinates for each point on the grid.

   A ____________ D ____________

   B ____________ E ____________

   C ____________ F ____________

2. In which quadrant is point *F* found?
   A. Quadrant I
   B. Quadrant II
   C. Quadrant III
   D. Quadrant IV

3. Plot the following points on the coordinate grid below.

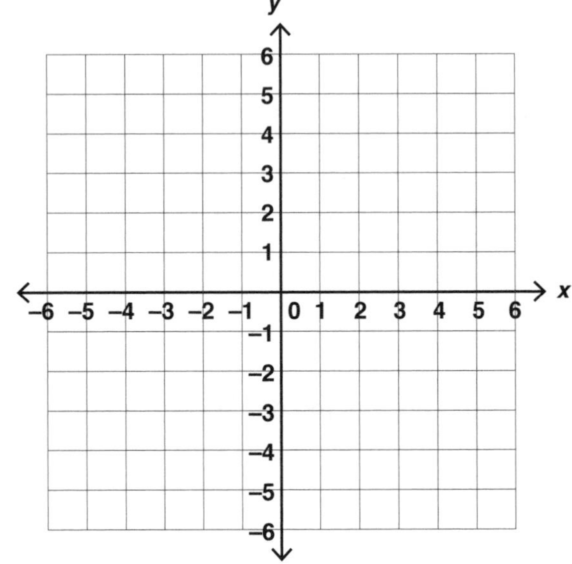

G = (1, –4) *J* = (0, 4)

H = (–3, 2) *K* = (–2, 0)

For each equation, complete the table of values.

4. $y = 7x + 4$

x	y
−2	
0	
2	
4	

5. $y = -x - 3$

x	y
−1	
0	
1	
2	

6. $3x - y = 5$

x	y
1	
2	
3	
4	

7. All but one of these points lie on the graph of the line $2x - y = 5$. Which point is not on the line?

A. (0, −5)

B. (2, −1)

C. (4, 5)

D. (6, 7)

For problems 8 and 9, find the *x*- and *y*-intercepts, plot the intercepts, and draw the graph of the line.

8. $3x - 4y = 12$

x-intercept: ____________

y-intercept: ____________

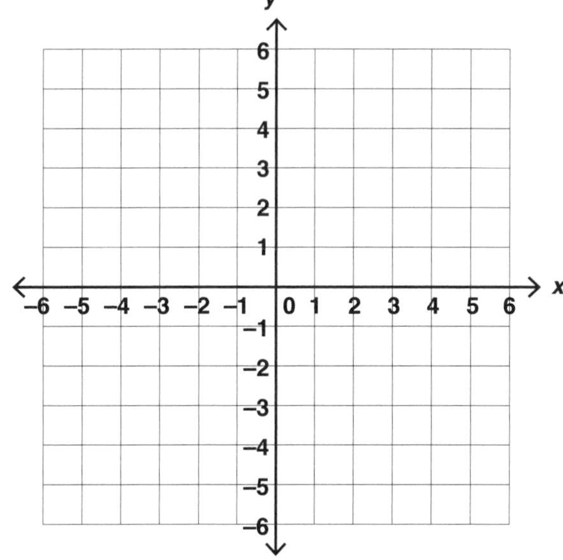

9. $5x - 3y = -15$

x-intercept: ____________

y-intercept: ____________

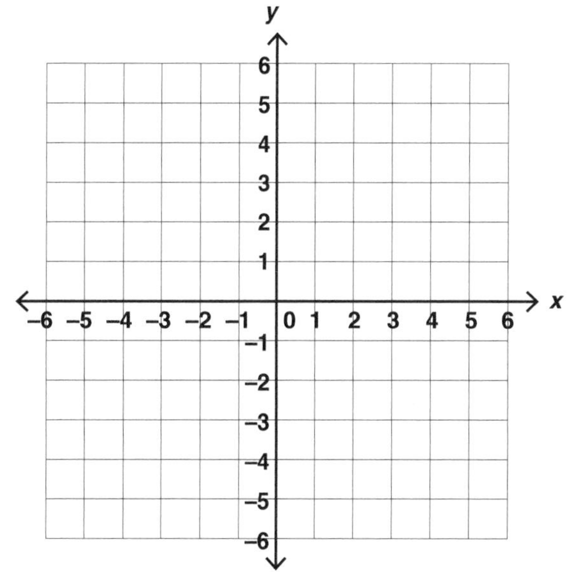

Solve.

10. Which of the lines on the graph below has a slope of $\frac{2}{3}$?

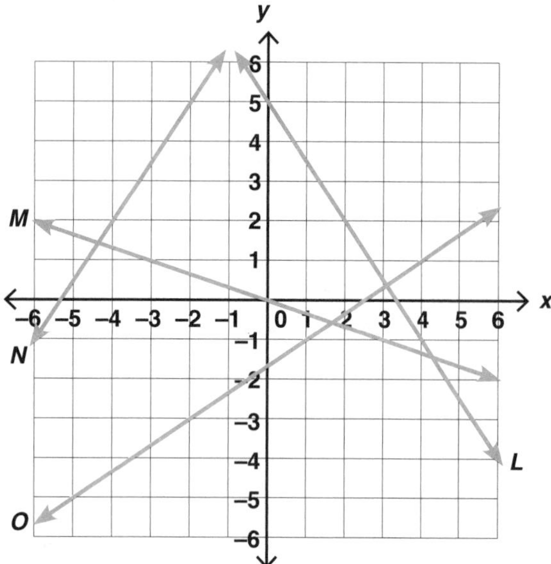

A. line L

B. line M

C. line N

D. line O

11. A line passes through point (–2, –1). If the slope of the line is undefined, which of the following points is also on the line?

A. (–2, 4)

B. (–1, 2)

C. (–1, –2)

D. (0, –1)

12. A line passes through points (–18, 16) and (–7, –6). What is the slope of the line?

13. Alan draws two lines on a graph. Line p passes through (–3, 0) and (2, 4). Line q passes through (–1, 0) and (4, –4).

Alan claims that lines p and q are perpendicular. Is he correct? Explain your reasoning.

14. A stage manager builds a step unit with 3 steps to reach a platform 18 inches above the floor. The slope of each step is $\frac{1}{2}$, or 0.5. If each of the steps is exactly the same size, how many inches is the tread (walking surface) of 1 step?

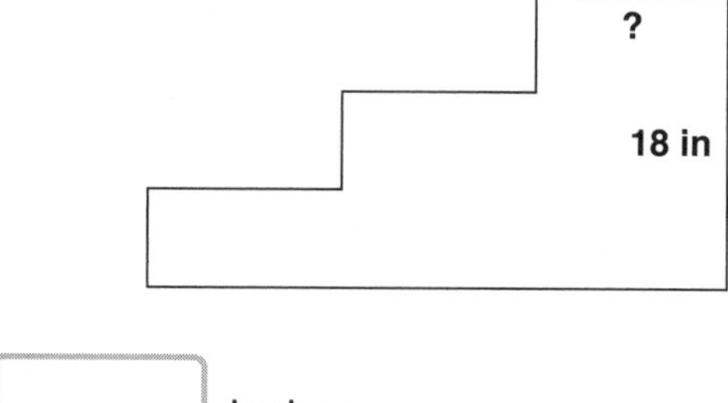

inches

For problems 15–18, write the equation of the line in slope-intercept form: $y = mx + b$

15.

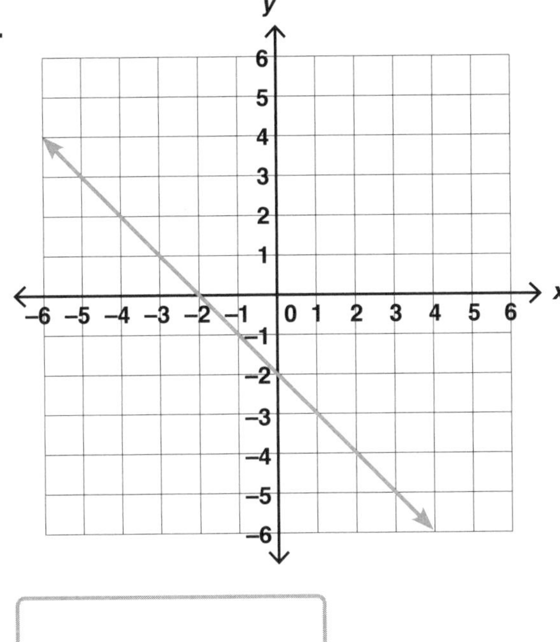

17.

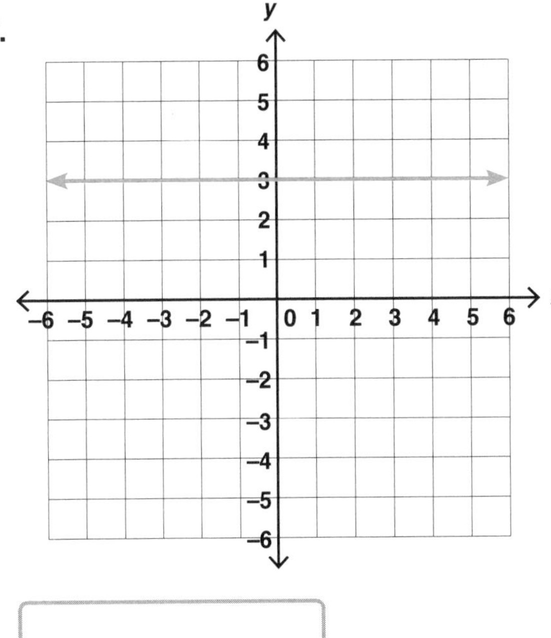

16.

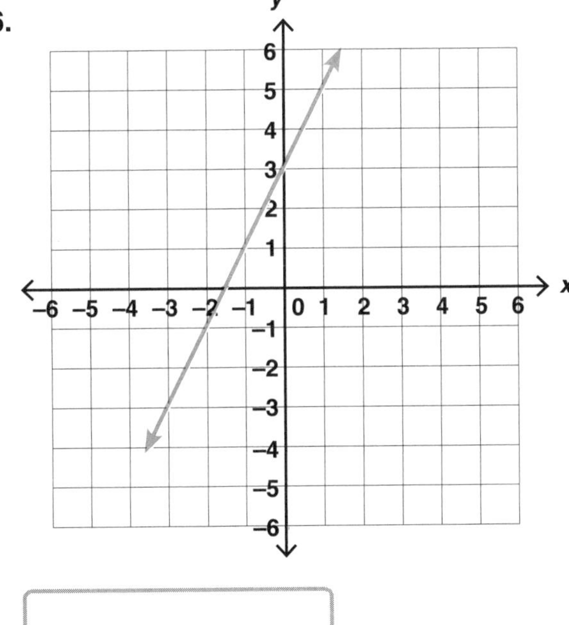

18.

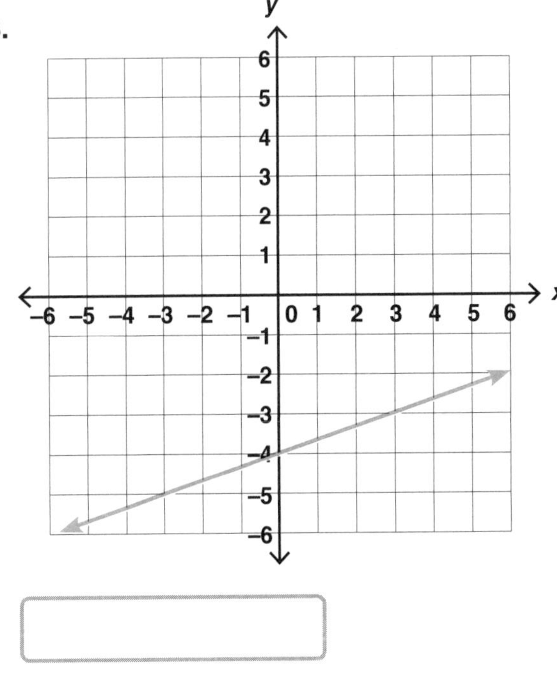

Answer problem 19 by writing a short response in the box.

19. Jenna claims that line *m* passes through points (–5, –9), (10, 0), and (5, –6).

Is this possible? How can you prove your answer without drawing a graph?

Solve.

20. Which is the equation of a line that passes through point (–1, –2) and has a slope of 3?

A. $3x - y = -1$

B. $-3x + y = -1$

C. $x - 3y = -1$

D. $x + 3y = 1$

21. Which is the equation of a line that passes through points (–2, 3) and (–4, –5)?

A. $y = 11x + 4$

B. $y = 4x + 11$

C. $y = 3x + 4$

D. $y = -4x - 5$

22. What is the distance in units between points (–3, 4) and (9, 4)?

units

23. What is the equation of a line that passes through (2, –1) and is perpendicular to the graph of $y = -\frac{1}{2}x - 4$?

Write your answer in slope-intercept form.

24. Both the *x*- and *y*-intercepts of a line are positive. Is the slope of the line positive or negative?

Explain how you know your answer is correct.

Problems 25 and 26 refer to the drawing below.

25. A student finds that a wooden block will begin to slide down a ramp when the angle of the ramp is 29.4°.

Which of the following best describes the slope of the ramp?

A. less than 0.5

B. equal to 0.5

C. greater than 0.5

D. slope cannot be determined

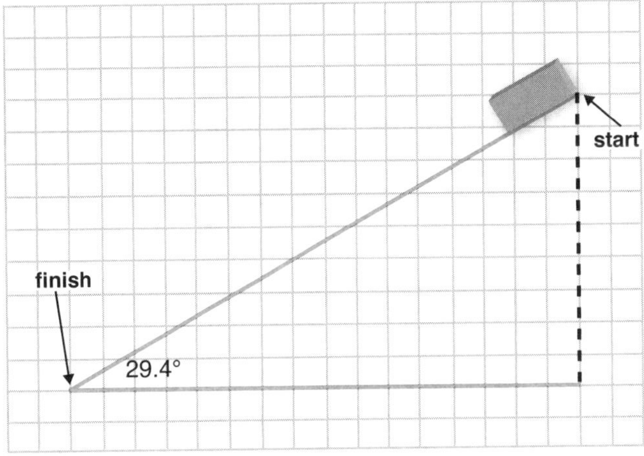

26. If each square on the grid measures 2 inches by 2 inches, how many inches will the block slide from start to finish? Round to the nearest inch.

[ ] inches

Answers start on page 211.

Simulated GED® Math Test

This 30-item simulated test will help you practice the skills you have learned in this book.

Solve as directed. Do not use your calculator for questions 1–5.

Question 1 refers to the number line. Select your answer from the choices.

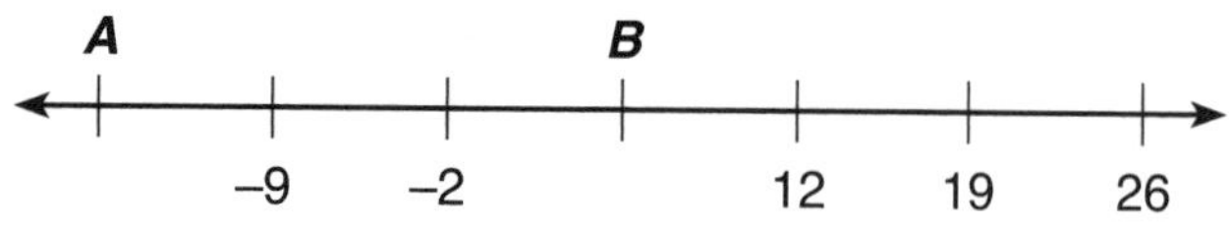

1. The markings on the number line are equally spaced. Find the values of A and B.

$A =$

–26
–20
–16
–12

$B =$

3
5
7
9

2. What is the value of the expression?

$$\frac{28}{4+|(-2)-1|}$$

A. –28
B. –4
C. 4
D. 28

Write your answer in the box.

3. What is the value of the expression?

$$3\sqrt{16} - (-2)^3 + 4(5 - 2^2)$$

Write your answer in the box.

4. Solve for x.

$$-3x - 13 = 7 - 2(3x + 1)$$

$x =$

Write your answer in the box. You may use numbers and the  symbol in your answer.

5. Write the expression in simplest form.

$$2\sqrt{54}$$

Solve as directed. You may use your calculator for questions 6–30.

Question 6 refers to the drawing.

The floor plan for a recreation room in a community center is shown below. All measurements are in feet. All angles are 90°.

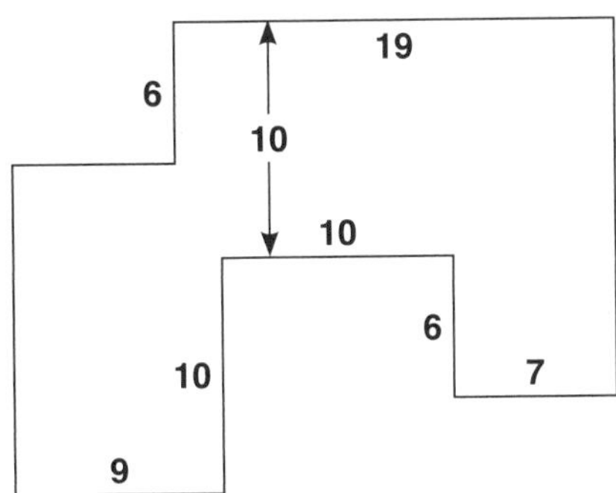

6. What is the perimeter of the recreation room in feet?
   A. 77
   B. 104
   C. 134
   D. 520

7. At 10 a.m., Dwayne and Mike are 36 miles apart and begin riding toward each other on bicycles. They finally meet at 11:30 a.m. Dwayne rides 4 miles per hour faster than Mike. What is Mike's average speed in miles per hour?

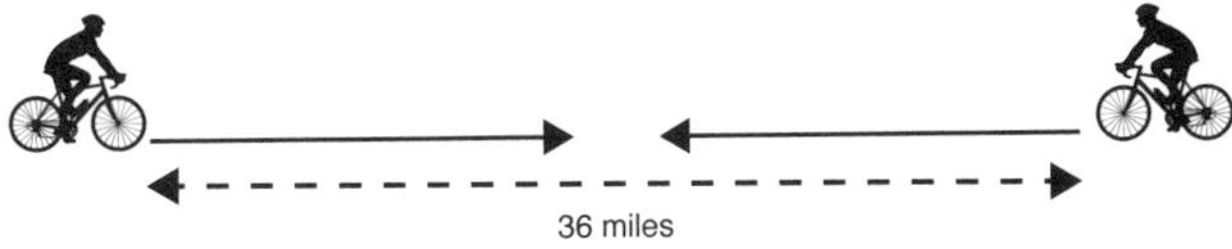

   A. 9
   B. 10
   C. 12
   D. 14

8. Scientists measure the length of a wave of light in meters. During an experiment, the wavelengths for several types of light are recorded. The results are shown in the table below.

Light	Wavelength
Ultraviolet light	9.0×10^{-8} m
Violet light	4.0×10^{-7} m
Red light	6.5×10^{-7} m
Infrared light	1.8×10^{-6} m

The wavelength of infrared light is about how many times greater than the wavelength of ultraviolet light?

   A. 0.2
   B. 2
   C. 20
   D. 200

Select your answer.

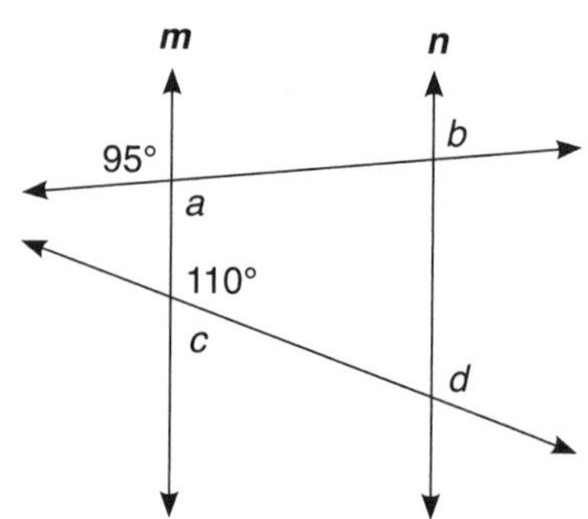

9. In the figure, lines *m* and *n* are parallel. Find the measures of the marked angles.

∠*a* = 70° / 85° / 95° / 110°

∠*b* = 70° / 85° / 95° / 110°

∠*c* = 70° / 85° / 95° / 110°

∠*d* = 70° / 85° / 95° / 110°

Write your answer in the box.

10. What is volume of the box in cubic centimeters?

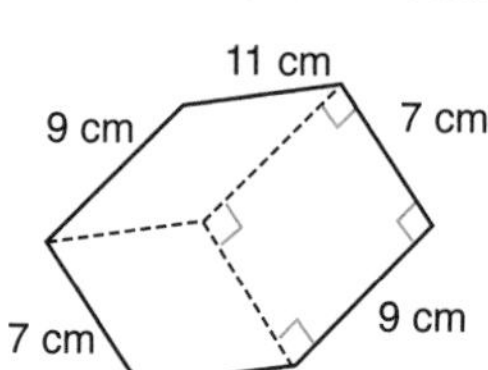

☐ cubic centimeters

11. What is the value of the expression when $x = -5$ and $y = -3$?

$$\frac{x-(x+10)}{2} \cdot (y+7)$$

A. 0

B. –20

C. –40

D. –50

Write your answer in the box.

12. Maggie and David played the same game twice. In Game 1, Maggie scored twice as many points as David. In Game 2, Maggie scored 10 fewer points than she did in Game 1. David's score in Game 2 was 12 points higher than his score in Game 1.

Maggie scored a total of 110 points in the two games. How many points did David score in the second game?

☐ points

Plot points and draw a line on the graph.

13. Complete the table. Then plot the points from the table, and draw the graph of the line for the equation.

$$3x + 2y = 2$$

x	*y*
–2	
0	
4	

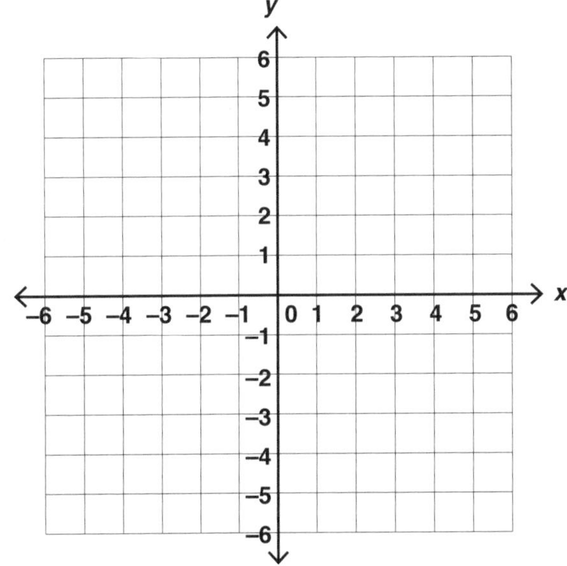

Write your answer in the box.

14. The formula for finding the perimeter of a rectangle can be written as $P = 2L + 2W$, where P = perimeter, L = length, and W = width.

Rewrite the formula to solve for W, the width of the rectangle.

$W =$ ☐

Question 15 refers to the following figure.

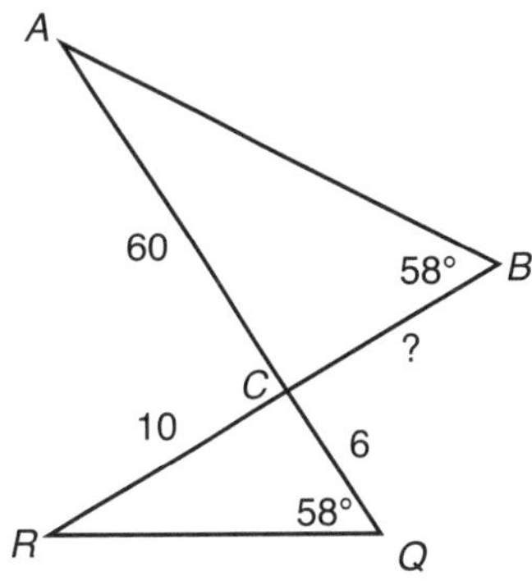

15. In the drawing, $\triangle CBA$ is similar to $\triangle CQR$. What is the length of side BC?

A. 10

B. 36

C. 100

D. 120

16. Three pipes connect to an underground storage tank.

Pipe A can fill the tank completely in 12 hours. Pipe B can do the job in 10 hours. Pipe C takes 15 hours.

If all three pipes are used at the same time, how many hours will it take to fill the tank?

A. 2

B. 4

C. 6

D. 12

17. Nick is playing a dice game with a friend. If he wins a round, he earns 9 points. If he loses a round, he loses 4 points. After 15 rounds, Nick has 18 points. How many rounds did he lose?

☐ rounds

Question 18 refers to the graph below.

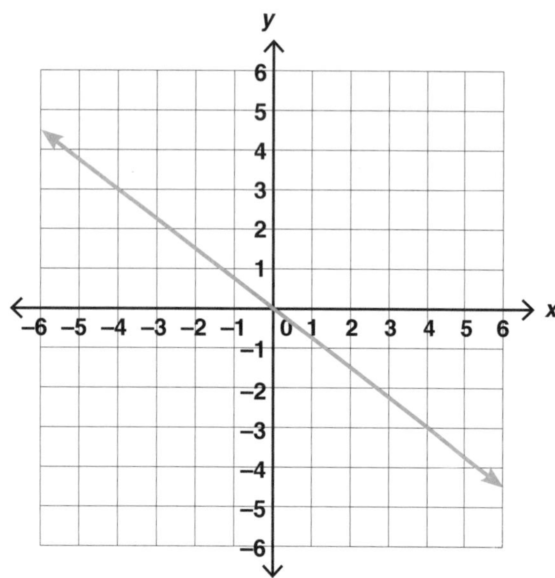

18. What is the slope of the line drawn on the graph?

A. $-\frac{4}{3}$

B. $-\frac{3}{4}$

C. $\frac{3}{4}$

D. $\frac{4}{3}$

19. A line passes through points (–1, 4) and (3, 2). What is the equation of the line in standard form?

A. $x + 2y = 7$

B. $x + 8y = 19$

C. $2x + y = 2$

D. $5x - 3y = 9$

20. The drawing shows the dimensions of the main floor of an apartment. The owner wants to install new hardwood flooring in the space.

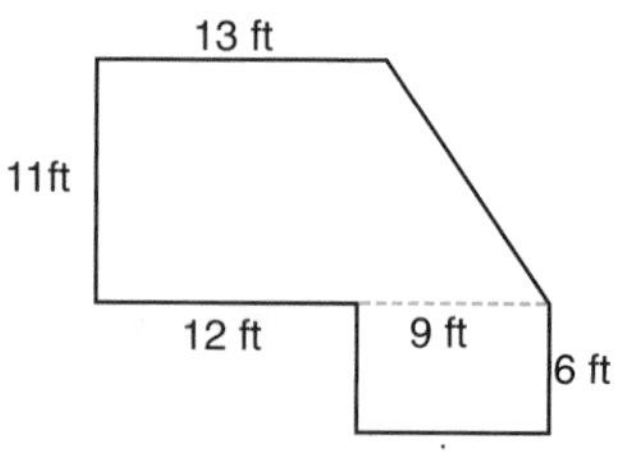

Hardwood Flooring charges $4.25 per square foot for engineered hardwood flooring. How much will the flooring cost?

A. $255.00

B. $794.75

C. $1,024.25

D. $1,211.25

21. Maureen has scores of 78, 83, 70, and 85 on four chemistry tests. She needs at least an 80 average in the class to get a B.

She has one more 100-point test. Which inequality represents the range of possible scores (*s*) that would allow her to get a B in the class?

A. $s \geq 80$

B. $80 \geq s < 100$

C. $84 \leq s \leq 100$

D. $84 < s < 100$

Question 22 refers to the following figure.

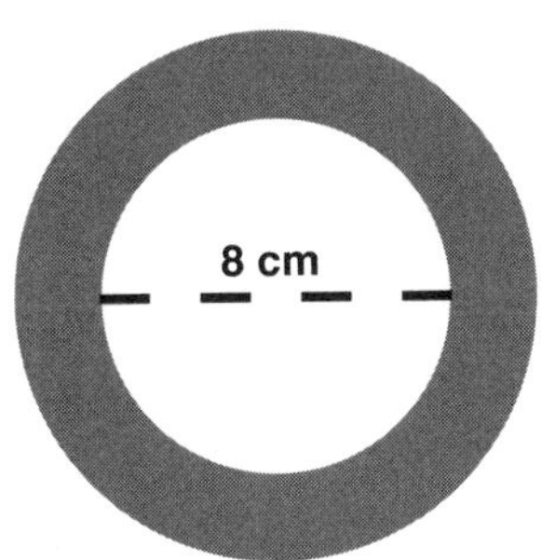

22. A metal washer is a circular piece of metal with a circular hole. What is the area of the washer, to the nearest square centimeter, if the circumference of the outside surface measures 12π cm?

A. 13

B. 50

C. 63

D. 113

Question 23 refers to the following figure.

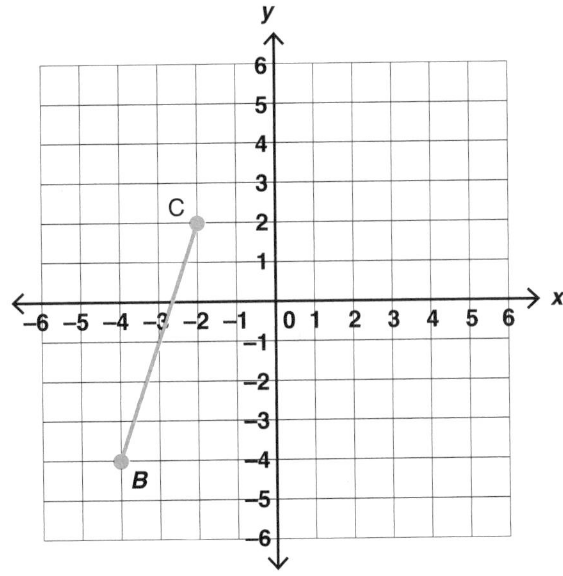

23. Which of the following is an equation of a line perpendicular to $\overline{BC}$ with an x-intercept of –6?

A. $y = -3x - 2$

B. $y = -3x + 2$

C. $y = \frac{1}{3}x + 2$

D. $y = -\frac{1}{3}x - 2$

Question 24 refers to the figure below. Write your answer in the box.

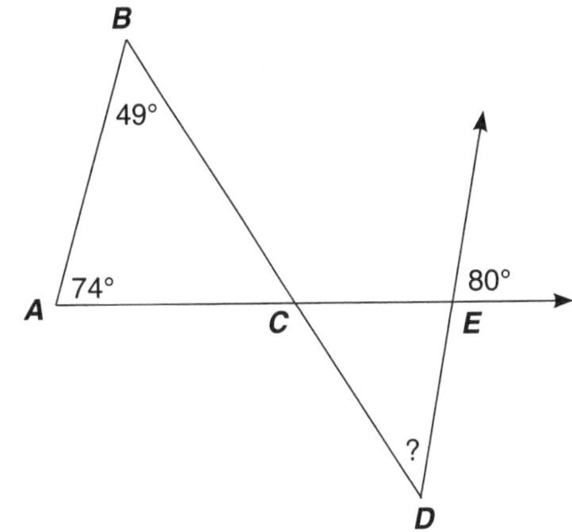

24. What is the measure of $\angle CDE$?

 degrees

25. Solve and graph the solution of the inequality on the number line.

$1 - 3x < -3 - 5x$

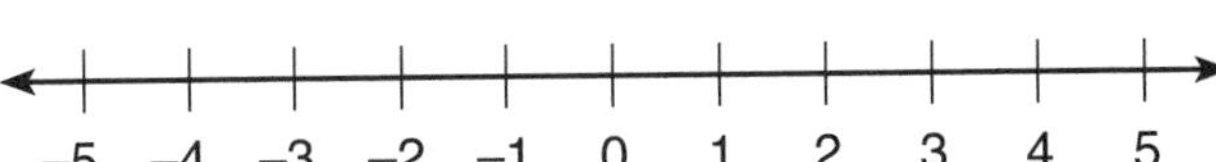

26. A ladder is placed against a wall so that the base of the ladder is 5 feet from the wall. The top of the ladder reaches a height 20 feet from the ground.

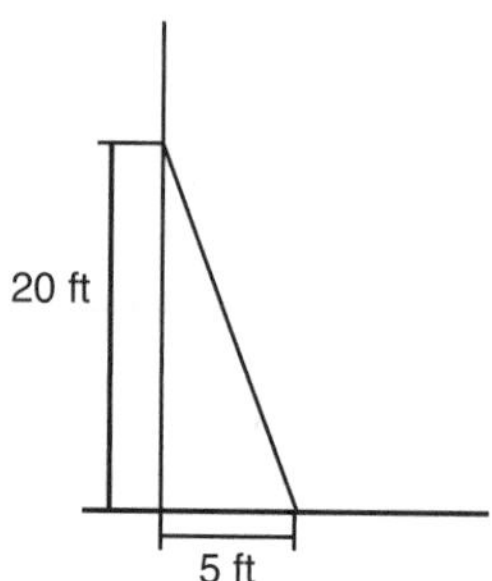

To the nearest tenth of a foot, what is the length of the ladder?

A. 20.6

B. 22.0

C. 24.4

D. 25.1

Write your answer in the box.

27. A line has a slope of –4 and passes through point (–2, 5). Write the equation of the line in slope-intercept form.

28. There are three consecutive even numbers. The sum of the first number and 2 times the third number is 46 more than the second number. What is the third number?

A. 20

B. 22

C. 24

D. 26

Question 29 refers to figure below. Write your answer in the box.

29. To the nearest square inch, what is the surface area of the figure?

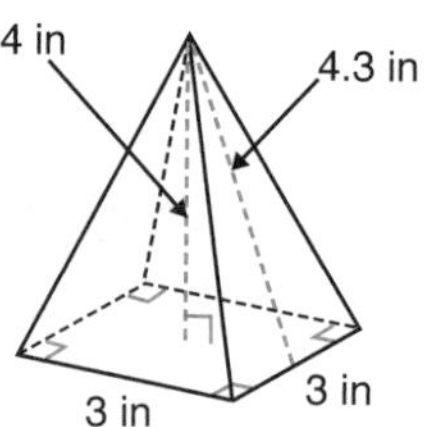

square inches

Explain your answer in the space below.

30. The following points are plotted on a coordinate plane:

A (–3, 4) *B* (–3, –5) *C* (5, –5)

The points are then connected to form a triangle. How could you find the perimeter of the triangle without graphing it?

Answers start on page 177.

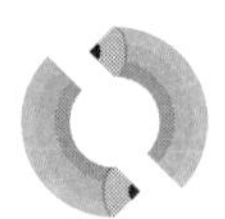 Simulated Test **Answer Key**

1. **$A = -16$, $B = 5$**
   The markings are 7 units apart.
   $-9 - 7 = -16$
   $12 - 7 = 5$

2. **C. 4**
   $\frac{28}{4+|(-2-)1|}$
   $= \frac{28}{4+|-3|}$
   $= \frac{28}{4+3}$
   $= \frac{28}{7}$
   $= 4$

3. **24**
   $3\sqrt{16} - (-2)^3 + 4(5 - 2^2)$
   $= 3(4) - (-8) + 4(5 - 4)$
   $= 3(4) - (-8) + 4(1)$
   $= 12 + 8 + 4$
   $= 24$

4. **6**
   $-3x - 13 = 7 - 2(3x + 1)$
   $-3x - 13 = 7 - 6x - 2$
   $-3x - 13 = 5 - 6x$
   $3x - 13 = 5$
   $3x = 18$
   $x = 6$

5. **$6\sqrt{6}$**
   $2\sqrt{54} = 2\sqrt{9 \times 6} = 3 \times 2\sqrt{6} = 6\sqrt{6}$

6. **B. 104**
   Fill in the missing side lengths.
   Rightmost side: 10 + 6 = 16 ft
   Leftmost side: 10 + (10 – 6) = 14 ft
   Let the missing horizontal side be x.
   $19 + x = 9 + 10 + 7$
   $19 + x = 26$
   $x = 7$
   $P = 19 + 16 + 7 + 6 + 10 + 10 + 9 + 14 + 7 + 6 = 104$

7. **B. 10**

	Rate	Time	Distance
Dwayne	$r + 4$	1.5	$1.5(r + 4)$
Mike	r	1.5	$1.5r$

   Equation:
   $1.5(r + 4) + 1.5r = 36$
   $1.5r + 6 + 1.5r = 36$
   $3r + 6 = 36$
   $3r = 30$
   $r = 10$

8. **C. 20**
   $1.8 \div 9.0 = 0.2$
   10^{-6} is 2 powers larger than 10^{-8}.
   $0.2 \times 10^2 = 20$
   The wavelength of infrared light is about 20 times greater than the wavelength of ultraviolet light.

9. $\angle a = 95°$
   $\angle b = 85°$
   $\angle c = 70°$
   $\angle d = 110°$

10. $V = 11 \times 7 \times 9 =$ **693 cm^3**

11. **B. –20**
   $\frac{-5-(-5+10)}{2} \times (-3 + 7)$
   $= \frac{-5-5}{2} \times 4$
   $= \frac{-10}{2} \times 4$
   $= -5 \times 4$
   $= -20$

12. **42 points**

	Game 1	Game 2
Maggie	$2x$	$2x - 10$
David	x	$x + 12$

   Equation:
   $2x + 2x - 10 = 110$
   $4x - 10 = 110$
   $4x = 120$
   $x = 30$
   David's second game: 30 + 12 = 42

13.

x	y
–2	4
0	1
4	–5

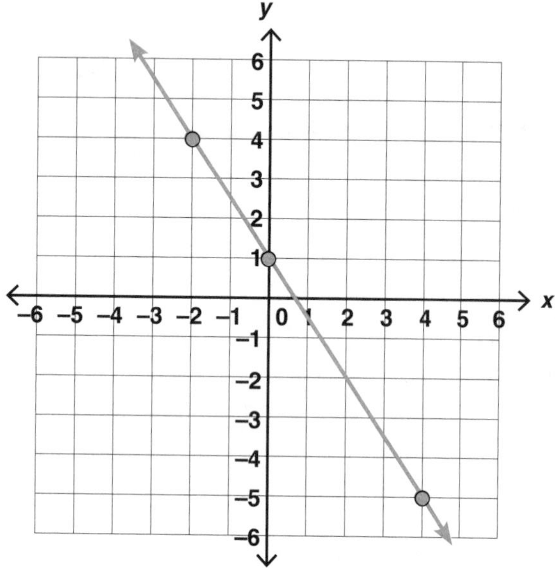

14. $P = 2L + 2W$

$P - 2L = 2W$

$\frac{P-2L}{2} = W$

$\mathbf{W = \frac{P-2L}{2}}$

or

$\mathbf{W = \frac{1}{2}(P - 2L)}$

or

$\mathbf{W = \frac{P}{2} - L}$

15. **B. 36**

$\frac{6}{10} = \frac{BC}{60}$

$10(BC) = 360$

$BC = 36$

16. **B. 4**

	Rate: Fraction of Job per Hour	Time Worked	Work Done per Time Worked
Pipe A	$\frac{1}{12}$	x	$\frac{1}{12}x$
Pipe B	$\frac{1}{10}$	x	$\frac{1}{10}x$
Pipe C	$\frac{1}{15}$	x	$\frac{1}{15}x$

Equation:

$\frac{1}{12}x + \frac{1}{10}x + \frac{1}{15}x = 1$

$5x + 6x + 4x = 60$

$15x = 60$

$x = 4$

17. **9 rounds**

	Number	Value
Won	x	$9x$
Lost	$15 - x$	$-4(15 - x)$

Equation:

$9x - 4(15 - x) = 18$

$9x - 60 + 4x = 18$

$13x = 78$

$x = 6$

Lost: $15 - 6 = 9$

18. **B. $-\frac{3}{4}$**

$m = \frac{3-0}{-4-0} = -\frac{3}{4}$

19. **A. $x + 2y = 7$**

$m = \frac{2-4}{3-(-1)} = \frac{-2}{4} = -\frac{1}{2}$

$y - 2 = -\frac{1}{2}(x - 3)$

$y - 2 = -\frac{1}{2}x + \frac{3}{2}$

$2y - 4 = -x + 3$

$x + 2y = 7$

20. **C. $1,024.25**

Area of the rectangle: 9(6) = 54 sq ft

Area of the trapezoid: $\frac{1}{2} \times 11 \times (13 + 21) = 187$ sq ft

Total area: 54 + 187 = 241 sq ft

Cost: 241 × $4.25 = $1,024.25

21. **C. $84 \le s \le 100$**

$\frac{78+83+70+85+s}{5} \ge 80$

$\frac{316+s}{5} \ge 80$

$316 + s \ge 400$

$s \ge 84$

Since Maureen's score cannot be greater than 100, the range of possible scores is $84 \le s \le 100$.

22. **C. 63**

Outside circumference: $C = \pi d$ so $d = 12$ cm

$C = 12\pi$ $r = 6$ cm

To find the area of the washer, subtract the area of the inner circle from the area of the larger circle.

Area of washer:

$A = (\pi \times 6^2) - (\pi \times 4^2)$

$= 36\pi - 16\pi$

$= 20\pi$

$\approx 20 \times 3.14$

≈ 63 cm

23. **D. $y = -\frac{1}{3}x - 2$**

Slope of BC: $m = \frac{2-(-4)}{-2-(-4)} = \frac{6}{2} = 3$

Slope of a line perpendicular to BC: $-\frac{1}{3}$

An x-intercept of –6: (–6, 0)

$y - y_1 = m(x - x_1)$

$y - 0 = -\frac{1}{3}(x - (-6))$

$y = -\frac{1}{3}(x + 6)$

$y = -\frac{1}{3}x - 2$

24. 43 degrees
$\angle ACB = 180° - (49° + 74°) = 57°$
$\angle CDE = 180° - (57° + 80°) = 43°$

25. $1 - 3x < -3 - 5x$
$1 + 2x < -3$
$2x < -4$
$\mathbf{x < -2}$

26. A. 20.6
$c^2 = a^2 + b^2$
$c^2 = 5^2 + 20^2$
$c = \sqrt{25 + 400}$
$c = \sqrt{425}$
$c \approx 20.6$ ft

27. $y - y_1 = m(x - x_1)$
$y - 5 = -4(x - (-2))$
$y - 5 = -4(x + 2)$
$y - 5 = -4x - 8$
$\mathbf{y = -4x - 3}$

28. C. 24
1st number: x
2nd number: $x + 2$
3rd number: $x + 4$
Equation:
$x + 2(x + 4) = x + 2 + 46$
$x + 2x + 8 = x + 48$
$3x + 8 = x + 48$
$2x = 40$
$x = 20$
3rd number: $20 + 4 = 24$

29. 35 sq in
$SA = \frac{1}{2}ps + B$
$p = 3 + 3 + 3 + 3 = 12$ in
$s = 4.3$ in
$B = 3^2 = 9$ sq in
$SA = \frac{1}{2}(12)(4.3) + 9 = 34.8$ sq in
$34.8 \approx 35$ sq in

30. Your answer may include the following ideas: Points *A* and *B* have the same *x*-coordinate, so they would form a vertical line. Points *B* and *C* have the same *y*-coordinate, so they would form a horizontal line. The intersection of sides *AB* and *BC* form a right angle, so the triangle is a right triangle. Use absolute value to find the lengths of *AB* and *BC,* and then use the Pythagorean theorem to find the hypotenuse *AC.*

Simulated Test Evaluation Chart

This simulated test measures how well you are able to apply the ideas taught in this book. The actual GED Math Test will include additional topics that you will study in Books 1 and 3 of this series.

On the chart below, circle the numbers of the problems that you answered incorrectly. Then review the skill area for each of those problems.

Problem Number	Skill Area	Unit
1, 2, 3	Numbers and Properties	1
4, 5, 8, 11, 25	The Basics of Algebra	2
7, 12, 14, 16, 17, 21, 28	Solving Problems with Algebra	3
6, 9, 10, 15, 20, 22, 24, 26, 29	Geometry Basics	4
13, 18, 19, 23, 27, 30	Connecting Algebra and Geometry	5

Answer Key

UNIT 1

The Number Line, pp. 16–17

From left to right:

1. 15, 20, 30
2. –8, –6, –5, –2, –1
3. –150, 100, 200

From top to bottom:

4. 3, –1
5. 20, –20, –60
6. –4, –5, –8

Core Connections: Positive or Negative?, p. 17

1. **negative**
   The contestant lost more than 200 points (1 correct answer).
2. **positive**
   The temperature dropped below 0° and then came back up.
3. **negative outcome**
   Ned lost money, for a negative outcome. He paid more for the cards than he sold them for.
4. **below normal**
   The patient's temperature dropped more degrees than the degrees above normal.

Comparing and Ordering Integers, pp. 18–19

1. $8 < 15$ $-8 < -6$ $5 > -5$
2. $9 > -3$ $-1 = -1$ $-11 > -12$
3. –22, –20, –17, –12
4. –2, –1, 0, 4
5. 2, –2, –6, –8
6. 30, 10, –20, –40
7. Montana
8. Your answer may vary. Craig's idea works most of the time. Of the states on the chart, Montana has the greatest elevation and the lowest temperature. But Nevada has a much greater elevation than Maine and Michigan, and their record low temperatures are equal or lower.
9. **7**
   They are –7, –6, –5, –4, –3, –2, and –1.
10. **4**
    They are 5, 6, 7, and 8.
11. **0**
    There are no numbers that are both to the right of –1 on the number line and to the left of –3.

Kinds of Numbers, pp. 20–21

1. 1, 3, 5, 15
2. 1, 2, 3, 6, 9, 18
3. 1, 2, 13, 26
4. 1, 2, 3, 4, 6, 8, 12, 24
5. 1, 2, 3, 5, 6, 10, 15, 30
6. 1, 2, 3, 4, 6, 9, 12, 18, 36
7. 10, 20, 30, 40, 50
8. 56
9. **35**
   Multiples of 5: 5, 10, 15, 20, 25, 30, 35
   Multiples of 7: 7, 14, 21, 28, 35
10. You should circle 6, 12, 18, 24, 30, and 36.

Core Connections: Using Divisibility Rules, p. 21

1. 20,720 and 103,080
2. 1,690; 20,720; and 103,080
3. 198 and 103,080
4. 375; 1,690; 20,720; and 103,080
5. Max is correct.
   Your answer may include the following ideas:
   9 is equal to 3 × 3, so dividing by 9 is like dividing by 3 and then dividing the result by 3 again.
   For example: $36 \div 3 = 12$ and $12 \div 3 = 4$
   $36 \div 9 = 4$
   This means that for a number to be divisible by 9, it must be divisible by 3.
6. Answers will vary. Your answer is correct if it follows the divisibility rules for 2, 3, 4, and 9.

Prime Numbers and Prime Factoring, pp. 22–23

Factor trees may vary slightly.

1. **2 × 3 × 3 × 5**

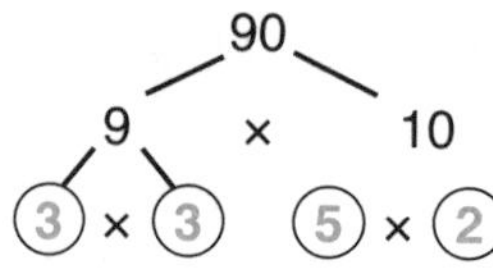

2. 3 × 3 × 3 × 5

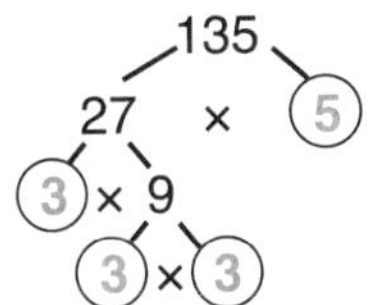

3. 2 × 3 × 3 × 3 × 3

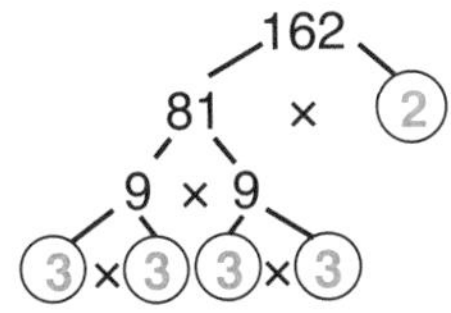

4. 2 × 2 × 3 × 5 × 5

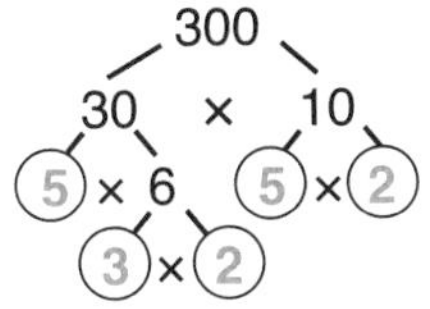

5. 18
18 = 2 × 3 × 3
54 = 2 × 3 × 3 × 3
90 = 2 × 3 × 3 × 5
2 × 3 × 3 = 18

6. 16
48 = 2 × 2 × 2 × 2 × 3
80 = 2 × 2 × 2 × 2 × 5
112 = 2 × 2 × 2 × 2 × 7
2 × 2 × 2 × 2 = 16

7. 1,300

8. 2
Find the greatest common factor of 178 and 1,386.
178 = 2 × 89 (Note that 89 is a prime number.)
1,386 = 2 × 3 × 231
The greatest number Carla could divide by is 2.

9. 41, 43, 47, 53, and 59

10. Your answer may include some of the following ideas:
Tamar is correct. A prime number has only two factors: one and itself. All even numbers are divisible by 2, so 2 is a factor of all even numbers. An even number greater than 2 has at least itself, 1, and 2 as factors. Therefore, 2 is the only even prime number.

Properties of Numbers, pp. 24–25

1. (99 + 1) + (98 + 2) + (97 + 3) = 100 + 100 + 100 = **300**

2. (11 × 12) + (11 × 7)

3. a. 20.8 fluid ounces
bottles: 4 × 0.7 = 2.8 fl oz
refill bottles: 4 × 4.5 = 18 fl oz
2.8 + 18 = 20.8 fl oz

b. 4(0.7 + 4.5) *and* (4 × 0.7) + (4 × 4.5)

4. 3 × (4 + 2)

5. a. commutative
b. associative
c. distributive

Adding and Subtracting Signed Numbers, pp. 26–27

1.	11	–2	11	–14
2.	–8	5	–15	7
3.	21	–17	–7	12
4.	6	16	–9	15
5.	–7	1	–10	8
6.	0	7	–14	
7.	–23	15	–2	

Absolute Value, pp. 28–29

1.	10	6	–5
2.	–14	7	18
3.	4	13	–8

4. | –6 | = **6**

5. point *B* and point *E*

6. point *C*
C: | –3 | = 3
D: | 1 | = 1

7. Find the absolute value of each point (its distance from zero). Then add the absolute values to find the distance from one point to the other.
| –3 | + | 5 | = 3 + 5 = 8
The distance from point *C* to point *F* is **8.**

8.	>	<	>
9.	=	>	<

Core Connections: True or False Questions, p. 29

1. True

2. False
Your explanation may include the following ideas: The absolute value of a number is its distance from zero, and distance is always positive. A large negative number is far from zero, so its absolute value would be a large positive number.

3. True

4. False
Your explanation may include the following ideas: The absolute value of a number is its distance from zero, and distance is always positive. Negative numbers have a positive absolute value. The absolute value of zero is zero, so it must be less than the absolute value of any negative number.

Multiplying and Dividing Signed Numbers, pp. 30–31

1. –42	–40	27	
2. –24	–27	24	
3. –32	20	–48	
4. –18	16	–4	
5. 60	–27	8	
6. 6	–21	–68	
7. 3	–1	5	–17
8. 0	–5	–17	5
9. –3	–11	–15	–5

Core Connections: Fractions and Division, p. 31

1. $\frac{210}{-15} \div \frac{5}{5} = \frac{42}{-3}$ $42 \div -3 = \mathbf{-14}$

$\frac{-828}{12} \div \frac{4}{4} = \frac{-207}{3}$ $-207 \div 3 = \mathbf{-69}$

$\frac{-720}{-48} \div \frac{8}{8} = \frac{-90}{-6}$ $-90 \div -6 = \mathbf{15}$

2. $\frac{600}{-24} \div \frac{6}{6} = \frac{100}{-4}$ $100 \div -4 = \mathbf{-25}$

$\frac{-1{,}080}{36} \div \frac{6}{6} = \frac{-180}{6}$ $-180 \div 6 = \mathbf{-30}$

$\frac{9{,}750}{150} \div \frac{10}{10} = \frac{975}{15}$ $\frac{975}{15} \div \frac{5}{5} = \frac{195}{3}$ $195 \div 3 = \mathbf{65}$

Powers and Roots, pp. 32–33

1. 49	27	8
2. 121	1	144
3. 125	64	729
4. 16	216	1,000

$2^2 = 4$	$5^2 = 25$	$8^2 = 64$	$11^2 = 121$	$14^2 = 196$
$3^2 = 9$	$6^2 = 36$	$9^2 = 81$	$12^2 = 144$	$15^2 = 225$
$4^2 = 16$	$7^2 = 49$	$10^2 = 100$	$13^2 = 169$	$20^2 = 400$

5. 10	11	7	8
6. 12	13	20	9

7. C. 7 and 8
$7 \times 7 = 49$
$8 \times 8 = 64$
50 is between 49 and 64.

8. B. 11 and 12
$11 \times 11 = 121$
$12 \times 12 = 144$
125 is between 121 and 144.

9. A. 3 and 4
$3 \times 3 = 9$
$4 \times 4 = 16$
10 is between 9 and 16.

10. Your answer should include some of these ideas from this sample answer:
To estimate, I thought of a perfect square that was near 90. $10 \times 10 = 100$. Because 100 is greater than 90, I tried a lower number: $9 \times 9 = 81$. Since 90 falls between 81 and 100, I know that the square root of 90 must be between 9 and 10.

Order of Operations, pp. 34–35

1. –14	5	44
2. 3	12	125
3. 4	45	–23
4. 1	4	–5
5. 121	12	81

6. B. $42 - 20$

7. A. $\frac{60}{10} - 5$

8. C. 2(3)

9. B. $\frac{39}{3}$

10. A. 13(3)

11. C. $15 + 6$

12. $\frac{7(\$9)+6(\$12)}{3}$

You may have set the problem up differently, but your answer should include these elements: multiplying \$9 by 7, multiplying \$12 by 6, adding these products, and dividing the sum by 3.

13. The order of operations is important in solving this problem. If you add before multiplying, you will get an incorrect answer.

Using a Calculator, pp. 36–37

1. –3	–240	–1
2. –9	–6	13
3. –2	–9	6
4. –399	9	10
5. –40	13	302

6. Your answer could include some of the following ideas:
First, I would do the operation inside the absolute value on the calculator: $8 - 15 = -7$. I know that the absolute value of –7 is 7. Then, I would multiply -3×7.

Unit 1 Review, pp. 38–39

1. 6	18	0
2. –25	–78	120
3. 50	–27	–10

4. commutative

5. associative

6. distributive

7. distributive

8. **C. 6**
Prime Factorization of 18: $2 \times 3 \times 3$
Prime Factorization of 30: $2 \times 3 \times 5$
$2 \times 3 = 6$

9. A. $<$

10. **D. 7**
Prime Factorization of 150: $2 \times 3 \times 5 \times 5$
7 is not one of the prime factors.

11. **D. 72**
Multiples of 12: 12, 24, 36, 48, 60, 72
Multiples of 9: 9, 18, 27, 36, 45, 54, 63, 72
36 and 72 are both common multiples. 72 is one of the answer choices.

12.	64	27	16	36
13.	11	14	30	9

14. **B. −10**
$11 - 6 \times 4 + 3$
$= 11 - 24 + 3$
$= -13 + 3$
$= -10$

15. **D. 2**
$\frac{(1-5)^2}{8}$
$= \frac{(-4)^2}{8}$
$= \frac{16}{8}$
$= 2$

16. **$458.12**
$638.00 - 20.38 + 120.50 - 280.00 = 458.12$

17. **−12**
$-2(9 + 2) - 5(4 - 6)$
$= -2(11) - 5(-2)$
$= -22 + (-5)(-2)$
$= -22 + 10$
$= -12$

18. **13 degrees**
$|-9| + |4|$
$= 9 + 4$
$= 13$

19. **2 × 2 × 3 × 3 × 5**
Your factor tree may look like this:

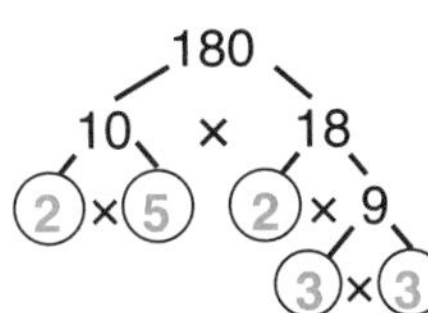

20. **B. 12 and 13**
$12^2 = 144$ and $13^2 = 169$
Since 155 is between 144 and 169, $\sqrt{155}$ must be between 12 and 13.

21. **40**
$|-7 - 8| + 5^2$
$= |-15| + 5^2$
$= |-15| + 25$
$= 15 + 25$
$= 40$

22. Your answer may include some of the following ideas:
Factors are numbers that multiply to make a certain product. The product of an even number and an odd number is always an even number.
For example: $5 \times 2 = 10$, $7 \times 2 = 14$, and $9 \times 2 = 18$
These products are even numbers, but they have an odd factor. The statement is **false.**

UNIT 2

Expressions and Variables, pp. 42–43

1. B. $6n$
2. C. $n - 12 = 19$
3. A. $2x - 1 = 15$
4. B. $\frac{x}{5} = x - 9$
5. $\frac{4n}{n+4}$
6. $3x + 15$

You may use any variable for problems 7–10.

7. $4n - 20$
8. $6(x + 2)$
9. $12 - 5n$
10. $\frac{30}{7x}$

Answers to problems 11–15 will vary.

11. The sum of *A* and *C*
A increased by *C*
12. The difference of *D* and *C*
D decreased by *C*
13. The product of *A* and *B*
A times *B*
14. The quotient of *C* and *D*
C divided by *D*
15. This statement says that the sum of *A, B,* and *C* is less than *D.* You can draw the conclusion that there are more blocks of type *D* than any other type of block. You can also draw the conclusion that there are more *D* blocks than all the other blocks combined.

Evaluating Expressions, pp. 44–45

1.	**a.** 5	**b.** 20
2.	**a.** −8	**b.** 2
3.	**a.** −46	**b.** 500

4. **a.** 3 **b.** 1

5. **a.** 2 **b.** 52

6. **a.** 7 **b.** –12

7. The greatest value this expression can have is –1. The following pairs give the expression a value of –1:
$x = -3, y = -5$ $x = -1, y = -3$ $x = 0, y = -1$
$x = 0, y = 1$ $x = 1, y = 3$ $x = 3, y = 5$

8. **No**
Your answer may include the following ideas:
The value of x^3 will not always be greater than the value of x^2. When x is a negative number, x^2 will be a positive number, but x^3 will still be a negative number. A positive number is always greater than a negative number, so in this case, x^2 would be greater.
For example: $(-3)^2 = 9$ and $(-3)^3 = -27$
$9 > -27$

Simplifying Expressions, pp. 46–47

1. $3x$
2. $-5k$
3. $-2t + 5$
4. $11a - 3$
5. $6m + 13$
6. $-6y + 25$
7. $-k - 8m$
8. $6c + 8d$
9. $-8s + t$
10. $\mathbf{x + 3}$
The expression for side $x + 3$ is 3 more than x and 1 more than side $x + 2$.
11. $P = x + x + 2 + x + 3$
12. $P = 3x + 5$ (*Note:* $3x$ means 3 times x.)
13. $P = 3(8) + 5 = 24 + 5 =$ **29**
14. $P = 3(25) + 5 = 75 + 5 =$ **80**
15. $P = m + m + 1 + m + m + 1$
16. $P = 4m + 2$ (*Note:* $4m$ means 4 times m.)
17. $P = 4(4.5) + 2 = 18 + 2 =$ **20**
18. $P = 4(18) + 2 = 72 + 2 =$ **74**
19. $P = c + c + c + c$
20. $P = 4c$
21. $P = 4(7) = 28$ cm
22. **16 cm**
$P = c - 3 + c - 3 + c - 3 + c - 3 = 4c - 12$
$P = 4(7) - 12 = 28 - 12 = 16$ cm
23. $n + n + 12 + n - 2 = 3n + 10$
24. **a.** $x - 5 + 9 = x + 4$
b. $x + x - 5 + x + 4 = 3x - 1$

The Rules of Exponents, pp. 48–49

1.	x^3	a^7	$3^3 = 27$
2.	$4^1 = 4$	$3^3 = 27$	$x^0 = 1$
3.	$6b$	$2m^2$	$5^3 = 125$
4.	2^{12}	x^{20}	b^6c^{12}
5.	3^{18}	$2k^8$	$n^0 = 1$

6. $2a = 2(2) = \mathbf{4}$
$4bc = 4(-3)(5) = \mathbf{-60}$
$c^2 = 5^2 = \mathbf{25}$
7. $b^4c^2 = (-3)^4 \times 5^2 = 81 \times 25 = \mathbf{2{,}025}$
$a = \mathbf{2}$
$b^2 = (-3)^2 = \mathbf{9}$
8. $a^2 = 2^2 = \mathbf{4}$
$6c^3 = 6 \times 5^3 = \mathbf{750}$
$2c = 2 \times 5 = \mathbf{10}$
9. Your answer may include the following ideas:
$(3n)^2$ is equal to $9n^2$. Use the rule $(xy)^a = x^ay^a$ to distribute the exponent: $(3n)^2 = 3^2 \times n^2 = 9n^2$

Negative Exponents, pp. 50–51

1.	3^{-4}	x^{-3}	2^{-5}
2.	a^{-2}	5^{-6}	x^{-7}
3.	$\frac{1}{36}$	$\frac{1}{125}$	$\frac{1}{64}$
4.	$\frac{1}{64}$	$\frac{1}{81}$	$\frac{1}{1} = 1$
5.	9	64	25

6. **a.** $\frac{y^3}{x^2} = \frac{(-2)^3}{(-4)^2} = -\frac{1}{2}$
b. $\frac{1}{x^2y^4} = \frac{1}{(-4)^2(-2)^4} = \frac{1}{256}$
c. $xy^3 = -4 \times (-2)^3 = 32$
7. **a.** $\frac{18a^3}{b^2} = \frac{18(-1)^3}{3^2} = -2$
b. $a^6b^4 = (-1)^6 \times 3^4 = 81$
c. $a^0b^0 = 1$
8. **a.** $\frac{20}{mn^4} = \frac{20}{5(2^4)} = \frac{20}{5(16)} = \frac{20}{80} = \frac{1}{4}$
b. $\frac{1}{n^2} = \frac{1}{2^2} = \frac{1}{4}$
c. $\frac{m^2}{n^4} = \frac{5^2}{2^4} = \frac{25}{16} = 1\frac{9}{16}$

Core Connections: Test Your Thinking, p. 51

You may test the situation with any values, but the result of the test should not vary.

1. **no**
Let $x = 3$ and $y = 2$.
$3^2 - 2^2 = 9 - 4 = 5$
$(3 - 2)^2 = (1)^2 = 1$

2. **yes**
Let $x = 2$ and $y = 4$.
$2^{-2} + 4^{-2} = \frac{1}{2^2} + \frac{1}{4^2} = \frac{1}{4} + \frac{1}{16} = \frac{5}{16}$
$\frac{1}{2^2} + \frac{1}{4^2} = \frac{1}{4} + \frac{1}{16} = \frac{5}{16}$

Scientific Notation, pp. 52–53

1.	1.9×10^4	7.35×10^5	6.4×10^6
2.	3.5×10^7	5.6×10^8	3.5×10^{-3}
3.	4.8×10^{-4}	5.0×10^{-6}	1.4×10^{-9}
4.	81,000	6,314,000	1,850
5.	250,000	36	0.000091
6.	0.000000742	0.0014	0.027

7. 197,000,000 sq mi
8. 67,000 mph
9. 239,000 mi
10. 0.000021 m

Simplifying Radicals, pp. 54–55

1. C. between 5 and 6
2. A. between 10 and 11
3. B. between 9 and 10

4.	$3\sqrt{7}$	$2\sqrt{2}$	$4\sqrt{2}$
5.	$3\sqrt{5}$	$2\sqrt{6}$	$4\sqrt{7}$
6.	$4\sqrt{5}$	$5\sqrt{2}$	$5\sqrt{7}$
7.	$9\sqrt{10}$	$6\sqrt{3}$	30
8.	$4\sqrt{19} \approx 17.4$	$51\sqrt{2} \approx 72.1$	$24\sqrt{2} \approx 33.9$
9.	$23\sqrt{3} \approx 39.8$	$12\sqrt{10} \approx 37.9$	$28\sqrt{5} \approx 62.6$

Mixed Review, pp. 56–57

You may choose any variable for problems 1–6.

1. $13 - 5n = 29$
2. $\frac{25}{3+x}$
3. $6 + 12n = 31$
4. $2(x + 8)$
5. $\frac{n}{3} - 15$
6. $\frac{7n}{n-11}$
7. **–1**
$9 - (-2^2 + 6)$
$= 9 - (4 + 6)$
$= 9 - 10$
$= -1$
8. **45**
$\frac{10(3)}{6} \times 3(3)$
$= \frac{30}{6} \times 9$
$= 5 \times 9$
$= 45$
9. **–19**
$|-17| - (3 + 3)^2$
$= 17 - 6^2$
$= 17 - 36$
$= -19$
10. **81**
$(7 - 4)^4$
$= 3^4$
$= 81$
11. **56**
$2(-8 + (-8 - (-2))^2)$
$= 2(-8 + (-6)^2)$
$= 2(-8 + 36)$
$= 2(28)$
$= 56$
12. –23
$5 - 4 \times \left| \frac{-21}{3+0} \right|$
$= 5 - 4 \times 7$
$= 5 - 28$
$= -23$

13.	x^7	3^{18}	a^3
14.	2^4	x^8	$\frac{b^2}{c^8}$
15.	$8n^9$	1	4
16.	27	$\frac{1}{x}$	$\frac{1}{m}$

17. $x + 3x - 4 + 2x + 1$
18. $6x - 3$
19. **21**
$6(4) - 3$
$= 24 - 3$
$= 21$
20. a. $\mathbf{2n - 6}$
1st piece: n
2nd piece: $2n$
3rd piece: $2n - 6$
b. $n + 2n + 2n - 6 = \mathbf{5n - 6}$
21. 1.97×10^6
22. 0.000000027
23. 43,500,000
24. 2.54×10^{-3}
25. $-6k + 12m + 15$
26. $\frac{24n^6}{m^3} = \frac{24 \times (-1)^6}{4^3} = \mathbf{\frac{3}{8}}$
27. $-6a - 22$

28.	$6\sqrt{2}$	$4\sqrt{6}$	$2\sqrt{30}$
29.	$\frac{\sqrt{5}}{6}$ or $\frac{1}{6}\sqrt{5}$	$\frac{4}{7}$	$\frac{\sqrt{21}}{12}$ or $\frac{1}{12}\sqrt{21}$
30.	$3\sqrt{13}$	$10\sqrt{2}$	$8\sqrt{3}$

Reading and Writing Equations, pp. 58–59

1. B. $x - 12 = 25$
2. A. $\frac{60}{n} = 15$
3. C. $a + 9 = 20$
4. A. $3w - 2 = 10$
5. B. $5b + 2 = 12$
6. A. $\frac{10}{z} = 3 - z$

Answers may vary, but should be similar to these sample answers.

7. The sum of five and a number is eight.
8. Twelve divided by a number is six.
9. Five less than four times a number is seven.
10. B. $\$320 + d = \$400$
11. C. $4s = 12$
12. B. $p - \$35 = \$85$
13. A. $\$1.15n = \$5.75$
14. A. $5d = 1{,}650$
15. Both equations mean the same thing. It doesn't matter which side of the equation the expressions are on as long as the sides are equal.

Solving Addition and Subtraction Equations, pp. 60–61

1. $a - 15 = 78$
   $a - 15 + 15 = 78 + 15$
   $\mathbf{a = 93}$

   $5.3 = x + 0.6$
   $5.3 - 0.6 = x + 0.6 - 0.6$
   $\mathbf{4.7 = x}$

   $532 = 189 + n$
   $532 - 189 = 189 + n - 189$
   $\mathbf{343 = n}$
2. $b + 3\frac{1}{2} = 9$
   $b + 3\frac{1}{2} - 3\frac{1}{2} = 9 - 3\frac{1}{2}$
   $\mathbf{b = 5\frac{1}{2}}$

   $10 = w - 8.2$
   $10 + 8.2 = w - 8.2 + 8.2$
   $\mathbf{18.2 = w}$

   $d - 11 = 33$
   $d - 11 + 11 = 33 + 11$
   $\mathbf{d = 44}$
3. $x + 6.4 = 100$
   $x + 6.4 - 6.4 = 100 - 6.4$
   $\mathbf{x = 93.6}$

   $1{,}050 + g = 8{,}000$
   $1{,}050 + g - 1{,}050 = 8{,}000 - 1{,}050$
   $\mathbf{g = 6{,}950}$

   $9\frac{1}{2} = y - 3\frac{1}{2}$
   $9\frac{1}{2} + 3\frac{1}{2} = y - 3\frac{1}{2} + 3\frac{1}{2}$
   $\mathbf{13 = y}$
4. $c + 28 - 7 = 84$
   $c + 21 = 84$
   $c + 21 - 21 = 84 - 21$
   $\mathbf{c = 63}$

   $h + 1.5 + 8.75 = 12.5$
   $h + 10.25 = 12.5$
   $h + 10.25 - 10.25 = 12.5 - 10.25$
   $\mathbf{h = 2.25}$
5. $95 - 25 + 15 + x = 105$
   $85 + x = 105$
   $85 + x - 85 = 105 - 85$
   $\mathbf{x = 20}$

   $5.375 = e - 0.9 + 2.05$
   $5.375 = e + 1.15$
   $5.375 - 1.15 = e + 1.15 - 1.15$
   $\mathbf{4.225 = e}$
6. $7 + x - (-10) = 46$
   $7 + x + 10 = 46$
   $17 + x = 46$
   $17 + x - 17 = 46 - 17$
   $\mathbf{x = 29}$

   $-18.1 = 2.9 + x - 2.4$
   $-18.1 = 0.5 + x$
   $-18.1 - 0.5 = 0.5 + x - 0.5$
   $\mathbf{-18.6 = x}$
7. $265 + m = 770$
   $m = 505$ miles
8. $\$580 + c = \$1{,}124$
   $\mathbf{c = \$544}$
9. $2.8 + 2.1 + a = 6.5$
   $4.9 + a = 6.5$
   $a = 1.6$ centimeters
10. You need to subtract 24 degrees from the high temperature. Since the high temperature, 18, is less than 24, you know the resulting low temperature will be a negative number.
    $18 - 24 = l$
    $-6 = l$
    The low temperature was **–6°F.**

Solving Multiplication and Division Equations, pp. 62–63

1. $\frac{w}{6} = 9$
   $6 \times \frac{w}{6} = 6 \times 9$
   $\mathbf{w = 54}$

$12n = 600$

$\frac{12n}{12} = \frac{600}{12}$

$\mathbf{n = 50}$

$\frac{z}{16} = 128$

$16 \times \frac{z}{16} = 16 \times 128$

$\mathbf{z = 2{,}048}$

2. $1.5x = 45$

$\frac{1.5x}{1.5} = \frac{45}{1.5}$

$\mathbf{x = 30}$

$\frac{p}{-2} = 56$

$-2 \times \frac{p}{-2} = -2 \times 56$

$\mathbf{p = -112}$

$25r = 40$

$\frac{25r}{25} = \frac{40}{25}$

$\mathbf{r = 1.6}$

3. $50c = 3{,}000$

$\frac{50c}{50} = \frac{3{,}000}{50}$

$\mathbf{c = 60}$

$\frac{y}{0.5} = 150$

$0.5 \times \frac{y}{0.5} = 0.5 \times 150$

$\mathbf{y = 75}$

$\frac{h}{32} = -3$

$32 \times \frac{h}{32} = 32 \times -3$

$\mathbf{h = -96}$

4. $-126 = -18x$

$\frac{-126}{-18} = \frac{-18x}{-18}$

$\mathbf{7 = x}$

$\frac{n}{2} = -4$

$2 \times \frac{n}{2} = 2 \times -4$

$\mathbf{n = -8}$

$-15k = 45$

$\frac{-15k}{-15} = \frac{45}{-15}$

$\mathbf{k = -3}$

5. $2 = \frac{b}{17}$

$17 \times 2 = \frac{b}{17} \times 17$

$\mathbf{34 = b}$

$-200 = 10c$

$\frac{-200}{10} = \frac{10c}{10}$

$\mathbf{-20 = c}$

$\frac{y}{6} = -9$

$6 \times \frac{y}{6} = 6 \times -9$

$\mathbf{y = -54}$

6. $\frac{2}{3}n = 12$

$\frac{3}{2} \times \frac{2}{3}n = 12 \times \frac{3}{2}$

$\mathbf{n = 18}$

$\frac{2}{5}y = 10$

$\frac{5}{2} \times \frac{2}{5}y = 10 \times \frac{5}{2}$

$\mathbf{y = 25}$

$-\frac{4}{9}b = -16$

$-\frac{9}{4} \times -\frac{4}{9}b = -16 \times -\frac{9}{4}$

$\mathbf{b = 36}$

7. $\frac{3}{7}a = -45$

$\frac{7}{3} \times \frac{3}{7}a = -45 \times \frac{7}{3}$

$\mathbf{a = -105}$

$\frac{7}{10}b = 56$

$\frac{10}{7} \times \frac{7}{10}b = 56 \times \frac{10}{7}$

$\mathbf{b = 80}$

$\frac{1}{4}m = -9$

$\frac{4}{1} \times \frac{1}{4}m = -9 \times \frac{4}{1}$

$\mathbf{m = -36}$

8. Let p equal the cost per pen.

$6p = \$6.72$

$\frac{6p}{6} = \frac{6.72}{6}$

$p = \$1.12$

Haskell paid **$1.12** per pen.

9. Let n equal the number.

$\frac{n}{-5} = 4$

$-5 \times \frac{n}{-5} = 4 \times -5$

$n = -20$

The number is **–20.**

10. Your answer may include the following ideas: Emily is correct. Usually, you would solve this equation using division, but dividing by 4 is the same as multiplying by $\frac{1}{4}$. You can solve this equation by multiplying by $\frac{1}{4}$.

$4a = -32$

$\frac{1}{4} \times 4a = -32 \times \frac{1}{4}$

$a = -8$

Solving Multistep Equations, pp. 64–65

1. $3m + 2 = 62$

$3m = 60$

$\mathbf{m = 20}$

$-8 = -3x + 7$

$-15 = -3x$

$\mathbf{5 = x}$

$-3 = \frac{x}{4} - 1$

$-2 = \frac{x}{4}$

$\mathbf{-8 = x}$

2. $4x - 7 = -83$
$4x = -76$
$\mathbf{x = -19}$

$4 = 3 + \frac{x}{12}$
$1 = \frac{x}{12}$
$\mathbf{12 = x}$

$\frac{s}{2} - 9 = -19$
$\frac{s}{2} = -10$
$\mathbf{s = -20}$

3. $8x + 1 = -55$
$8x = -56$
$\mathbf{x = -7}$

$-1 = 2 + \frac{m}{5}$
$-3 = \frac{m}{5}$
$\mathbf{-15 = m}$

$\frac{w}{5} - 3 = 0$
$\frac{w}{5} = 3$
$\mathbf{w = 15}$

4. $\frac{b}{2} - 4 = -7$
$\frac{b}{2} = -3$
$\mathbf{b = -6}$

$-9 - 7x = 5$
$-7x = 14$
$\mathbf{x = -2}$

$-4n + 9 = -35$
$-4n = -44$
$\mathbf{n = 11}$

5. $\frac{a}{3} - 1 = 1$
$\frac{a}{3} = 2$
$\mathbf{a = 6}$

$10 = 8 - \frac{k}{8}$
$2 = -\frac{k}{8}$
$\mathbf{-16 = k}$

$-3 + 7n = 137$
$7n = 140$
$\mathbf{n = 20}$

6. $-8 = -5 + \frac{m}{3}$
$-3 = \frac{m}{3}$
$\mathbf{-9 = m}$

$\frac{n}{5} - 9 = -6$
$\frac{n}{5} = 3$
$\mathbf{n = 15}$

$-3 - 9y = 69$
$-9y = 72$
$\mathbf{y = -8}$

Core Connections: Working Backward, p. 65

1. If you knew the number, you would add 9 and multiply by 3. Working backward:
$63 \div 3 = 21$
$21 - 9 = 12$
The number is **12.**

2. If you knew the number of hours, you would multiply by \$8 and add \$150. Working backward:
\$414 – \$150 = \$264
\$264 ÷ \$8 = 33
Kira needs to work **33** more hours.

Solving Equations with Separated Terms, pp. 66–67

1. $-5x + 7 = 3 - 6x$
$x + 7 = 3$
$\mathbf{x = -4}$

$2m - 16 - m = -m - 6$
$m - 16 = -m - 6$
$2m - 16 = -6$
$2m = 10$
$\mathbf{m = 5}$

$-19 + 5a = -40 + 8a$
$-19 - 3a = -40$
$-3a = -21$
$\mathbf{a = 7}$

2. $1 - 5k = 10k - 14$
$1 - 15k = -14$
$-15k = -15$
$\mathbf{k = 1}$

$10 - 5c + 21 = 3c + 7$
$31 - 5c = 3c + 7$
$31 - 8c = 7$
$-8c = -24$
$\mathbf{c = 3}$

$2 + 10x = 9x - 16 - 7$
$2 + 10x = 9x - 23$
$2 + x = -23$
$\mathbf{x = -25}$

3. $5b + 30 = -b$
$6b + 30 = 0$
$6b = -30$
$\mathbf{b = -5}$

$12 + 7p = 2p + 4 + p$
$12 + 7p = 3p + 4$
$12 + 4p = 4$
$4p = -8$
$\mathbf{p = -2}$

$8 - 6m = 5 - 18m + 3$
$8 - 6m = 8 - 18m$
$8 + 12m = 8$
$12m = 0$
$\mathbf{m = 0}$

4. $20 + a - 33 = 3 + 9a$
$-13 + a = 3 + 9a$
$-13 - 8a = 3$
$-8a = 16$
$\mathbf{a = -2}$

$25 + 30d = d - 19 + 7d$
$25 + 30d = 8d - 19$
$25 + 22d = -19$
$22d = -44$
$\mathbf{d = -2}$

$21 + 2n = 4n - 63 + 5n$
$21 + 2n = 9n - 63$
$21 - 7n = -63$
$-7n = -84$
$\mathbf{n = 12}$

5. $52 + 5x = 12x - 4$
$52 - 7x = -4$
$-7x = -56$
$\mathbf{x = 8}$

$-2a + 60 + 2a = -8a + 140$
$60 = -8a + 140$
$-80 = -8a$
$\mathbf{10 = a}$

$13n + 9 = 14n + 104 - 96n$
$13n + 9 = -82n + 104$
$95n + 9 = 104$
$95n = 95$
$\mathbf{n = 1}$

Core Connections: Apply a Rule, p. 67

1.	27	31	35	39	43	47
2.	–17	–9	–1	7	15	23

Solving Equations with Parentheses, pp. 68–69

1. $8(x + 5) = 96$
$8x + 40 = 96$
$8x = 56$
$\mathbf{x = 7}$

$-6(6y - 1) = -102$
$-36y + 6 = -102$
$-36y = -108$
$\mathbf{y = 3}$

$2(4 - 6k) = 92$
$8 - 12k = 92$
$-12k = 84$
$\mathbf{k = -7}$

2. $2 + 4(1 - 3a) = 42$
$2 + 4 - 12a = 42$
$6 - 12a = 42$
$-12a = 36$
$\mathbf{a = -3}$

$4(3n + 3) + 2 = 50$
$12n + 12 + 2 = 50$
$12n + 14 = 50$
$12n = 36$
$\mathbf{n = 3}$

$-64 = 4(-3m - 4)$
$-64 = -12m - 16$
$-48 = -12m$
$\mathbf{4 = m}$

3. $4(1 - d) = 3(d - 1)$
$4 - 4d = 3d - 3$
$4 - 7d = -3$
$-7d = -7$
$\mathbf{d = 1}$

$2(4 - m) + 4m = -(2 + 3m)$
$8 - 2m + 4m = -2 - 3m$
$8 + 2m = -2 - 3m$
$8 + 5m = -2$
$5m = -10$
$\mathbf{m = -2}$

4. $4(m + 5) = 2(m - 1)$
$4m + 20 = 2m - 2$
$2m + 20 = -2$
$2m = -22$
$\mathbf{m = -11}$

$4(3 - 2x) + 2 = -6(x + 1)$
$12 - 8x + 2 = -6x - 6$
$14 - 8x = -6x - 6$
$14 - 2x = -6$
$-2x = -20$
$\mathbf{x = 10}$

5. $\frac{3m + 1}{2} = 2m + 1$
$3m + 1 = 4m + 2$
$-m + 1 = 2$
$-m = 1$
$\mathbf{m = -1}$

$n + 3 = \frac{8n}{5}$
$5n + 15 = 8n$
$-3n + 15 = 0$
$-3n = -15$
$\mathbf{n = 5}$

$\frac{-3a - 11}{7} = a - 3$
$-3a - 11 = 7a - 21$
$-10a - 11 = -21$
$-10a = -10$
$\mathbf{a = 1}$

6. $\frac{7-5x}{-3} = x - 7$
$7 - 5x = -3x + 21$
$7 - 2x = 21$
$-2x = 14$
$\mathbf{x = -7}$
$6p + 8 = \frac{2(p-12)}{7}$
$6p + 8 = \frac{2p-24}{7}$
$42p + 56 = 2p - 24$
$40p + 56 = -24$
$40p = -80$
$\mathbf{p = -2}$
$\frac{1+n}{2} = 2(n + 4)$
$\frac{1+n}{2} = 2n + 8$
$1 + n = 4n + 16$
$1 - 3n = 16$
$-3n = 15$
$\mathbf{n = -5}$

7. $\frac{3k+5}{2} = 6k - 2$
$3k + 5 = 12k - 4$
$-9k + 5 = -4$
$-9k = -9$
$\mathbf{k = 1}$
$-8m + 5 = \frac{30+m}{6}$
$-48m + 30 = 30 + m$
$-49m + 30 = 30$
$-49m = 0$
$\mathbf{m = 0}$
$4 + b = \frac{b+9}{2}$
$8 + 2b = b + 9$
$8 + b = 9$
$\mathbf{b = 1}$

8. $\frac{7(n-4)}{2} = n - 4$
$\frac{7n-28}{2} = n - 4$
$7n - 28 = 2n - 8$
$5n - 28 = -8$
$5n = 20$
$\mathbf{n = 4}$
$a + 10 = \frac{a+40}{6}$
$6a + 60 = a + 40$
$5a + 60 = 40$
$5a = -20$
$\mathbf{a = -4}$
$5(1 - x) = \frac{5(x+3)}{-3}$
$5 - 5x = \frac{5x+15}{-3}$
$-15 + 15x = 5x + 15$
$-15 + 10x = 15$
$10x = 30$
$\mathbf{x = 3}$

Graphing Inequalities, pp. 70–71

1. –3 –2 –1 0 1 2 3
2. –3 –2 –1 0 1 2 3
3. –3 –2 –1 0 1 2 3
4. –3 –2 –1 0 1 2 3
5. –3 –2 –1 0 1 2 3
6. –3 –2 –1 0 1 2 3
7. **a.** no **b.** yes **c.** no
8. **a.** no **b.** yes **c.** yes
9. **a.** yes **b.** no **c.** yes
10. Your answer may include the following ideas:
Look for values that the blue line touches on all three graphs. The line goes through the values between 0 and –1 on all three graphs. All three graphs include zero, but they don't all include –1. Values that are greater than –1 and less than or equal to 0 belong in all three solution sets.
11. $-3 \le x \le 4$
12. $x < 2$ or $x > 3$
13. $x < -2$ or $x > 3$
14. $-4 < x \le 0$

Solving Inequalities, pp. 72–73

1. $8x - 1 < 7$
$8x < 8$
$\mathbf{x < 1}$
$5(a + 2) \ge 45$
$5a + 10 \ge 45$
$5a \ge 35$
$\mathbf{a \ge 7}$
$18 > 3c + 4 - c$
$18 > 2c + 4$
$14 > 2c$
$7 > c$
$\mathbf{7 > c}$ or $\mathbf{c < 7}$

2. $-2n - 3 > 9$
$-2n > 12$
$\mathbf{n < -6}$
$4(m - 3) < 20$
$4m - 12 < 20$
$4m < 32$
$\mathbf{m < 8}$

$36 \le 9(y - 6)$
$36 \le 9y - 54$
$90 \le 9y$
$\mathbf{10 \le y}$ **or** $\mathbf{y \ge 10}$

3. $8(m + 2) < 6(m + 5)$
$8m + 16 < 6m + 30$
$2m + 16 < 30$
$2m < 14$
$\mathbf{m < 7}$

$81 \ge -3(1 - 7x)$
$81 \ge -3 + 21x$
$84 \ge 21x$
$\mathbf{4 \ge x}$ **or** $\mathbf{x \le 4}$

$-2(7n + 2) \ge 108$
$-14n - 4 \ge 108$
$-14n \ge 112$
$\mathbf{n \le -8}$

4. $17 - 3a > -4(6a + 1)$
$17 - 3a > -24a - 4$
$17 + 21a > -4$
$21a > -21$
$\mathbf{a > -1}$

$-8n + 2 > 6(7n - 8)$
$-8n + 2 > 42n - 48$
$-50n + 2 > -48$
$-50n > -50$
$\mathbf{n < 1}$

$-3(1 + 4k) > -7k + 32$
$-3 - 12k > -7k + 32$
$-3 - 5k > 32$
$-5k > 35$
$\mathbf{k < -7}$

5. $-2 < n + 4 < 9$
$\mathbf{-6 < n < 5}$

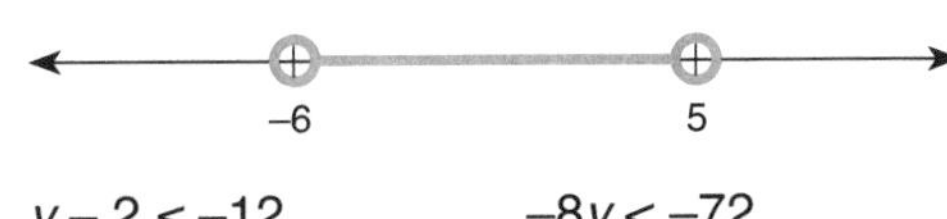

$y - 2 \le -12$ $\quad$ $-8y < -72$
$y \le -10$ $\quad$ $y > 9$
$\mathbf{y \le -10}$ **or** $\mathbf{y > 9}$

6. $6 + a \ge 4$ $\quad$ $-2a \ge 20$
$a \ge -2$ $\quad$ $a \le -10$
$\mathbf{a \ge -2}$ **or** $\mathbf{a \le -10}$

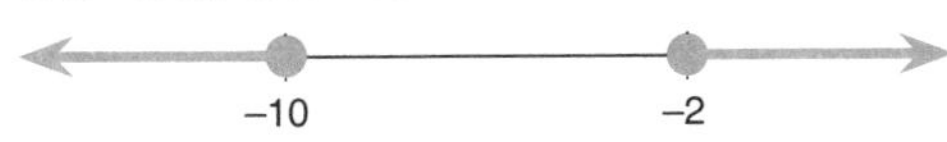

$-3 < n - 5 \le 2$
$\mathbf{2 < n \le 7}$

7. $0 > -7x \ge -7$
$\mathbf{0 < x \le 1}$

$k - 2 < -2$ $\quad$ $k - 2 > 7$
$k < 0$ $\quad$ $k > 9$
$\mathbf{k < 0}$ **or** $\mathbf{k > 9}$

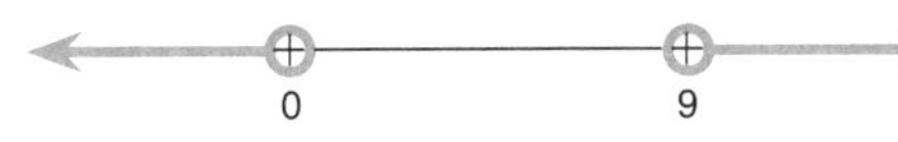

8. $\frac{a}{10} \le 0$ $\quad$ $a - 6 > 0$
$a \le 0$ $\quad$ $a > 6$
$\mathbf{a \le 0}$ **or** $\mathbf{a > 6}$

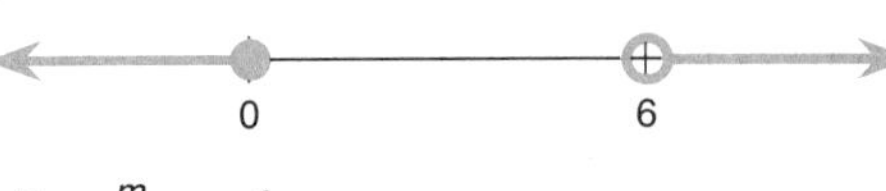

$-5 < \frac{m}{2} < -4$
$\mathbf{-10 < m < -8}$

Try the Answer Choices, pp. 74–75

1. **C. 22**
$\frac{n+3}{5} = 5$
$\frac{22+3}{5} = 5$
$\frac{25}{5} = 5$
$5 = 5$

2. **D. 690**
$\frac{2}{3}x = 460$
$\frac{2}{3} \times 690 = 460$
$460 = 460$

3. **D. 85**
$\frac{73+82+x}{3} = 80$
$\frac{73+82+85}{3} = 80$
$\frac{240}{3} = 80$
$80 = 80$

4. **B. 11.6**
$l \times 5.9 = 68.44$
$11.6 \times 5.9 = 68.44$
$68.44 = 68.44$

5. **A. 5**
$3(x - 1) + 12 = 24$
$3(5 - 1) + 12 = 24$
$3(4) + 12 = 24$
$12 + 12 = 24$
$24 = 24$

6. **C. 16**
$0.75w = 12$
$0.75 \times 16 = 12$
$12 = 12$

7. **B. 15 in**
   $40 < 10 + 16 + x < 45$
   $40 < 10 + 16 + 15 < 45$
   $40 < 41 < 45$
8. **C. 35**
   $\$10.25h = \$358.75$
   $\$10.25 \times 35 = \$358.75$
   $\$358.75 = \$358.75$

Unit 2 Review, pp. 76–77

1. **B. 4**
   $3(5 - x) + 3 = 6(x - 3)$
   $15 - 3x + 3 = 6x - 18$
   $-3x + 18 = 6x - 18$
   $-9x + 18 = -18$
   $-9x = -36$
   $x = 4$
2. A. $17 + \frac{n}{9}$
3. C. $\$45.86 + c = \$50$
4. **D. –14**
   $y + 5 = \frac{2y - 8}{4}$
   $4y + 20 = 2y - 8$
   $2y + 20 = -8$
   $2y = -28$
   $y = -14$
5. **B. 2.5×10^{-11}**
6. **D. $2,440**
   Let r equal the total rent.
   $\frac{r}{4} = \$610$
   $\frac{r}{\not{4}} \times \frac{\not{4}}{1} = \$610 \times 4$
   $r = \$2{,}440$
7. yes
8. no
9. no
10. yes
11. **–44**
    $12 = -10 - \frac{x}{2}$
    $22 = -\frac{x}{2}$
    $44 = -x$
    $x = -44$
12. **D. 30**
    $\sqrt{900} = \sqrt{9} \times \sqrt{100} = 3 \times 10 = 30$
13. **4**
    $9a - 10 + 9a - 10 + a + 2 + a + 2 = 64$
    $20a - 16 = 64$
    $20a = 80$
    $a = 4$
14. **–9**
    $-4(y - 1) = 40$
    $-4y + 4 = 40$
    $-4y = 36$
    $y = -9$
15. $-7(x + 3) \geq 4x + 12$
    $-7x - 21 \geq 4x + 12$
    $-11x - 21 \geq 12$
    $-11x \geq 33$
    $\boldsymbol{x \leq -3}$

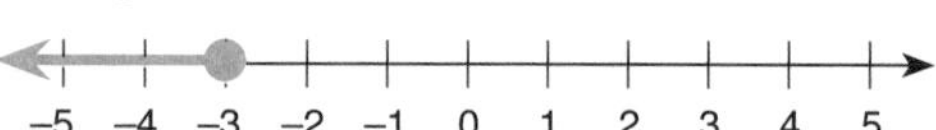

You may use any variable for problems 16 and 17.

16. $9x - 18$
17. $5n + 8$
18. **B. –2**
    $5 + 15a = -17 - a - 10$
    $5 + 15a = -a - 27$
    $5 + 16a = -27$
    $16a = -32$
    $a = -2$
19. A. $\frac{x^6}{y^2}$
20. **–18**
    $\frac{2(m - 12)}{-5} = -(m + 6)$
    $\frac{2m - 24}{-5} = -m - 6$
    $2m - 24 = 5m + 30$
    $-3m - 24 = 30$
    $-3m = 54$
    $m = -18$
21. $4 + 5n > 24$
    $5n > 20$
    $\boldsymbol{n > 4}$

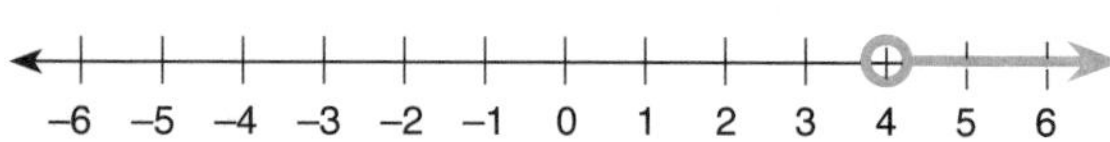

22. **$45 ≤ x ≤ $60**
    Your explanation may include the following ideas: Customers will pay no more than $60, which means that the price must be less than or equal to $60. The store must sell the game for at least $45, which means that the price must be greater than or equal to $45. A compound inequality will show that the price of the game is between $45 and $60.

UNIT 3

Translating Words to Equations, pp. 80–81

1. 46 hours

Ethan	Anna	Cole	Total Hours
$2x + 6$	x	$x + 10$	96

Equation: $2x + 6 + x + x + 10 = 96$
$4x = 80$
$x = 20$
Ethan: $2(20) + 6 = 46$ hours

2. 46 in, 58 in

Piece 1	Piece 2	Total Length
x	$x + 12$	104 in

Equation: $x + x + 12 = 104$
$2x = 92$
$x = 46$
Piece 2: $46 + 12 = 58$ in

3. 2,100 votes

Reyes	Glass	Tynan	Total Votes
$x + 600$	x	$2x$	4,800

Equation: $x + 600 + x + 2x = 4{,}800$
$4x = 4{,}200$
$x = 1{,}050$
Tynan: $2(1{,}050) = 2{,}100$ votes

4. $770

Washer	Dryer	Total
$x + \$60$	x	$1,600

Equation: $x + \$60 + x = \$1{,}600$
$2x = \$1{,}540$
$x = \$770$

5. 65 games

First Year	Second Year	Third Year	Total Wins
x	$x + 15$	$x + 23$	164

Equation: $x + x + 15 + x + 23 = 164$
$3x + 38 = 164$
$3x = 126$
$x = 42$
Third year: $42 + 23 = 65$ games

6. 12 years old

Mike	Jacob	Difference
$4x - 3$	x	33

Equation: $4x - 3 - x = 33$
$3x = 36$
$x = 12$

7. 200 miles

First Day	Second Day	Third Day	Total Miles
x	$x + 150$	$x - 60$	870

Equation: $x + x + 150 + x - 60 = 870$
$3x + 90 = 870$
$3x = 780$
$x = 260$
Third day: $260 - 60 = 200$ miles

8. 42, 60

First Number	Second Number	Sum of the Numbers
x	$x + 18$	102

Equation: $x + x + 18 = 102$
$2x = 84$
$x = 42$
Second number: $42 + 18 = 60$

OR

First Number	Second Number	Sum of the Numbers
x	$x - 18$	102

Equation: $x + x - 18 = 102$
$2x = 120$
$x = 60$
Second number: $60 - 18 = 42$

Number Puzzles and Age Problems, pp. 82–83

1. 4
Equation: $5(n + 11) = 75$
Solution: $n = 4$

2. 29, 30, 31
1st number: n
2nd number: $n + 1$
3rd number: $n + 2$
Equation: $n + n + 1 + n + 2 = 90$
n: 29
$n + 1$: 30
$n + 2$: 31

3. 45
Equation: $\frac{n}{9} = n - 40$
Solution: $n = 45$

4. 12
Equation: $4n - 9 = 39$
Solution: $n = 12$

5. 172 and 173
1st page: n
2nd page: $n + 1$
Equation: $n + n + 1 = 345$
1st page: 172
2nd page: 173

6. 6

Let n be the number.

Equation: $8n - 8 = 5n + 10$

Solution: $n = 6$

7. 77 and 83

1st number: n

2nd number: $n + 6$

Equation: $n + n + 6 = 160$

1st number: 77

2nd number: 83

8. 19

	Age Now	Age in 9 Years
Rhonda	$3x + 2$	$3x + 11$
Greg	x	$x + 9$

Equation: $3x + 11 + x + 9 = 60$

$x = 10$

Greg's age in 9 years: 10 + 9 = 19

9. 14 years old

	Age 8 Years Ago	Age Now
Lucy	$\frac{x}{2}$	$\frac{x}{2} + 8$
Laura	x	$x + 8$

Equation: $\frac{x}{2} + 8 + x + 8 = 34$

$x = 12$

Laura's age 8 years ago: 12

Lucy's age now: 14

10. 16 years old

	Age Now	Age Next Year
Samantha	$x + 3$	$x + 4$
twin 1	x	$x + 1$
twin 2	x	$x + 1$

Equation: $x + 4 + x + 1 + x + 1 = 45$

$x = 13$

Samantha's age: 13 + 3 = 16 years old

11. 15 years ago

	Age Now	Age x Years Ago
Johnsons'	35	$35 - x$
Moys'	25	$25 - x$

Equation: $35 - x = 2(25 - x)$

$x = 15$

12. Cal: 20 years, Phil: 26 years

	Years Worked Now	Years Worked in 2 Years
Cal	x	$x + 2$
Phil	$x + 6$	$x + 8$

Equation: $x + 2 + x + 8 = 50$

$x = 20$

Cal: 20 years

Phil: 20 + 6 = 26 years

Solve Equations with Fractions and Decimals, pp. 84–85

1. $-\frac{11}{4} = \frac{1}{2}x - \frac{1}{4}$

$-11 = 2x - 1$

$-10 = 2x$

$\mathbf{-5 = x}$

$\frac{1}{3} + \frac{3}{2}a = \frac{11}{6}$

$2 + 9a = 11$

$9a = 9$

$\mathbf{a = 1}$

$\frac{1}{3}m - 1 = -\frac{1}{3}$

$m - 3 = -1$

$\mathbf{m = 2}$

2. $\frac{13}{3} = -\frac{8}{3} - \frac{7}{2}y$

$26 = -16 - 21y$

$42 = -21y$

$\mathbf{-2 = y}$

$\frac{5}{2}n - \frac{1}{3} = 8$

$15n - 2 = 48$

$15n = 50$

$\mathbf{n = \frac{10}{3}}$ **or** $\mathbf{3\frac{1}{3}}$

$-\frac{3}{2}x + \frac{7}{3} = \frac{11}{24}$

$-36x + 56 = 11$

$-36x = -45$

$\mathbf{x = \frac{5}{4}}$ **or** $\mathbf{1\frac{1}{4}}$

3. $0.48 = 2.4 - 1.6a$

$48 = 240 - 160a$

$-192 = -160a$

$\mathbf{1.2 = a}$

$-9.28 - 3.2n = 0.736$

$-9{,}280 - 3{,}200n = 736$

$-3{,}200n = 10{,}016$

$\mathbf{n = -3.13}$

$18.12 = -2.8x + 4.4$

$1{,}812 = -280x + 440$

$1{,}372 = -280x$

$\mathbf{-4.9 = x}$

4. $-2.5 + 2.6m = -5.1$
$-25 + 26m = -51$
$26m = -26$
$\mathbf{m = -1}$

$-0.036 = 3.6 + 4.04k$
$-36 = 3{,}600 + 4{,}040k$
$-3{,}636 = 4{,}040k$
$\mathbf{-0.9 = k}$

$0.8 - 1.7x = -4.13$
$80 - 170x = -413$
$-170x = -493$
$\mathbf{x = 2.9}$

5. **16 years**
Let x equal the number of years the tree will grow.
Equation: $\frac{23}{4}x = 92$
Solution: $x = 16$

6. **160 points**

Sean	Carrie	Silas	Total Points
$\frac{1}{4}x$	$\frac{1}{2}x$	x	560

Equation: $\frac{1}{4}x + \frac{1}{2}x + x = 560$
$7x = 2240$
$x = 320$
Carrie: $\frac{1}{2} \times 320 = 160$

7. **40**
Let n be the number.
Equation: $\frac{3}{5}n - 9 = 15$
Solution: $n = 40$

8. **6.4 miles**

Day 1	Day 2	Day 3	Day 4	Total Miles
x	x	x	2.8	22

Equation: $x + x + x + 2.8 = 22$
Solution: $x = 6.4$

9. **$3.40**

New Patio Size	Cost per Square Foot	Total Cost
600 + 0.15(600)	x	$2,346

Equation: $690x = \$2{,}346$
Solution: $x = \$3.40$

10. **$9.80**
Let x equal the price per share in the beginning.

Initial Value	End of 1st Month Value	20 shares	Total End Value
x	$x - 0.1x$	$20(x - 0.1x)$	$176.40

Equation: $20(x - 0.1x) = \$176.40$
$20x - 2x = \$176.40$
$18x = \$176.40$
$x = \$9.80$
Art paid $9.80 per share, the initial value.

11. **90**
Let n be the number.
Equation: $1.5n - 70 = n - 25$
Solution: $n = 90$

12. **15**
Let n be the number.
Equation: $\frac{2}{3}n = n - 5$
Solution: $n = 15$

Solving Motion Problems, pp. 86–87

1. $50 \times t = 175$
$\mathbf{t = 3.5}$ **hours**

2. $20 \times 2.5 = d$
$\mathbf{d = 50}$ **miles**

3. $r \times 12 = 60$
$\mathbf{r = 5}$ **feet per second**

4. $600 \times t = 1{,}800$
$\mathbf{t = 3}$ **hours**

5. a. Lee: $r \times 3$
Ned: $(r + 10) \times 3$
b. $3r + 3(r + 10) = 318$
$\mathbf{r = 48}$ **mph**

6. a. Your diagram may look something like this:

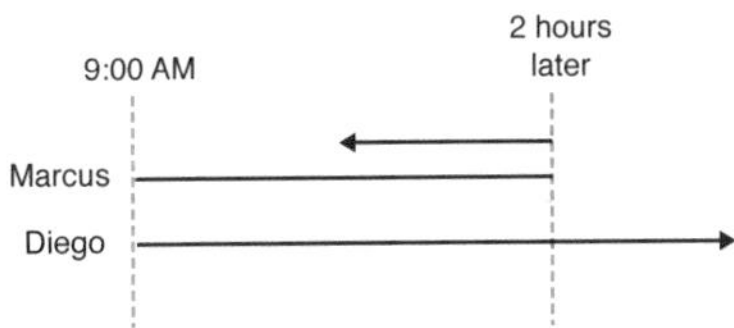

b. rate and time
c. To find how far apart Marcus and Diego are, find the difference between their distances from the starting point.
Diego's distance from the start: $d = 16 \times 3$
Marcus's distance from the start:
$d = 16 \times 2 - 16 \times 1$
Equation: $d = 16 \times 3 - (16 \times 2 - 16 \times 1)$
Solution: $\mathbf{d = 32}$ **miles**

You could also recognize that 2 hours after the start is 11 a.m., and noon is 1 hour from then. After heading in opposite directions for 1 hour:
$16 \times 1 + 16 \times 1 = d$, and $d = 32$.

7. **6 miles per hour**

	Rate	Time	Distance
Nita	4	$\frac{30 \text{ minutes}}{60 \text{ minutes}} = \frac{1}{2}$	$\frac{1}{2}(4)$
Pat	r	$\frac{20 \text{ minutes}}{60 \text{ minutes}} = \frac{1}{3}$	$\frac{1}{3}r$

Equation: $\frac{1}{2}(4) = \frac{1}{3}r$
Solution: $r = 6$ mph

8. 2.5 hours

	Rate	Time	Distance
Dave	45	t	$45t$
Frank	55	t	$55t$

Equation: $55t - 45t = 25$
Solution: $t = 2.5$ hours

9. Lap 1: 30 minutes, Lap 2: 24 minutes

	Rate	Time	Distance
1st Lap	4 mph	t	$4t$
2nd Lap	5 mph	$\frac{9}{10} - t$	$5(\frac{9}{10} - t)$

Equation: $4t = 5(\frac{9}{10} - t)$
1st lap: $t = \frac{1}{2}$ hour or 30 minutes
2nd lap: $\frac{9}{10} - \frac{1}{2} = \frac{2}{5}$ hour or 24 minutes

10. 10:10 a.m.

	Rate	Time	Distance
Garcias	48 mph	t	$48t$
Parkers	60 mph	$t - \frac{1}{3}$	$60(t - \frac{1}{3})$

Equation: $48t = 60(t - \frac{1}{3})$
The Garcias' time: $t = 1\frac{2}{3}$ hours or 100 minutes
8:30 + 100 minutes = 10:10 a.m.

Solving Value Problems, pp. 88–89

1. 4 nickels, 12 dimes, 8 quarters

	Number	Value
Nickels	x	$0.05x$
Dimes	$3x$	$0.1(3x)$
Quarters	$2x$	$0.25(2x)$

Equation: $0.05x + 0.1(3x) + 0.25(2x) = 3.40$
$x = 4$
Nickels: 4
Dimes: 3(4) = 12
Quarters: 2(4) = 8

2. 4 bills

	Number	Value
\$5 bills	x	$5x$
\$10 bills	$12 - x$	$10(12 - x)$

Equation: $5x + 10(12 - x) = 100$
$x = 4$

3. 32 hours

	Number	Value
Regular	$4x$	$14(4x)$
Weekend	x	$28x$

Equation: $14(4x) + 28x = 672$
$x = 8$
Weekend hours: 8
Regular hours: 8(4) = 32

4. 21 dimes

	Number	Value
Dimes	x	$0.1x$
Quarters	$x - 8$	$0.25(x - 8)$

Equation: $0.1x + 0.25(x - 8) = 5.35$
$x = 21$

5. 12 coins

	Number	Value
Emma	x	$0.1x$
John	x	$0.25x$

Equation: $0.25x - 0.1x = 1.80$
$x = 12$

6. 4 hits

	Number	Point Value
Hits	x	$20x$
Misses	$15 - x$	$-5(15 - x)$

Equation: $20x - 5(15 - x) = 25$
$x = 4$

7. 5 shots

	Number	Point Value
1-point	x	x
2-point	$2(x + 2)$	$4(x + 2)$
3-point	$x + 2$	$3(x + 2)$

Equation: $x + 4(x + 2) + 3(x + 2) = 38$
$x = 3$
1-point shots: 3
3-point shots: 3 + 2 = 5

8. 8 vests

	Number	Fabric Used
Vests	x	$\frac{3}{4}x$
Shirts	x	$\frac{9}{4}x$

Equation: $\frac{3}{4}x + \frac{9}{4}x = 24$
$x = 8$

9. 6 small boxes

	Number	Total Panels
Small	x	$5x$
Large	$16 - x$	$9(16 - x)$

Equation: $5x + 9(16 - x) = 120$
$x = 6$

10. 12 questions

	Number	Point Value
3-point	x	$3x$
8-point	$20 - x$	$8(20 - x)$

Equation: $3x + 8(20 - x) = 100$
$x = 12$

11. 9 regular muffins

	Number	Value
Regular	x	x
Deluxe	$24 - x$	$1.75(24 - x)$

Equation: $x + 1.75(24 - x) = 35.25$
$x = 9$

Solving Work Problems, pp. 90–91

1. $\frac{6}{5}$ or $1\frac{1}{5}$ hours

	Rate: Fraction of Job per Hour	Time Worked	Work Done per Time Worked
Copier	$\frac{1}{3}$	x	$\frac{1}{3}x$
Faster Copier	$\frac{1}{2}$	x	$\frac{1}{2}x$

Equation: $\frac{1}{3}x + \frac{1}{2}x = 1$
Solution: $x = \frac{6}{5}$ or $1\frac{1}{5}$ hours

2. $\frac{76}{9}$ or $8\frac{4}{9}$ hours

	Rate: Fraction of Job per Hour	Time Worked	Work Done per Time Worked
Pipe A	$\frac{1}{12}$	x	$\frac{1}{12}x$
Pipe B	$\frac{1}{15}$	$x - 4$	$\frac{1}{15}(x - 4)$

Equation: $\frac{1}{12}x + \frac{1}{15}(x - 4) = 1$
Solution: $x = \frac{76}{9}$ or $8\frac{4}{9}$ hours

3. $\frac{40}{3}$ or $13\frac{1}{3}$ minutes

	Rate: Fraction of Job per Minute	Time Worked	Work Done per Time Worked
Rafael	$\frac{1}{60}$	x	$\frac{1}{60}x$
Kim	$\frac{1}{40}$	x	$\frac{1}{40}x$
Nick	$\frac{1}{30}$	x	$\frac{1}{30}x$

Equation: $\frac{1}{60}x + \frac{1}{40}x + \frac{1}{30}x = 1$
Solution: $x = \frac{40}{3}$ or $13\frac{1}{3}$ minutes

4. 91 minutes

	Rate: Fraction of Job per Second	Time Worked	Work Done per Time Worked
Mike	$\frac{1}{60}$	x	$\frac{1}{60}x$
Vanessa	$\frac{1}{50}$	x	$\frac{1}{50}x$

Equation: $\frac{1}{60}x + \frac{1}{50}x = 1$

Solution: $x = \frac{300}{11}$ seconds

$\frac{300}{11} \times 200 = \frac{60{,}000}{11}$ seconds

$\frac{60{,}000}{11} \div 60 = \frac{1{,}000}{11}$ minutes

$\frac{1{,}000}{11} \approx 90.9 \approx 91$ minutes

5. Your answer may include some of the following ideas:

	Rate: Fraction of Job per Hour	Time Worked	Work Done per Time Worked
Elaine	$\frac{1}{25}$	x	$\frac{1}{25}x$
Stan	$\frac{1}{25}$	x	$\frac{1}{25}x$

Equation: $\frac{1}{25}x + \frac{1}{25}x = 1$
Solution: $x = 12.5$ hours
Elaine should work with Stan. Even though she will slow down, the job will be completed in 12.5 hours. Since it would take her 20 hours without Stan, she would save time by working with him.

Use Inequalities to Solve Word Problems, pp. 92–93

1. 12
Let x be the number of Super Burgers with cheese.
Inequality: $\$2.39x \leq \$30$
Solution: $x \leq 12.552$
Round down to the nearest whole burger. Frank can buy 12 Super Burgers with cheese for $30 or less.

2. 7

Let x be the number of meals.

Inequality: $(\$1.59 + \$0.99 + \$1.29)x \leq 30$

Solution: $x \leq 7.751$

Round down to the nearest whole meal. Frank can buy 7 meals for $30 or less.

3. 12

Let x be the number of Junior Burgers.

Inequality: $10(\$.99) + \$1.59x \leq \$30$

Solution: $x \leq 12.64$

Round down to the nearest whole burger. Frank can buy 12 Junior Burgers with the remaining money.

4. 13

Let x be the number of small drinks.

Inequality: $\$.99x \leq 10(\$1.29)$

Solution: $x \leq 13$

5. C. $n \geq -4$

Let n be the number.

Inequality: $n + 10 \geq 6$

Solution: $n \geq -4$

6. A. 4

Try the answer choices:

A. $2(4 - 5) > -2$
   $-2 > -2$ false

B. $2(6 - 5) > -2$
   $2 > -2$ true

C. $2(8 - 5) > -2$
   $6 > -2$ true

D. $2(10 - 5) > -2$
   $10 > -2$ true

7. B. $n > 5$

Let n be the number.

Inequality: $-4n + 19 < -1$

Solution: $n > 5$

8. D. 0

Try the answer choices.

A. $-8 < 5(-6) + 2$
   $-8 < -28$ false

B. $-8 < 5(-4) + 2$
   $-8 < -18$ false

C. $-8 < 5(-2) + 2$
   $-8 < -8$ false

D. $-8 < 5(0) + 2$
   $-8 < 2$ true
   $4 - 0 \leq 8$
   $4 \leq 8$ true

Using Formulas, pp. 94–95

1. 192 feet

$d = rt$

$d = 24 \times 8$

$d = 192$ feet

2. 25°C

$C = \frac{5}{9}(F - 32)$

$C = \frac{5}{9}(77 - 32)$

$C = 25°$

3. 400 sq cm

$A = \frac{1}{2}bh$

$A = \frac{1}{2} \times 40 \times 20$

$A = 400$ sq cm

4. Loan B

Loan A: $I = prt$
$I = \$10{,}000 \times 0.04 \times 6$
$I = \$2{,}400$

Loan B: $I = prt$
$I = \$10{,}000 \times 0.05 \times 4$
$I = \$2{,}000$

5. 4.2 sq in

$A = bh$

$A = 2.8 \times 1.5$

$A = 4.2$ sq in

6. 313.6 meters

$d = \frac{1}{2}g(t \times t)$

$d = \frac{1}{2} \times 9.8 \times (8 \times 8)$

$d = 313.6$ meters

Rewriting Formulas, pp. 96–97

1. a. $c = P - a - b$
   b. $c = 72 - 20 - 18 =$ **34 cm**
2. a. $F = \frac{9}{5}C + 32$
   b. $F = \frac{9}{5}(60) + 32 =$ **140°**
3. a. $w = \frac{P - 2l}{2}$
   b. $w = \frac{30 - 2 \times 9}{2} =$ **6 in**
4. a. $y = 3A - x - z$
   b. $y = 3(87) - 86 - 81 =$ **94**
5. a. $b = \frac{2A}{h}$
   b. $b = \frac{2 \times 414}{18} =$ **46 in**
6. a. $t = \frac{I}{pr}$
   b. $t = \frac{\$480}{\$4{,}000 \times 0.04} =$ **3 yr**
7. a. $n = \frac{C}{r}$
   b. $n = \frac{\$261}{\$21.75} =$ **12 T-shirts**
8. $p = w \times r$
   $r = \frac{p}{w}$
   $w = \frac{p}{r}$
   Real-life situations will vary.

Unit 3 Review, pp. 98–99

1. a.

Class A	Class B	Class C	Total
$n + 12$	n	$2n - 23$	85

b. Equation: $n + 12 + n + 2n - 23 = 85$
Solution: $n =$ **24 students**

2. **C. 48**
Jordan: $4x$
Grace: x
Equation: $4x - x = 36$
$x = 12$
Jordan: $4(12) = 48$

3. **C. 17**

	Number	Value
$5 bills	$3x$	$5(3x)$
$10 bills	x	$10x$
$20 bills	$2x - 1$	$20(2x - 1)$

Equation: $5(3x) + 10x + 20(2x - 1) = 175$
$x = 3$
$5 bills: $3(3) = 9$
$10 bills: 3
$20 bills: $2(3) - 1 = 5$
Total bills: $9 + 3 + 5 = 17$

4. **B. 24 and 31**
Equation: $6x - 5 + 4x + 6x - 5 + 4x = 110$
$x = 6$
Length: $6(6) - 5 = 31$ meters
Width: $4(6) = 24$ meters

5. a.

	Rate	Time	Distance
Up	2	x	$2x$
Down	4	$3 - x$	$4(3 - x)$

b. **B. 1**
Equation: $2x = 4(3 - x)$
$x = 2$
Downhill: $3 - 2 = 1$

6. **14 kids**

	Number	Value
Car flags	x	$13x$
Plush mascots	x	$19x$
Bobbleheads	$4x$	$15(4x)$
Baseballs	$20 - 6x$	$5(20 - 6x)$

Equation: $13x + 19x + 15(4x) + 5(20 - 6x) = 162$
$x = 1$
Baseballs: $20 - 6(1) = 14$

7. **C. between 6 and 7 hours**

	Rate: Fraction of Job per Hour	Time Worked	Work Done per Time Worked
Bob	$\frac{1}{10}$	2	$\frac{1}{10}(2)$
Ellen	$\frac{1}{8}$	$2 + x$	$\frac{1}{8}(2 + x)$

Equation: $\frac{1}{10}(2) + \frac{1}{8}(2 + x) = 1$
$x = 4\frac{2}{5}$
Total time for the job: $2 + 4\frac{2}{5} = 6\frac{2}{5}$
The job will take between 6 and 7 hours.

8. **16**

1st Number	2nd Number	Total
$\frac{5}{2}x$	x	56

Equation: $\frac{5}{2}x + x = 56$
Solution: $x = 16$

9. **26 nickels**

	Number	Value
Nickels	x	$0.05x$
Quarters	$40 - x$	$0.25(40 - x)$

Equation: $0.05x + 0.25(40 - x) \geq 4.80$
Solution: $x \leq 26$
Brandon has no more than 26 nickels.

10. **B. $n < 6$**
Equation: $-2n + 15 > 3$
Solution: $n < 6$

11. $h = \frac{3V}{b}$

12. $s = p - 0.3p$
$\mathbf{s = 0.7p}$

13. Let n be the number of sales.
$\mathbf{4n + 180 \geq 450}$

UNIT 4

Points, Lines, and Angles, pp. 102–103

1. 3
2. **No, lines *r* and *p* are not perpendicular.**
Explanations may vary but should include some of the following ideas:
Since point J is at the intersection of perpendicular lines, lines r and $\overline{GJ}$ are perpendicular. In order for lines r and p to be perpendicular, line p would have to be parallel to $\overline{GJ}$.
3. $\overline{GH}, \overline{KH}, \overline{HJ}, \overline{GJ}$
4. Answers could include: $\overrightarrow{GJ}$, $\overrightarrow{HJ}$, $\overrightarrow{HK}$, $\overrightarrow{GH}$, or $\overrightarrow{KH}$

5. **d,** an acute angle
   c, a right angle
   b, an obtuse angle
   a, a straight angle
6. A. because the opening between the rays is smallest

Using Protractors, pp. 104–105

1. **a.** 75°
   b. 60°
   c. 110°
   d. 150°
2. **b.** 180°
   a. 90°
   c. 30°
   d. 135°
3. 72°
4.

Angle	Type	Degrees
∠POS	obtuse	125°
∠QOS	acute	80°
∠POR	acute	70°

5. **$\angle d = 30°$ and $\angle c = 90°$**
   Let $x = \angle d$.
   $3x + x = 120°$
   $4x = 120°$
   $x = 30°$
   $3x = 90°$

Working with Angles, pp. 106–107

1. $m\angle a = 90° - 26° = \mathbf{64°}$
2. $m\angle d = 180° - 129° = \mathbf{51°}$
3. $\angle x$ and $\angle z$; $\angle w$ and $\angle y$
4. $\angle x$ and $\angle z$
5. 70°
6. 110°; because $\angle x$ and $\angle z$ are vertical angles, and vertical angles are equal.
7. $\angle MOQ$
8. **$\angle POQ = 30°$**
   $\angle MOP + \angle POQ = 90°$
   $90° - \angle MOP = \angle POQ$
   $90° - 60° = 30°$

Core Connections: Angle Relationships, p. 107

1. $\angle h$, $\angle b$, and $\angle d$
2. **$\angle a = 43°$**; $\angle b = 137°$ because $\angle b$ and $\angle f$ are corresponding angles. $\angle b$ and $\angle a$ are supplementary angles. $180° - 137° = 43°$

Quadrilaterals, pp. 108–109

1. *CD*
2. *AB* and *CD*
3. *AC* and *BD*
4. $\angle ADC$
5. **$\angle ADC = 83°$**
   $\angle DAB + \angle ABC + \angle BCD + \angle ADC = 360°$
   $80° + 114° + 2(\angle ADC) = 360°$
   $2(\angle ADC) = 360° - 194°$
   $2(\angle ADC) = 166°$
   $\angle ADC = 83°$
6. The opposite sides are equal and parallel; all angles are right angles; and the diagonals are equal.
7. **True**
   The main property of a parallelogram (opposite sides are equal and parallel) is true of a square, a rectangle, and a rhombus.
8. Rhombus
9. **False**
   Even though a trapezoid has only one pair of parallel sides, it can have no more than two right angles.
10. **No**
    Since both pairs of opposite sides are equal, the opposite angles must be equal.
11. **Square**
    Sides *WX* and *YZ* are equal, as are sides *XY* and *WZ*. Since the adjacent sides *WX* and *WZ* are equal, all four sides must be equal. The figure must be a square.
12. Yes for both. See the examples below.

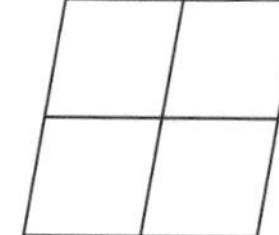

Triangles, pp. 110–111

1. right triangle
2. equilateral triangle
3. isosceles triangle
4. scalene triangle
5. Each group could form triangles:
   50°, 80°, 50°
   45°, 60°, 75°
   50°, 60°, 70°
6. Side *CD*, because it is opposite the largest angle.
7. Angle *MNO*, because it is opposite the longest side.
8. $\angle U = 40°$
9. **$\angle A = 20°$ and $\angle C = 40°$**
   $120 + x + 2x = 180$
   $3x = 60$
   $x = 20, 2x = 40$

10. Each measures **65°.**
You know that $\angle V$ and $\angle X$ are equal, so let x represent the measure of each.
$x + x + 50 = 180$
$2x + 50 = 180$
$2x = 130$
$x = 65°$

11. $180° + 180° =$ **360°**

12. $\angle D$

13. Yes.

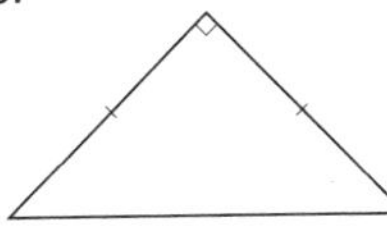

The Pythagorean Theorem, pp. 112–113

1. **20 in**
$12^2 + 16^2 = c^2$
$\sqrt{144 + 256} = c$
$\sqrt{400} = c$
$20 = c$

2. **12 cm**
$5^2 + b^2 = 13^2$
$b^2 = 13^2 - 5^2$
$b = \sqrt{169 - 25}$
$b = \sqrt{144}$
$b = 12$

3. **26 in**
$10^2 + 24^2 = c^2$
$\sqrt{100 + 576} = c$
$\sqrt{676} = c$
$26 = c$

4. **24 cm**
$7^2 + b^2 = 25^2$
$b^2 = 25^2 - 7^2$
$b = \sqrt{625 - 49}$
$b = \sqrt{576}$
$b = 24$

5. ***FG* = 41 cm**
$9^2 + 40^2 = c^2$
$\sqrt{81 + 1{,}600} = c$
$\sqrt{1{,}681} = c$
$41 = c$

6. **width = 6 in**
$a^2 + 8^2 = 10^2$
$a^2 = 10^2 - 8^2$
$a = \sqrt{100 - 64}$
$a = \sqrt{36}$
$a = 6$

7. **82 ft**
$18^2 + 80^2 = c^2$
$\sqrt{324 + 6{,}400} = c$
$\sqrt{6{,}724} = c$
$82 = c$

8. **127.3 ft**
$90^2 + 90^2 = c^2$
$\sqrt{8{,}100 + 8{,}100} = c$
$\sqrt{16{,}200} = c$
$127.3 \approx c$

Core Connections: Pythagorean Triples, p. 113

1.

a	*b*	*c*
12	16	20
15	20	25

2.

a	*b*	*c*
5	12	13
10	24	26
15	36	39
20	48	52

Similar Geometric Figures, pp. 114–115

1. **Yes.** Both figures have the same shape.
2. **Yes.** Both figures are isosceles right triangles.
3. **No.** The ratio of length to width is not the same.
4. **Yes.** Although the triangles are in different positions, the corresponding sides have the same ratio.
5. ***x* = 40 and *y* = 24**
$\frac{x}{24} = \frac{30}{18}$
$30 \times 24 = 18x$
$720 = 18x$
$40 = x$
$\frac{y}{18} = \frac{32}{24}$
$32 \times 18 = 24y$
$576 = 24y$
$24 = y$
6. **$4\frac{1}{2}$ inches**
Set up a proportion:
$\frac{3}{5} = \frac{x}{7\frac{1}{2}}$
$3 \times 7.5 = 5x$
$22.5 = 5x$
$4.5 = x$
7. **26 feet**
$\frac{4}{6} = \frac{x}{39}$
$4 \times 39 = 6x$
$156 = 6x$
$26 = x$

8. **140 yards**

$\frac{1.75 \text{ cm}}{2.5 \text{ cm}} = \frac{w}{200 \text{ yd}}$

$1.75 \times 200 = 2.5w$

$350 = 2.5w$

$140 = w$

9. **$4\frac{1}{2}$ or 4.5**

Set up a proportion:

$\frac{XY}{YZ} = \frac{XV}{VW}$

$\frac{12}{9} = \frac{6}{x}$

$9 \times 6 = 12x$

$54 = 12x$

4.5 or $4\frac{1}{2} = x$

10. **78 feet**

$\frac{6}{5} = \frac{x}{65}$

$6 \times 65 = 5x$

$390 = 5x$

$78 = x$

11. a. **True.** The sides in any equilateral triangle are equal, so the ratio must always be the same.
    b. **True.** The sides are always equal in any square, so the sides must maintain the same ratio.
    c. **False.** The lengths of the sides may not maintain the same ratio.
    d. **False.** The lengths of the sides may not maintain the same ratio.

Finding Patterns in Algebra and Geometry, pp. 116–117

1. 18; add 3
2. 55; subtract 9
3. 10,000; multiply by 10
4. 32; multiply by 2
5. 95; add twice the difference of the previous value
6. $\frac{1}{16}$; divide by 2
7. 7:00
8. U
9. 36
10. 4 ft 6 in
11. 64

Rectangle	Length	Width	Perimeter
ABCD	2	1	6
EFGH	3	2	10
IJKL	4	3	14
MNOP	5	4	18
QRST	6	5	22
UVWX	7	6	26

12. 22
13. 8

Number of steps	2	3	4	5	6
Number of cubes	3	6	10	15	21

14. 36
15. 20; The number of blocks in the bottom row is the number of steps.

Mixed Review, pp. 118–119

1. 65°
2. 127°
3. 42°
4. 120°
5. C. perpendicular
6. B. right
7. A. vertical
8. 60°
9. 77°; acute
10. right
11. 135°; obtuse
12. **C. 40°, 50°, 100°**
    The sum of the angles in a triangle is 180°. These angle measures add up to 190°.
13. **Angle *H***
    In a triangle, the longest side is opposite the largest angle. *GI* is the longest side, and it is opposite angle *H*.
14. **Yes**
    Ratio of long sides: $\frac{5}{20} = \frac{1}{4}$
    Ratio of short sides: $\frac{4}{16} = \frac{1}{4}$
15. **Yes**
    Ratio of long sides: $\frac{10}{15} = \frac{2}{3}$
    Ratio of short sides: $\frac{6}{9} = \frac{2}{3}$
16. **No**
    Ratio of long sides: $\frac{9}{20}$
    Ratio of middle sides: $\frac{8}{16} = \frac{1}{2}$
    Ratio of short sides: $\frac{6}{14} = \frac{3}{7}$
17. **33**

$\frac{8}{11} = \frac{24}{x}$

$8x = 264$

$x = 33$

18. **21.6 m**

$\frac{9}{10} = \frac{x}{24}$

$10x = 216$

$x = 21.6$

19. 30
$\frac{x}{9} = \frac{40}{12}$
$12x = 360$
$x = 30$

20. 60 ft
$\frac{x}{40} = \frac{3}{2}$
$2x = 120$
$x = 60$

21. a. $90° - 65° =$ **25°**

b. 27 cm
$12^2 + 24^2 = c^2$
$\sqrt{144 + 576} = c$
$\sqrt{720} = c$
$27 \approx c$

22. 48 ft
$14^2 + b^2 = 50^2$
$b^2 = 50^2 - 14^2$
$b = \sqrt{2{,}500 - 196}$
$b = \sqrt{2{,}304}$
$b = 48$

23. 14.4 in
$\frac{3}{5} = \frac{x}{24}$
$5x = 72$
$x = 14.4$

24. 22.4 in
$10^2 + 20^2 = c^2$
$\sqrt{100 + 400} = c$
$\sqrt{500} = c$
$22.4 \approx c$

Perimeter, pp. 120–121

1. 12 + 5 + 12 + 5 = **34 ft**
2. 4 × 6.5 = **26 cm**
3. 7 + 3 + 9 + 8 = **27 in**
4. 2.5 + 2.5 + 3 + 4 + 5.5 + 6.5 = **24 units**
5. 10 + 8 + 8 + 10 + 8 + 8 = **52 ft**
6. **54**
$y = 5 + 5 + 5 = 15$
$x = 4 + 4 + 4 = 12$
$P = 15 + 12 + 5 + 4 + 5 + 4 + 5 + 4 = 54$
7. **40**
$s = 4 + 6 = 10$
$t = 4$
$P = 4 + 4 + 10 + 8 + 4 + 10 = 40$
8. **40**
$a = 3 + 4 = 7$
$b = 2 + 6 + 2 = 10$
$c = 3 + 4 = 7$
$P = 7 + 10 + 7 + 2 + 3 + 6 + 3 + 2 = 40$
9. **30**
The missing side is 9 units.
$P = 9 + 9 + 12 = 30$
10. **36 ft**
Each side of both squares is 6 ft. Remember, perimeter is the distance around the outside of a figure.
6 + 6 + 6 + 6 + 6 + 6 = 36
11. **24 inches**
Let x be the width.
Let $3x$ be the length.
$P = x + 3x + x + 3x$
$64 = 8x$
$x = 8$
Length: 3 × 8 = 24 inches
12. Your explanation may include some of the following ideas:
Side *a* is the hypotenuse of a right triangle. You could find side *a* by using the Pythagorean theorem.
Side *b* is equal to the sum of the sides labeled 9 feet and 3 feet. You could find side *b* by adding those two sides.

Area of Squares, Rectangles, and Parallelograms, pp. 122–123

1. 4 × 4 = **16 sq in**
2. 3.4 × 5.3 = **18.02 cm^2**
3. 12 × 9 = **108 sq in**
4. 8 × 6.9 = **55.2 sq mi**
5. 0.7 × 0.6 = **0.42 cm^2**
6. 3.7 × 3.7 = **13.69 sq mi**
7. 27 × 78 = **2,106 sq ft**
8. 27 × 18 = **486 sq ft**
9. 13.5 × 21 = **283.5 sq ft**
10. **312 sq yd**
36 × 78 = 2,808 sq ft
2,808 ÷ 9 = 312 sq yd
11. No, the rectangles will have different perimeters. Explanations and examples will vary but should include similar ideas:
A rectangle with a width of 2 and a length of 8 will have an area of 16 square units and a perimeter of 20 units. A square with a side of 4 will have an area of 16 square units and a perimeter of 16 units.
12. Drawings will vary. Be sure that the height of the parallelogram is labeled, not the width.

Area of Triangles and Trapezoids, pp. 124–125

1. $\frac{1}{2}(8)(4.3) =$ **17.2 sq in**
2. $\frac{1}{2}(6)(8) =$ **24 sq in**
3. $\frac{1}{2}(3)(3 + 8) =$ **16.5 m^2**
4. $\frac{1}{2}(6)(10.1 + 4.9) =$ **45 sq in**

5. $\frac{1}{2}(2)(5.6) =$ **5.6 cm²**

6. $\frac{1}{2}(7)(3 + 8) =$ **38.5 sq yd**

7. $\frac{1}{2}(12)(15) =$ **90 sq ft**

8. $\frac{1}{2}(14)(9) =$ **63 sq in**

9. a. $\frac{1}{2}(6)(6 + 12) =$ **54 cm²**

   b. *First figure:*

   triangle: $\frac{1}{2}(6)(6) = 18 \text{ cm}^2$

   parallelogram: $6(6) = 36 \text{ cm}^2$

   total: $18 + 36 = 54 \text{ cm}^2$

   Second figure:

   square: $6(6) = 36 \text{ cm}^2$

   triangle: $\frac{1}{2}(6)(6) = 18 \text{ cm}^2$

   total: $36 + 18 = 54 \text{ cm}^2$

Circumference and Area of Circles, pp. 126–127

1. Circumference: $3.14(10) =$ **31.4 cm**
   Area: $3.14(5^2) =$ **78.5 cm²**
2. Circumference: $3.14(22) \approx$ **69.1 in**
   Area: $3.14(11^2) \approx$ **379.9 sq in**
3. Circumference: $3.14(4.2) \approx$ **13.2 m**
   Area: $3.14(2.1^2) \approx$ **13.8 m²**
4. **22 packets**
   Area of garden: $3.14(9^2) = 254.34$ sq ft
   Seed packets: $254.34 \div 12 = 21.195$
   Sasha can buy only whole seed packets, and 21 won't be enough to fill the entire garden. Round up to 22 packets.
5. **9.6 ft**
   $C = \pi d$
   $30 \approx 3.14d$
   $30 \div 3.14 \approx d$
   $9.6 \approx d$
6. **8.1 in**
   Circumference of lid: $3.14(2.5) = 7.85$ in
   Length of strip: $7.85 + 0.25 = 8.1$ in

Core Connections: Lines of Symmetry, p. 127

1. Rectangle: 4 lines
   Oval: 2 lines
   Equilateral triangle: 3 lines
   Trapezoid: 1 line
   Parallelogram: 0 lines
2. A circle

Area of Complex Figures, pp. 128–129

1. large rectangle: $9 \times 5 = 45$ sq yd
   small rectangle: $3 \times 4 = 12$ sq yd
   total: $45 + 12 =$ **57 sq yd**
2. square: $8 \times 8 = 64 \text{ cm}^2$
   half-circle: $\frac{1}{2} \times 3.14 \times 4^2 \approx 25.12 \text{ cm}^2$
   total: $64 + 25.12 =$ **89.12 cm²**
3. rectangle: $25 \times 20 = 500$ sq ft
   triangle: $\frac{1}{2} \times 10 \times 25 = 125$ sq ft
   total: $500 - 125 =$ **375 sq ft**
4. large rectangle: $9 \times 5 = 45$ sq yd
   small rectangle: $3 \times 4 = 12$ sq yd
   total: $45 - 12 =$ **33 sq yd**
5. triangle: $\frac{1}{2} \times 8 \times 7 = 28 \text{ cm}^2$
   circle: $3.14 \times 1.5^2 \approx 7.1 \text{ cm}^2$
   total: $28 - 7.1 =$ **20.9 cm²**
6. triangle: $\frac{1}{2} \times 10 \times 25 = 125$ sq ft
   rectangle: $20 \times 25 = 500$ sq ft
   total: $125 + 500 =$ **625 sq ft**
7. diameter of large circle: $6 + 3 + 3 = 12$
   large circle: $3.14 \times 6^2 \approx 113.04$ sq ft
   small circle: $3.14 \times 3^2 \approx 28.26$ sq ft
   walkway: $113.04 - 28.26 = 84.78 \approx$ **84.8 sq ft**
   or $113 - 28.3 =$ **84.7 sq ft**
8. There are several ways to find the area of the X. One way is to find the area of the two rectangles and subtract the area of the square inside the X.
   rectangle: $11 \times 6 = 66$ sq in
   area of both rectangles: $66 + 66 = 132$ sq in
   area of inner square: $6 \times 6 = 36$ sq in
   area of X $= 132 - 36 =$ **96 sq in**
9. area of square: $32 \times 32 = 1{,}024$ sq ft
   area of triangle: $\frac{1}{2} \times 16 \times 18 = 144$ sq ft
   area of walkway: $1{,}024 - 144 =$ **880 sq ft**
10. area of square: $60 \times 60 = 3{,}600$ sq ft
    Together, the ends of the course create a circle with a diameter of 60 feet.
    area of circle: $3.14 \times 30^2 = 2{,}826$ sq ft
    area of course: $3{,}600 + 2{,}826 =$ **6,426 sq ft**
11. a. $\frac{3}{4} \times 3.14 \times 9^2 \approx$ **190.8 sq in**
    b. $\sqrt{190.8} \approx 13.8 \approx$ **14 in**

Volume of Prisms and Cylinders, pp. 130–131

1. $3.14 \times 3^2 \times 7 \approx$ **197.8 cm³**
2. $(6)(8)(2) =$ **96 in³**
3. $3^3 =$ **27 m³**
4. $3.14 \times 3^2 \times 10 =$ **282.6 ft³**
5. $3.14 \times 7^2 \times 4 \approx$ **615.4 cm³**
6. $10 \times 20 \times 1\frac{1}{2} =$ **300 ft³**
7. 1st box: $(8)(5)(4) = 160 \text{ ft}^3$
   2nd box: $5^3 = 125 \text{ ft}^3$
   difference: $160 - 125 =$ **35 ft³**
8. a. $\frac{1}{2} \times 6 \times 48 =$ **144 ft³**
   b. $144 \div 27 =$ **$5\frac{1}{3}$ yd³**

9. $3.14 \times 8^2 \times 20 =$ **$4{,}019.2\ ft^3$**

10. Volume of can: $3.14 \times 5^2 \times 12 = 942\ in^3$
Volume of box: $(5)(15)(12) = 900\ in^3$
No, the box will overflow because the can holds more than the box does.

Volume of Pyramids, Cones, and Spheres, pp. 132–133

1. $\frac{1}{3} \times 5 \times 5 \times 6 =$ **$50\ in^3$**
2. $\frac{1}{3} \times 3.14 \times 5^2 \times 10 \approx$ **$261.7\ km^3$**
3. $\frac{4}{3} \times 3.14 \times 2^3 \approx$ **$33.5\ cm^3$**
4. $\frac{1}{3} \times 3 \times 2 \times 2 =$ **$4\ m^3$**
5. $\frac{1}{3} \times 3.14 \times 3^2 \times 8 \approx$ **$75.4\ cm^3$**
6. $\frac{4}{3} \times 3.14 \times 3^3 \approx$ **$113\ ft^3$**
7. The height of 1 pyramid is 4 inches. Multiply the volume of 1 pyramid by 2.
$2 \times \frac{1}{3} \times 4 \times 4 \times 4 \approx$ **$43\ in^3$**
8. volume of box: $24^3 = 13{,}824\ cm^3$
volume of ball: $\frac{4}{3} \times 3.14 \times 11.9^3 \approx 7{,}055\ cm^3$
unused space: $13{,}824 - 7{,}055 =$ **$6{,}769\ cm^3$**
9. cone: $\frac{1}{3} \times 3.14 \times 1^2 \times 6 = 6.28\ in^3$
cylinder: $3.14 \times 1^2 \times 10 = 31.4\ in^3$
total: $31.4 + 6.28 \approx$ **$38\ in^3$**
10. pyramid: $\frac{1}{3} \times 5 \times 3 \times 2 = 10\ ft^3$
prism: $5 \times 3 \times 4 = 60\ ft^3$
total: $10 + 60 =$ **$70\ ft^3$**

Surface Area, pp. 134–135

1. **$184\ m^2$**
Top: $8 \times 4 = 32$
Bottom: $8 \times 4 = 32$
Left side: $5 \times 4 = 20$
Right side: $5 \times 4 = 20$
Front: $8 \times 5 = 40$
Back: $8 \times 5 = 40$
Sum: $32 + 32 + 20 + 20 + 40 + 40 = 184\ m^2$
Or use the formula $SA = ph + 2B$.
$SA = 24 \times 5 + 2 \times 32 = 184\ m^2$
2. **314 sq yd**
$SA = 4\pi r^2$
$4 \times 3.14 \times 5^2 = 314$ sq yd
3. **226.1 sq yd**
$SA = 2\pi rh + 2\pi r^2$
$2 \times 3.14 \times 3 \times 9 + 2 \times 3.14 \times 3^2 \approx 226.1$ sq yd
4. **$24\ cm^2$**
All of the faces have the same area. Since there are 6 faces on a cube, multiply the area of a single face by 6.
$(6)(2)(2) = 24\ cm^2$
Or use the formula $SA = ph + 2B$.
$SA = 8 \times 2 + 2 \times 4 = 24\ cm^2$
5. **105.6 sq ft**
$SA = \frac{1}{2}ps + B$
$\frac{1}{2} \times (6 \times 4) \times 5.8 + 36 = 105.6$ sq ft
6. **$40.8\ m^2$**
$SA = \pi rs + \pi r^2$
$3.14 \times 2 \times 4.5 + 3.14 \times 2^2 \approx 40.8\ m^2$
7. **202 sq ft**
Bottom: $8 \times 11 = 88$
Front: $3 \times 8 = 24$
Back: $3 \times 8 = 24$
Left side: $3 \times 11 = 33$
Right side: $3 \times 11 = 33$
Sum: $88 + 24 + 24 + 33 + 33 = 202$ sq ft
Or use the formula $SA = ph + 2B$. Note that there is no need to multiply the base by 2 since there is no top to the truck bed.
$SA = 38 \times 3 + 88 = 202$ sq ft
8. a. **Crunchy Oats**
Crunchy Oats:
Top: $2 \times 8 = 16$
Bottom: $2 \times 8 = 16$
Left side: $2 \times 11 = 22$
Right side: $2 \times 11 = 22$
Front: $8 \times 11 = 88$
Back: $8 \times 11 = 88$
Sum: $16 + 16 + 22 + 22 + 88 + 88 = 252$ sq in

Bran Crisps:
Top: $3 \times 7 = 21$
Bottom: $3 \times 7 = 21$
Left side: $3 \times 10 = 30$
Right side: $3 \times 10 = 30$
Front: $7 \times 10 = 70$
Back: $7 \times 10 = 70$
Sum: $21 + 21 + 30 + 30 + 70 + 70 = 242$ sq in

b. **Bran Crisps**
Crunchy Oats: $(8)(11)(2) = 176\ in^3$
Bran Crisps: $(7)(10)(3) = 210\ in^3$

Choosing Area, Perimeter, Volume, or Surface Area, pp. 136–137

1. Solve for: volume
Solution: $7 \times 7 \times 15 =$ **$735\ ft^3$**
2. Solve for: area
Solution: πr^2
$3.14 \times 18^2 \approx$ **1,017 sq ft**

3. Solve for: perimeter
   Solution: $2\frac{1}{2} + 2\frac{1}{2} + 4 + 4 =$ **13 ft**
4. Solve for: surface area
   Solution: $SA = 2\pi rh + 2\pi r^2$
   $2 \times 3.14 \times 10 \times 25 + 2 \times 3.14 \times 10^2 \approx$ **2,198 m²**
5. Solve for: perimeter
   Solution: $72 + 72 + 60 + 60 =$ **264 in**
6. Solve for: area
   Solution: $22(15) = 330$ sq ft
   area per tile: 1^2
   $330 \div 1 =$ **330 tiles**
7. Solve for: surface area
   Solution: 40 sq yd
   Top: $3 \times 4 = 12$
   Left side: $4 \times 2 = 8$
   Right side: $4 \times 2 = 8$
   Front: $3 \times 2 = 6$
   Back: $3 \times 2 = 6$
   Sum: $12 + 8 + 8 + 6 + 6 =$ **40 sq yd**
8. Solve for: volume
   Solution: $\pi r^2 h$
   $3.14 \times 2.5^2 \times 1 \approx 19.625 \approx$ **20 ft³**

Using Algebra in Geometry Problems, pp. 138–139

1. **75°**
   $3x + 4x + 5x = 180$
   $12x = 180$
   $x = 15$
   $m\angle F = 5(15) = 75°$
2. **192 cm²**
   Let x represent side TU.
   Let $\frac{1}{3}x$ represent side SV.
   $x + \frac{1}{3}x + 10 + 10 = 68$
   $x = 36$
   $TU = 36$ cm and $SV = 12$ cm
   $A = \frac{1}{2}h(b_1 + b_2)$
   $\frac{1}{2} \times 8 \times (12 + 36) = 192 \text{ cm}^2$
3. **40°**
   $60 + 11x + 3 + 5x + 5 = 180$
   $x = 7$
   $m\angle A = 5(7) + 5 = 40°$
4. **B. length = 10 ft, height = 10 ft, volume = 400 ft³**
   Find the missing dimension in each answer choice. Then compare to the requirements.
   A. $V = 8 \times 5 \times 9 = 360 \text{ ft}^3$
      Does not meet requirements
   B. $400 = 10 \times w \times 10$
      $400 = 100w$
      $w = 4$ ft
      Meets requirements
   C. $400 = 5 \times w \times 4$
      $400 = 20w$
      $w = 20$
      Does not meet requirements
5. **9 in**
   $V = \frac{1}{3}\pi r^2 h$
   $151 = \frac{1}{3}(3.14) \times 4^2 \times h$
   $9 \approx h$
6. **$x = 4$ or $x = 1$**
   Isosceles triangles have two equal sides. Set pairs of sides equal to each other and solve for x.
   $3x - 2 = 2x + 2$
   $x = 4$ — x could equal 4
   $3x - 2 = x$
   $x = 1$ — x could equal 1
   $2x + 2 = x$
   $x = -2$ — The sides of a figure must have positive lengths. x cannot equal -2

Unit 4 Review, pp. 140–141

1. **$m\angle x = 80°$**
   The vertical angle to $\angle B$ and the 60° angle are corresponding angles, so $\angle B$ is also 60°.
   $\angle B + 40° + x = 180°$
   $60° + 40° + x = 180°$
   $x = 80°$
2. **C. scalene**
   The interior angles of triangle ABC are 80°, 60°, and 40°. Since the angles are different sizes, the sides are all different lengths. The triangle is a scalene triangle.
3. **59.2 cm**
   The formula for circumference of a circle is $C = \pi d$. Find three-fourths of the circumference and add to the remaining sides.
   $(\frac{3}{4} \times 3.14 \times 9) + 9 + 10 + 10 + 9 \approx 59.2$ cm
4. **C. 281 sq in**
   The side length of one square is $\frac{1}{2} \times 15 = 7.5$.
   Area of a square: $7.5^2 = 56.25$
   Area of 5 squares: $56.25 \times 5 \approx 281$ sq in
5. **82 ft³**
   $V = \frac{1}{3}Bh$
   $\frac{1}{3} \times 7 \times 7 \times 5 \approx 82 \text{ ft}^3$
6. **176 cm**
   $15 + x + 15 = 45$
   $x = 15$
   $13 + 17 + y = 43$
   $y = 13$
   $P = 43 + 15 + 17 + 15 + 13 + 15 + 13 + 45 = 176$ cm

7. **D. 50**
Volume of container:
$V = Bh = (20)(30)(20) = 12{,}000 \text{ in}^3$
Gallons of cider: $12{,}000 \div 230 \approx 52$
50 gallons of cider is the best estimate.

8. **537 sq ft**
$SA = 2\pi rh + 2\pi r^2$
Since the bottom of the tank is not being painted, there is no need to multiply πr^2 by 2.
$2 \times 3.14 \times 9 \times 5 + 3.14 \times 9^2 = 536.94$ sq ft
$536.94 \approx 537$ sq ft

9. **A. 6**
The corresponding angles in the triangles are equal, so the triangles are similar.
$\frac{8}{12} = \frac{x}{9}$
$12x = 72$
$x = 6$

10. Explanations may vary, but your answer should include some of the following ideas:
Since the ice cream cone is the shape of a cone, use the formula for volume of a cone. The scoop of ice cream is a half-sphere. The scoop extends 1.5 in above the cone, which is equal to the radius. You can find the volume of the whole sphere and divide by 2.

11. **D. 540**
Volume of the cone:
$V = \frac{1}{3}\pi r^2 h$
$\frac{1}{3} \times 3.14 \times 1.5^2 \times 7 \approx 16.5 \text{ in}^3$
Volume of the half-sphere:
$V = \frac{4}{3}\pi r^3$
$\frac{4}{3} \times 3.14 \times 1.5^3 \approx 14.13 \text{ in}^3$
$14.13 \div 2 \approx 7.1 \text{ in}^3$
Total volume: $16.5 + 7.1 = 23.6 \text{ in}^3$
Ice cream calories: $23.6 \times 20 = 472$
Total calories: $472 + 70 = 542$
The best estimate is 540 calories.

12. **17 miles**
Use the Pythagorean theorem: $c^2 = a^2 + b^2$
$c^2 = 8^2 + 15^2$
$c = \sqrt{289}$
$c = 17$

UNIT 5

The Coordinate Plane, pp. 144–145

1. (2, 2)
2. (–3, 0)
3. (–1, –1)
4. (2, –4)
5. (5, 1)
6. (–2, 4)

Refer to the coordinate grid for problems 7–12.

7. *G*
8. *H*
9. *I*
10. *J*
11. *K*
12. *L*

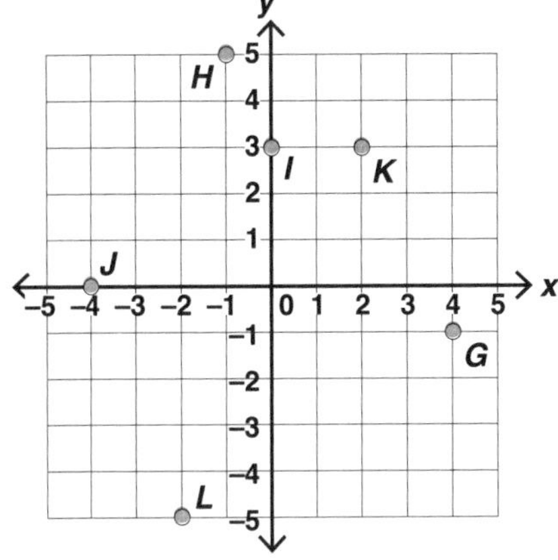

13. II
14. IV
15. I
16. III
17. II
18. I

Make a Table to Graph an Equation, pp. 146–147

1.

x	y
–2	–11
0	–5
2	1

2.

x	y
2	7
4	11
5	13

3.

x	y
1	4
3	2
5	0

For problems 4–7, tables of values may vary, but graphs should be as shown.

4.

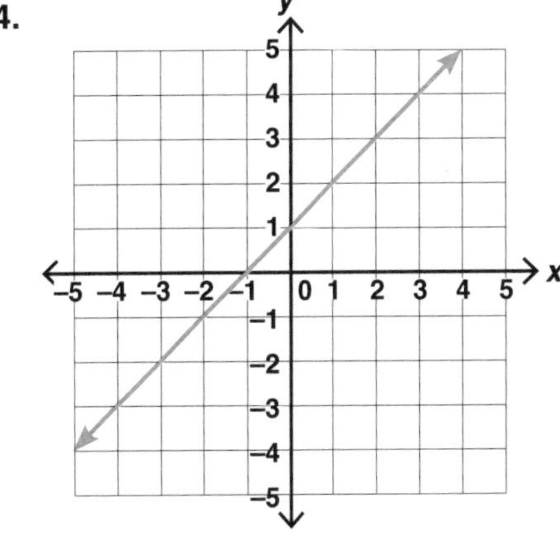

5.

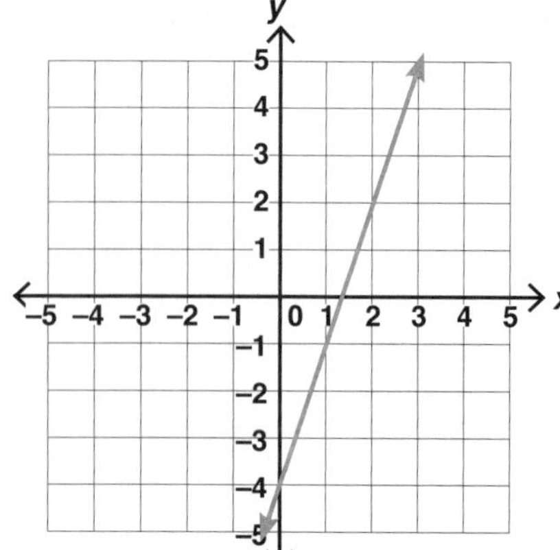

6.

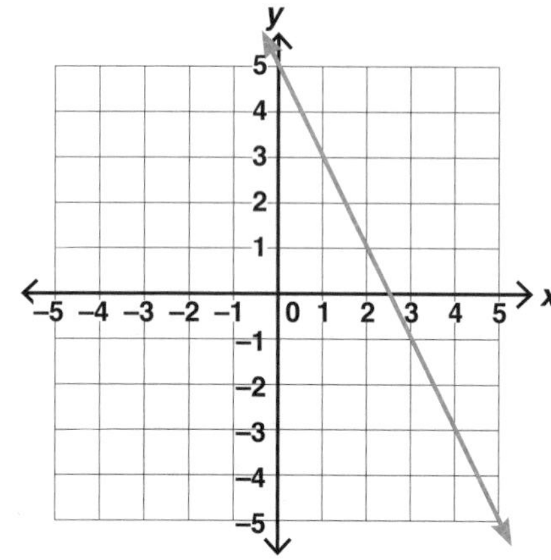

7.

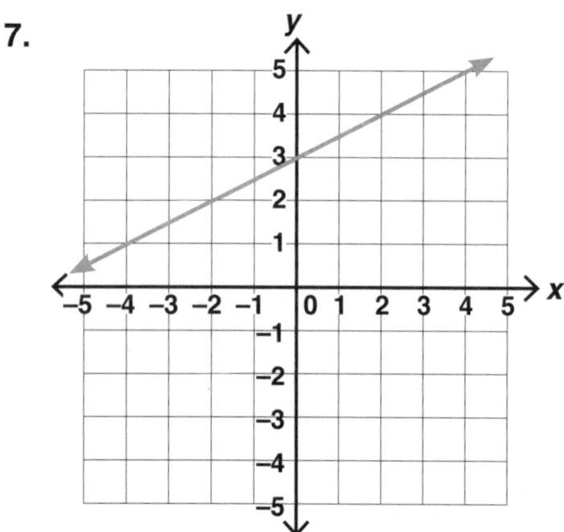

Use Intercepts to Graph a Line, pp. 148–149

1. y-intercept: $y = 3(0) - 3$ **(0, –3)**
   $y = -3$
   x-intercept: $0 = 3x - 3$ **(1, 0)**
   $3 = 3x$
   $x = 1$

2. y-intercept: $0 + 5y = -10$ **(0, –2)**
   $5y = -10$
   $y = -2$
   x-intercept: $x + 5(0) = -10$ **(–10, 0)**
   $x = -10$

3. y-intercept: $4(0) - 3y = 12$ **(0, –4)**
   $-3y = 12$
   $y = -4$
   x-intercept: $4x - 3(0) = 12$ **(3, 0)**
   $4x = 12$
   $x = 3$

4. y-intercept: $-2(0) + 4y = 8$ **(0, 2)**
   $4y = 8$
   $y = 2$
   x-intercept: $-2x + 4(0) = 8$ **(–4, 0)**
   $-2x = 8$
   $x = -4$

5. **C. $2x + y = 4$**
   Check each answer choice to see if the intercepts match the graph. Both intercepts must match.
   A. y-intercept: (0, –4)
   B. y-intercept: (0, 4)
      x-intercept: (–2, 0)
   C. y-intercept: (0, 4)
      x-intercept: (2, 0)
   D. y-intercept: (0, –4)
   Choice C matches the x- and y-intercepts on the graph.

6. y-intercept: $2(0) + 3y = 6$ **(0, 2)**
   $3y = 6$
   $y = 2$
   x-intercept: $2x + 3(0) = 6$ **(3, 0)**
   $2x = 6$
   $x = 3$

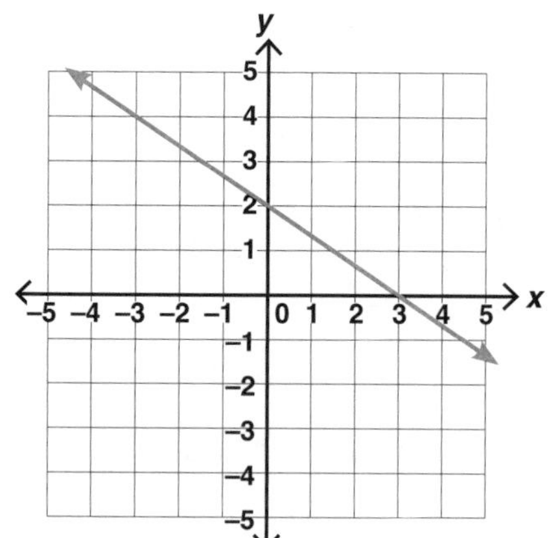

7. *y*-intercept: $0 - y = 4$ **(0, –4)**

$y = -4$

x-intercept: $x - 0 = 4$ **(4, 0)**

$x = 4$

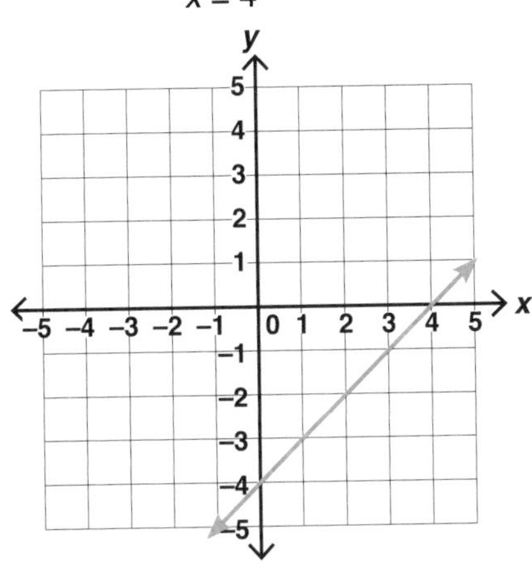

8. *y*-intercept: $3(0) + y = 3$ **(0, 3)**

$y = 3$

x-intercept: $3x + 0 = 3$ **(1, 0)**

$3x = 3$

$x = 1$

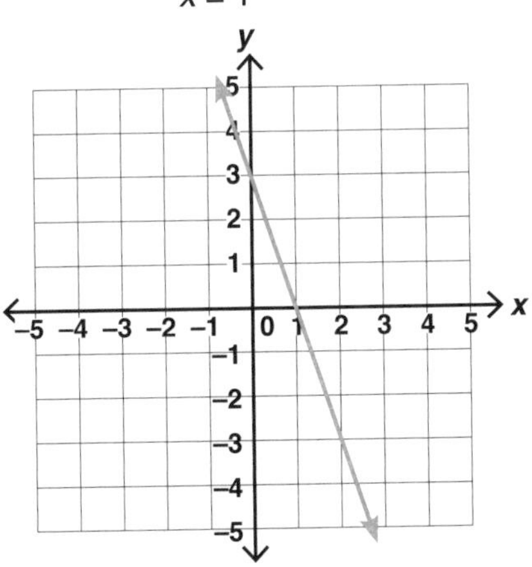

9. *y*-intercept: $y = 0 + 2$ **(0, 2)**

$y = 2$

x-intercept: $0 = -x + 2$ **(2, 0)**

$-2 = -x$

$2 = x$

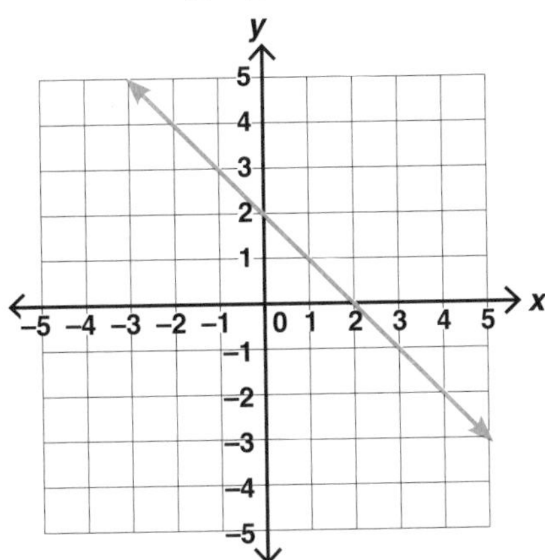

10. Yes. Both the *x*- and *y*-axes share point (0, 0). Imagine a line that passes through point (0, 0). That line will have the same *x*- and *y*-intercepts.

Slope: Rise over Run, pp. 150–151

For problems 1 and 2, points may vary, but the slope should be as shown.

1. Slope: –3
2. Slope: $\frac{1}{2}$
3. $\frac{5-4}{2-(-2)} = \mathbf{\frac{1}{4}}$
4. $\frac{-2-(-7)}{5-6} = \frac{5}{-1} = \mathbf{-5}$
5. $\frac{6-3}{-1-(-5)} = \mathbf{\frac{3}{4}}$
6. $\frac{3-8}{-1-0} = \frac{-5}{-1} = \mathbf{5}$
7. $\frac{7-2}{4-4} = \frac{5}{0}$ **undefined**
8. $\frac{-6-(-5)}{-9-(-4)} = \frac{-1}{-5} = \mathbf{\frac{1}{5}}$
9. $\frac{3-0}{0-(-3)} = \frac{3}{3} = \mathbf{1}$
10. $\frac{9-9}{5-(-1)} = \frac{0}{6} = \mathbf{0}$
11. $\frac{2-2}{1-5} = \frac{0}{-4} = \mathbf{0}$
12. $\frac{3-1}{8-6} = \frac{2}{2} = \mathbf{1}$

Parallel and Perpendicular Lines, pp. 152–153

1. **–2**

   Slope of *MN*: $\frac{-3-3}{-1-(-4)} = \frac{-6}{3} = -2$
2. $\mathbf{\frac{1}{2}}$

   The negative reciprocal of –2 is $\frac{1}{2}$.
3. Slope of *OP*: $\frac{0-1}{2-(-1)} = \frac{-1}{3} = -\frac{1}{3}$

   Slope of *ST*: $\frac{-4-(-3)}{2-(-2)} = \frac{-1}{4} = -\frac{1}{4}$

   The slopes of the lines are not the same, so the lines are not parallel.
4. Slope of *OP*: $-\frac{1}{3}$

   Slope of *OR*: $\frac{1-4}{-1-0} = \frac{-3}{-1} = \frac{3}{1} = 3$

   The slopes are negative reciprocals of each other, so the lines are perpendicular.

Core Connections: Slope and Line Graphs, p. 153

1. In Year 1, sales increased by 2. In Year 2, sales increased by 1. Sales increased more in Year 1.
2. From April to May, sales increased by 2. From May to June, sales increased by 3. From June to July, sales increased by 2. Sales increased the most from May to June.

Problem Solving with Slope, pp. 154–155

1. $\frac{24}{50.4} \approx 0.476 \approx \mathbf{0.48}$

2. Find the rise and the tread. This staircase has 4 stairs, so divide the height and the width of the staircase by 4.
   Rise: 24 ÷ 4 = 6 in
   Tread: 50.4 ÷ 4 = 12.6 in
   Substitute these values in the builder's rule.
   2 × 6 + 12. 6 = 24.6
   Yes, the staircase follows the rule.
3. **a.** $\frac{4}{25}$ or 0.16
   b. Yes. $\frac{4}{25}$ = 0.16 or 16%, which is greater than 15%.
4. **a. 7.5 ft**
   $a^2 + b^2 = c^2$
   $4^2 + b^2 = 8.5^2$
   $b^2 = 8.5^2 - 4^2$
   $b = \sqrt{56.25}$
   $b = 7.5$
   b. $\frac{4}{7.5} \approx 0.53$
5. advanced
   $\frac{5}{12} \approx 0.42 = 42\%$
6. advanced
   $\frac{9}{20} = 0.45 = 45\%$
7. intermediate
   $\frac{25}{90} \approx 0.28 = 28\%$
8. advanced
   $\frac{60}{140} \approx 0.43 = 43\%$

Write the Equation of a Line, pp. 156–157

1. Slope (m): $\frac{2}{-1} = -2$
   y-intercept: (0, –3)
   Equation: $y = -2x - 3$
2. Slope (m): 1
   y-intercept: (0, 4)
   Equation: $y = x + 4$
3. Slope (m): $\frac{3}{1} = 3$
   y-intercept: (0, 0)
   Equation: $y = 3x$
4. Slope (m): $\frac{2}{-5} = -\frac{2}{5}$
   y-intercept: (0, 1)
   Equation: $y = -\frac{2}{5}x + 1$

5. and **6.**

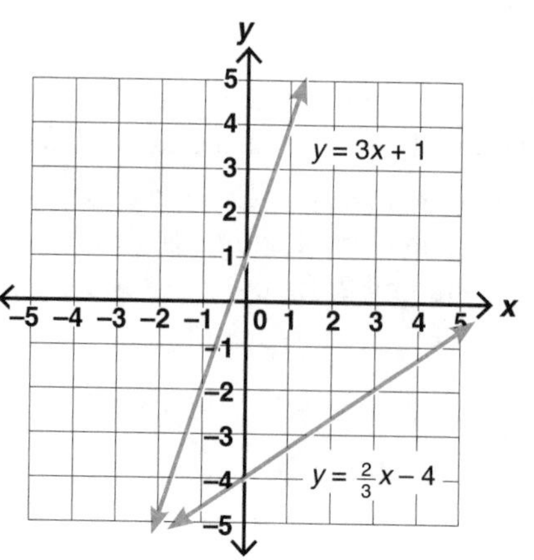

Use Point-Slope Form, pp. 158–159

1. $3x - y = 4$
   $-y = -3x + 4$
   $\mathbf{y = 3x - 4}$
2. $5x + 5y = 15$
   $5y = -5x + 15$
   $\mathbf{y = -x + 3}$
3. $-2x + y = 1$
   $\mathbf{y = 2x + 1}$
4. $-2x + 6y = -12$
   $6y = 2x - 12$
   $\mathbf{y = \frac{1}{3}x - 2}$
5. $5x + 4y = 28$
   $4y = -5x + 28$
   $\mathbf{y = -\frac{5}{4}x + 7}$
6. $3x + 8y = 40$
   $8y = -3x + 40$
   $\mathbf{y = -\frac{3}{8}x + 5}$
7. $y - y_1 = m(x - x_1)$
   $y - 3 = 3(x - 1)$
   $y - 3 = 3x - 3$
   $\mathbf{y = 3x}$
8. $y - y_1 = m(x - x_1)$
   $y - (-1) = -2(x - (-1))$
   $y - (-1) = -2(x + 1)$
   $y + 1 = -2x - 2$
   $\mathbf{y = -2x - 3}$
9. $m = \frac{4-(-8)}{3-(-1)} = \frac{12}{4} = 3$
   $y - y_1 = m(x - x_1)$
   $y - 4 = 3(x - 3)$
   $y - 4 = 3x - 9$
   $\mathbf{y = 3x - 5}$
10. $m = \frac{-5-(-1)}{-1-(-3)} = \frac{-4}{2} = -2$
    $y - y_1 = m(x - x_1)$
    $y - (-5) = -2(x - (-1))$
    $y + 5 = -2(x + 1)$
    $y + 5 = -2x - 2$
    $\mathbf{y = -2x - 7}$
11. $m = \frac{-4-(-4)}{0-5} = \frac{0}{-5} = 0$
    $y - y_1 = m(x - x_1)$
    $y - (-4) = 0(x - 5)$
    $y + 4 = 0$
    $\mathbf{y = -4}$
12. $y - y_1 = m(x - x_1)$
    $y - 1 = -\frac{1}{2}(x - (-2))$
    $y - 1 = -\frac{1}{2}(x + 2)$
    $y - 1 = -\frac{1}{2}x - 1$
    $\mathbf{y = -\frac{1}{2}x}$
13. $x = 5$

14. $y - y_1 = m(x - x_1)$
$y - 5 = -7(x - 3)$
$y - 5 = -7x + 21$
$\mathbf{y = -7x + 26}$

15. $m = \frac{-4-0}{1-0} = \frac{-4}{1} = -4$
$y - y_1 = m(x - x_1)$
$y - 0 = -4(x - 0)$
$\mathbf{y = -4x}$

16. $m = \frac{5-(-4)}{4-4} = \frac{9}{0}$ undefined
$\mathbf{x = 4}$

17. $y - y_1 = m(x - x_1)$
$y - (-5) = 4(x - (-2))$
$y + 5 = 4(x + 2)$
$y + 5 = 4x + 8$
$\mathbf{y = 4x + 3}$

18. $m = \frac{3-2}{5-0} = \frac{1}{5}$
$y - y_1 = m(x - x_1)$
$y - 2 = \frac{1}{5}(x - 0)$
$y - 2 = \frac{1}{5}x$
$\mathbf{y = \frac{1}{5}x + 2}$

Distance between Points, pp. 160–161

1. $|4 - -4| = |8| =$ **8 units**
2. $|-2 - 4| = |-6| =$ **6 units**
3. **10 units**
$6^2 + 8^2 = c^2$
$\sqrt{36 + 64} = c$
$\sqrt{100} = c$
$10 = c$
4. $|4 - -1| = |5| =$ **5 units**
5. **D. between 6 and 7**
$3^2 + 6^2 = c^2$
$\sqrt{9 + 36} = c$
$\sqrt{45} = c$
$\sqrt{45}$ is between 6 and 7
6. $|-6 - 6| = |-12| =$ **12 units**
7. $|1 - -4| = |5| =$ **5 units**
8. **13 units**
$12^2 + 5^2 = c^2$
$\sqrt{144 + 25} = c^2$
$\sqrt{169} = c$
$13 = c$
9. $|-1 - 1| = |-2| =$ **2 units**
10. **B. between 10 and 11**
$8^2 + 7^2 = c^2$
$\sqrt{64 + 49} = c$
$\sqrt{113} = c$
$\sqrt{113}$ is between 10 and 11

Geometric Figures on the Coordinate Plane, pp. 162–163

1. **D. 32**
Use the distance formula to find the length of the side of a square.
$4^2 + 4^2 = c^2$
$\sqrt{16 + 16} = c$
$\sqrt{32} = c$
$A = (\sqrt{32})^2 = 32$
2. Find the slope of $\overline{FE}$ and $\overline{CD}$.
$\overline{FE}$: $m = \frac{5-3}{2-(-1)} = \frac{2}{3}$
$\overline{CD}$: $m = \frac{4-(-3)}{-4-1} = \frac{7}{-5} = -\frac{7}{5}$
The slopes are not negative reciprocals of each other, so $\overline{FE}$ and $\overline{CD}$ are not perpendicular and will not intersect at a right angle.
3. If triangle *PQR* is a right triangle, then angle *Q* must be a right angle. Find the slopes of *PQ* and *QR*.
PQ: $m = \frac{4-2}{-4-4} = \frac{2}{-8} = -\frac{1}{4}$
QR: $m = \frac{2-(-2)}{4-3} = \frac{4}{1} = 4$
The slopes of *PQ* and *QR* are negative reciprocals of each other, so they are perpendicular. Triangle *PQR* is a right triangle.
4. **(2, –2)**
First, find the slopes of *DE* and *CD*.
Slope of *DE*: $m = \frac{3-2}{3-(-3)} = \frac{1}{6}$
Slope of *CD*: $m = \frac{2-(-3)}{-3-(-4)} = \frac{5}{1} = 5$
Side *EF* must be parallel to side *CD,* and side *CF* must be parallel to side *DE*. Estimate where point *F* must go so that opposite sides are parallel.
(2,–2) looks like the right place to put the point.
Check the slopes of *CF* and *EF*.
Slope of *CF*: $m = \frac{-2-(-3)}{2-(-4)} = \frac{1}{6}$
Slope of *EF*: $m = \frac{-2-3}{2-3} = \frac{-5}{-1} = 5$
Opposite sides are parallel. The coordinates of point *F* are (2, –2).

Unit 5 Review, pp. 164–169

1. *A:* (–5, 4)
B: (0, 1)
C: (4, 5)
D: (5, 0)
E: (1, –3)
F: (–4, –2)
2. C. Quadrant III

3.

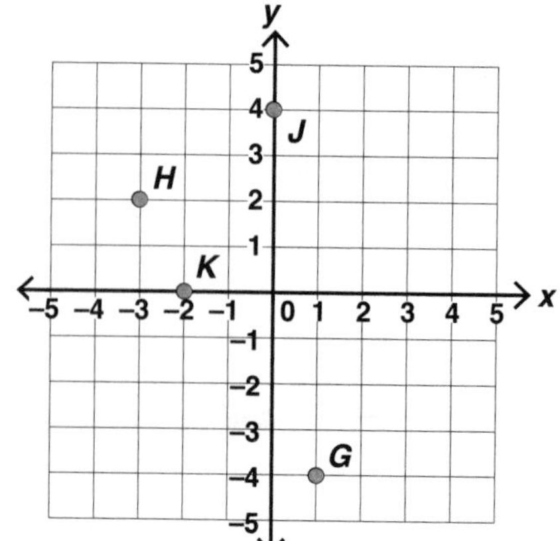

4.

x	y
−2	−10
0	4
2	18
4	32

5.

x	y
−1	−2
0	−3
1	−4
2	−5

6.

x	y
1	−2
2	1
3	4
4	7

7. C. (4, 5)

Test each point in the equation of the line.

A. $2(0) - (-5) = 5$
$0 + 5 = 5$
$5 = 5$ true

B. $2(2) - (-1) = 5$
$4 + 1 = 5$
$5 = 5$ true

C. $2(4) - 5 = 5$
$8 - 5 = 5$
$3 = 5$ false

D. $2(6) - 7 = 5$
$12 - 7 = 5$
$5 = 5$ true

Point (4, 5) is not on the line.

8. x-intercept: $3x - 4(0) = 12$ **(4, 0)**
$3x = 12$
$x = 4$
y-intercept: $3(0) - 4y = 12$ **(0, −3)**
$-4y = 12$
$y = -3$

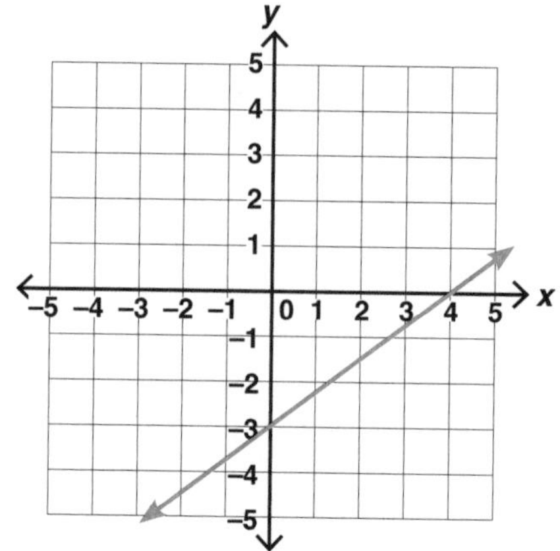

9. 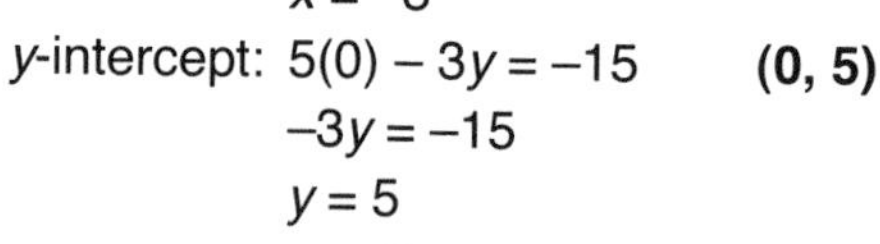
x-intercept: $5x - 3(0) = -15$ **(−3, 0)**
$5x = -15$
$x = -3$
y-intercept: $5(0) - 3y = -15$ **(0, 5)**
$-3y = -15$
$y = 5$

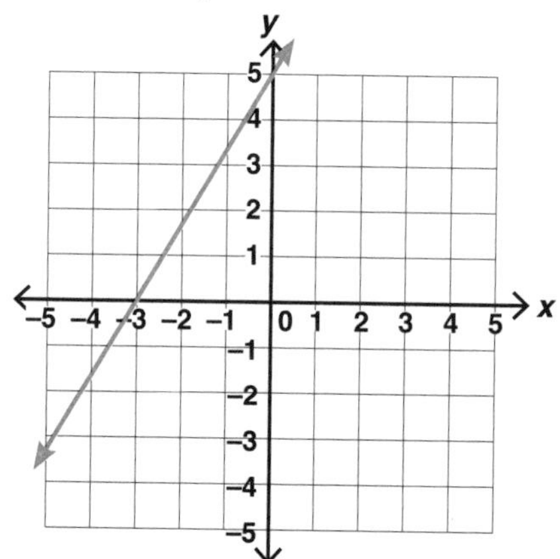

10. D. line *O*

Choose two points and find the slope of each line. You may choose any points.

line L: $m = \frac{5-2}{0-2} = \frac{3}{-2} = -\frac{3}{2}$

line M: $m = \frac{1-0}{-3-0} = \frac{1}{-3} = -\frac{1}{3}$

line N: $m = \frac{2-5}{-4-(-2)} = \frac{-3}{-2} = \frac{3}{2}$

line O: $m = \frac{-5-(-3)}{-5-(-2)} = \frac{-2}{-3} = \frac{2}{3}$

Only line O has a slope of $\frac{2}{3}$.

11. A. (−2, 4)

12. −2

$m = \frac{-6-16}{-7-(-18)} = \frac{-22}{11} = -2$

13. No, Alan is incorrect.

Find the slope of both lines.

Line p: $m = \frac{4-0}{2-(-3)} = \frac{4}{5}$

Line q: $m = \frac{-4-0}{4-(-1)} = \frac{-4}{5} = -\frac{4}{5}$

The slopes of lines p and q are not negative reciprocals of each other, so they are not perpendicular.

14. 12 inches

Since there are three steps, the rise of one step is:

$18 \div 3 = 6$ in

The rise over run of each step must be $\frac{1}{2}$.

$\frac{6}{x} = \frac{1}{2}$

$x = 12$

The tread of one step is 12 inches.

15. $y = -x - 2$

16. $y = 2x + 3$

17. $y = 3$

18. $y = \frac{1}{3}x - 4$

19. Your answer may include the following ideas:

This is impossible. These three points do not lie on the same line. You can prove your answer by finding the slope between each pair of points. If the points all lie on the same line, then the slope will be the same for each pair.

(–5, –9) and (10, 0): $m = \frac{0-(-9)}{10-(-5)} = \frac{9}{15} = \frac{3}{5}$

(10, 0) and (5, –6): $m = \frac{-6-0}{5-10} = \frac{-6}{-5} = \frac{6}{5}$

(–5, –9) and (5, –6): $m = \frac{-6-(-9)}{5-(-5)} = \frac{3}{10}$

The slope is different for each pair of points. They cannot be on the same line.

20. A. $3x - y = -1$

Use point-slope form. Then use algebra to rewrite the equation so that it matches one of the answer choices.

$y - y_1 = m(x - x_1)$

$y - (-2) = 3(x - (-1))$

$y + 2 = 3(x + 1)$

$y + 2 = 3x + 3$

$-3x + y = 1$

$3x - y = -1$

You could also rewrite each choice in slope-intercept form and test the point.

$3x - y = -1$

$-y = -3x - 1$ This line has a slope of 3.

$y = 3x + 1$

Test point (–1, –2).

$-2 = 3(-1) + 1$

$-2 = -3 + 1$

$-2 = -2$

21. B. $y = 4x + 11$

$m = \frac{-5-3}{-4-(-2)} = \frac{-8}{-2} = 4$

$y - 3 = 4(x - (-2))$

$y - 3 = 4(x + 2)$

$y - 3 = 4x + 8$

$y = 4x + 11$

22. 12 units

These points have the same y-coordinate. To find the distance, subtract the x-coordinates and take the absolute value.

$|-3 - 9| = |-12| = 12$

23. $y = 2x - 5$

Slope of the new line: 2

$y - (-1) = 2(x - 2)$

$y + 1 = 2(x - 2)$

$y + 1 = 2x - 4$

$y = 2x - 5$

24. negative

Your answer may include the following ideas:

Picture a coordinate grid. If the y-intercept is positive, then it lies above the x-axis. If the x-intercept is positive, then it lies to the right of the y-axis. This line would fall from left to right, so it has a negative slope.

25. C. greater than 0.5

Rise: 9 units

Run: 16 units

Slope: $\frac{9}{16} = 0.5625$

26. 37 inches

Horizontal distance: 16 squares × 2 inches = 32 in

Vertical distance: 9 squares × 2 inches = 18 in

$18^2 + 32^2 = c^2$

$\sqrt{324 + 1{,}024} = c$

$\sqrt{1{,}348} = c$

$36.7 \approx c$

$36.7 \approx 37$

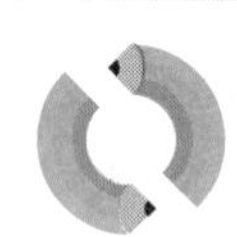

Glossary

adjacent angles two angles that share a side (p. 106)

$\angle a$ and $\angle b$ are adjacent.

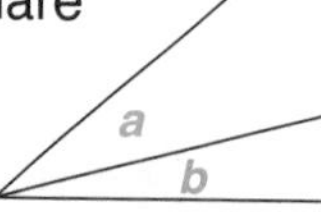

area the measure of the surface of a flat figure; measured in square units (p. 122)

associative property a rule stating that numbers being added or multiplied can be grouped in any order and the answer will be the same (p. 24)

$(a + b) + c = a + (b + c)$
$(a \times b) \times c = a \times (b \times c)$

base a number that is multiplied by itself in a power (p. 32)

exponent

$3^2 = 3 \times 3 = 9$

base

circumference the distance around a circle (p. 126)

coefficient the number multiplying a variable (p. 46)

The coefficient of $12x$ is 12.

commutative property a rule stating that numbers can be added or multiplied in any order and the answer will be the same (p. 24)

$a + b = b + a$
$a \times b = b \times a$

complementary angles two angles that add up to 90° (p. 106)

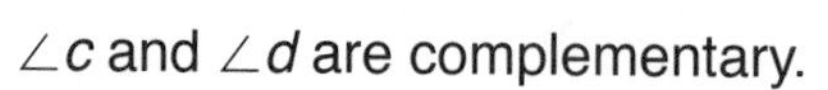
$\angle c$ and $\angle d$ are complementary.

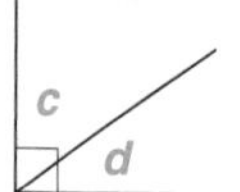

composite number a number that has more than two factors (p. 22)

9 is a composite number because its factors are 1, 3, and 9.

corresponding angles equal angles formed by a transversal. Corresponding angles are in the same position related to the parallel lines (p. 107).

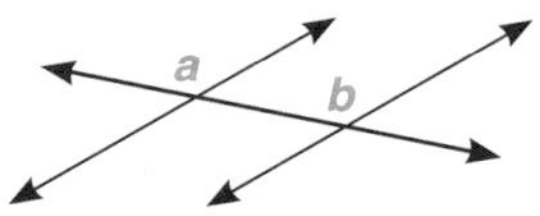

$\angle a$ and $\angle b$ are corresponding angles.

diameter a line segment passing through the center of a circle, reaching from one side of the circle to the other side (p. 126)

distributive property a rule stating that a number multiplying a sum or difference in parentheses can be distributed to each value in parentheses (p. 24)

$a(b + c) = ab + ac$
$a(b - c) = ab - ac$

divisible a number is divisible by another number if there is no remainder after dividing (p. 20)

15 is divisible by 5.

equation a number sentence that contains an equal sign (p. 42)

even number a number that can be divided exactly by 2. The ones place of an even number is a 0, 2, 4, 6, or 8 (p. 20).

exponent a number that is multiplied by itself in a power (p. 32)

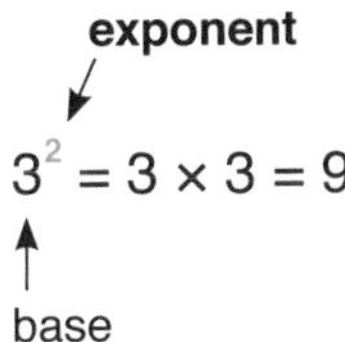

expression a mathematical amount written with symbols (p. 42)

factors the two numbers being multiplied in a multiplication fact (p. 20)

In $3 \times 4 = 12$, 3 and 4 are factors of 12.

formula an equation that shows a constant relationship between variables (p. 94)

horizontal running left and right (p. 102)

hypotenuse the side opposite the right angle of a right triangle (p. 112)

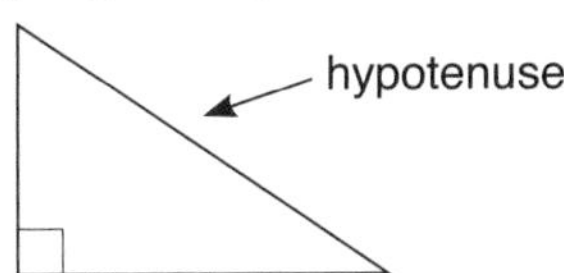

inequality a statement that expressions or amounts are not equal (p. 42)

$2 < 5$	"2 is less than 5"
$8 > -1$	"8 is greater than –1"

integer any number in the set $\{..., -5, -4, -3, -2, -1, 0, 1, 2, 3, ...\}$ (p. 18)

intersect to cross (p. 102)

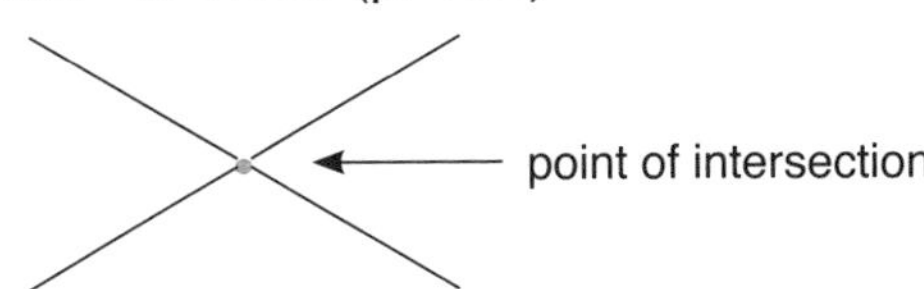

like terms terms that have the same variable (p. 46)

$3x$ and $5x$ are like terms. x^2 and $8x^2$ are like terms.

line a straight path of points that continues in two directions (p. 102)

line segment a straight path of points with definite length (p. 102)

linear equation an equation that, when graphed, forms a straight line on a coordinate grid (p. 146)

multiple the product in a multiplication fact (p. 20)

The number 20 is a multiple of both 4 and 5 because $4 \times 5 = 20$.

negative reciprocal the opposite, inverted fraction of the original (p. 152)

The negative reciprocal of $\frac{1}{3}$ is $-\frac{3}{1}$ or -3.

odd number any number that is not even is odd (p. 20)

opposite across from (p. 108)

Side *AB* is opposite side *CD*.

order of operations the acceptable order in which to do computation in a multistep problem (p. 34)

1. Do operations in grouping symbols.
2. Evaluate expressions involving powers and roots.
3. Do any multiplication or division in order, working from left to right.
4. Do any addition or subtraction in order, working from left to right.

ordered pair the coordinates of a point on the coordinate grid; written in the order (x, y) (p. 144)

parallel running in the same direction at a constant distance apart (p. 102)

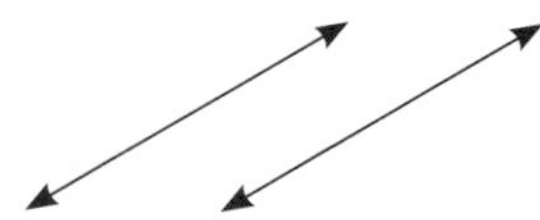

perimeter the distance around a geometric shape. To find the perimeter, add the lengths of all the sides of the figure (p. 120).

perpendicular meeting at right angles (p. 102)

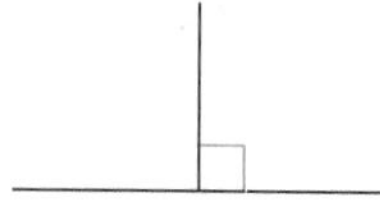

point-slope form equation of a line written as $y - y_1 = m(x - x_1)$, where m = slope and (x_1, y_1) is a point on the line (p. 158)

prime number a number that has exactly two factors: itself and 1 (p. 22)

13 is a prime number. Its factors are 1 and 13.

product the answer in a multiplication problem (p. 20)

$12 \times 5 = 60$

↑

product

radius a line segment passing from the center of a circle to any point on the circle; half the diameter (p. 126)

ray a straight path of points that starts at one point and continues infinitely in one direction (p. 102)

reciprocal the result of inverting a fraction (p. 63)

$\frac{9}{2}$ is the reciprocal of $\frac{2}{9}$.

scientific notation a method of representing very large or very small numbers with powers of ten (p. 52)

$270{,}000 = 2.7 \times 10^5$

$0.000027 = 2.7 \times 10^{-5}$

signed numbers the set of numbers that includes positive and negative numbers. Zero is neither positive nor negative (p. 16).

slope the ratio of rise (vertical distance) to run (horizontal distance) (p. 150)

slope-intercept form equation of a line written as $y = mx + b$, where m = slope and b is the y-intercept (p. 156)

standard form equation of a line written as $Ax + By = C$, where A, B, and C are numbers (p. 158)

supplementary angles two angles that add up to 180° (p. 106)

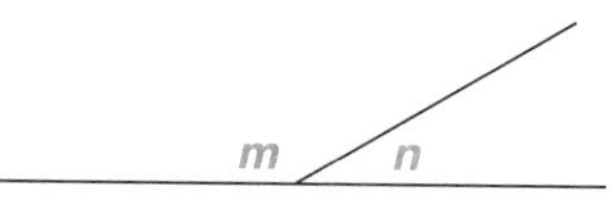

$\angle m$ and $\angle n$ are supplementary.

surface area the sum of the areas of the faces of a three-dimensional figure (p. 134)

symmetry a property that describes a figure that can be divided into two parts that are mirror images of each other (p. 127)

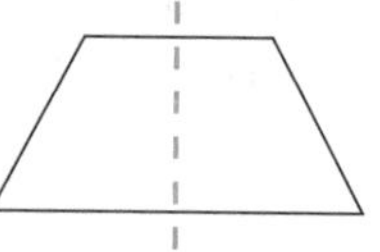

transversal a line that crosses two parallel lines (p. 107)

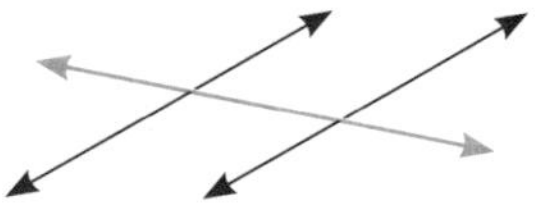

variable a letter used to represent an unknown value in an expression or an equation (p. 42)

$c + 15 = 25$ *c* is the variable.

vertex a point where two rays or two line segments meet (p. 103)

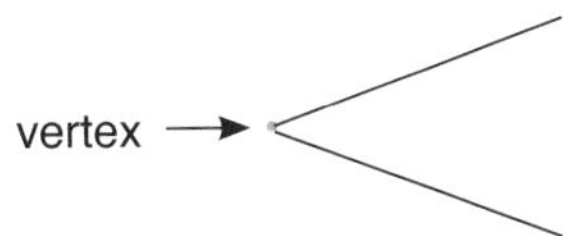

vertical running straight up and down (p. 102)

vertical angles two angles that do not share a side but are opposite each other when two lines intersect. Vertical angles are equal (p. 106).

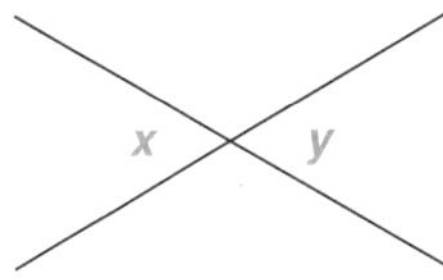

volume the measure of the space inside a three-dimensional object; measured in cubic units (p. 130)

whole numbers the set of numbers that starts at 0 and is used for counting (p. 16)

0, 1, 2, 3, 4, 5, . . .

***x*-intercept** the point where the graph of a linear equation crosses the *x*-axis; the *y*-value equals zero (p. 148)

***y*-intercept** the point where the graph of a linear equation crosses the *y*-axis; the *x*-value equals zero (p. 148)

Tool Kit

CALCULATOR BASICS

A scientific calculator has many functions. You will need only a few of the functions to do the math on the GED® Math Test. Study the diagram to find the keys you will need. If you are using a different scientific calculator, the keys may be located in a different place, but they will have the same purpose.

Certain keys have more than one assigned function. To access a function written in small letters above a main key, first press the 2nd function key: [2nd]. Then press the key.

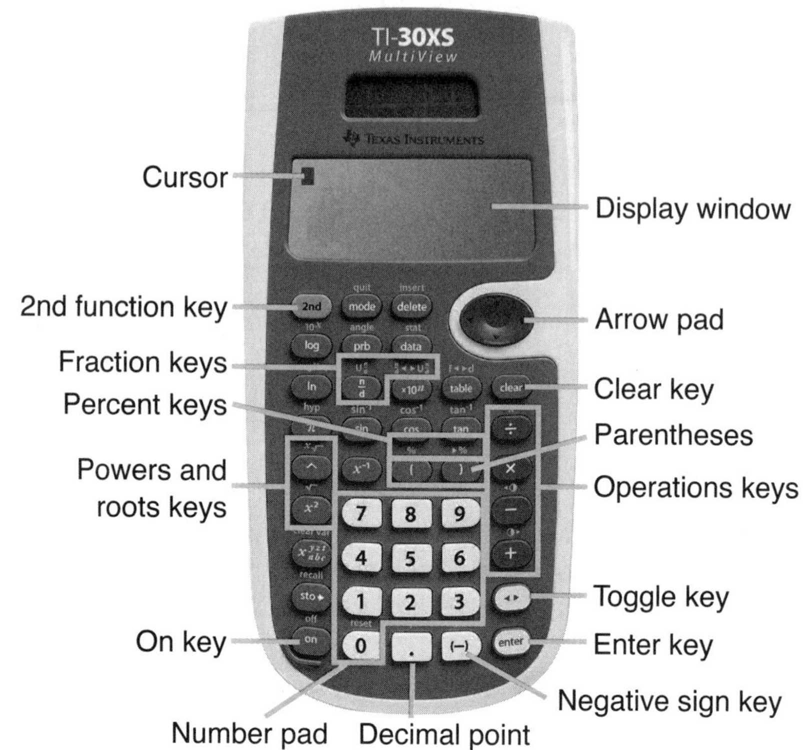

EXPLANATION OF SPECIAL KEYS

[clear]	Clears the display window. The memory is not erased.
[enter]	The enter key is used to process the operations you have entered. Think of it as an equal key (=).
x^2	Used to square a number.
^	Used to enter an exponent.
$\sqrt{\ }$ $\sqrt[x]{\ }$	Second functions used to find square roots and other roots.
( )	Used to enter parentheses or brackets to group operations.
[◄ ►]	The toggle key changes the form of the answer. It can change fractions or roots to decimals and back.
[(–)]	Used to enter a negative number. Do not enter a negative number using the subtraction symbol.
$\frac{n}{d}$	Used to input fractions.
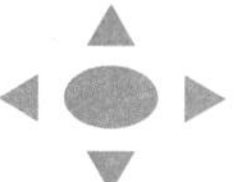	The arrow pad is used to move the cursor in the display window. Press an arrow to move in that direction.

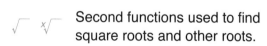

BASIC COMPUTATIONS

A scientific calculator always follows the order of operations. If you enter a chain of operations, it multiplies and divides before performing addition and subtraction steps. Use parentheses when a different order is needed. You can embed one set of parentheses inside another if more grouping symbols are needed.

Examples:	Press:	The display reads:	
$-5 \cdot 6 - 9$	[(–)] 5 × 6 – 9 [enter]	-5*6-9	-39
$-5(6 - 9)$	[(–)] 5 (6 – 9) [enter]	-5(6-9)	15
$\frac{-2+12}{-5}$	$\frac{n}{d}$ [(–)] 2 + 12 ▼ [(–)] 5 [enter]	$\frac{-2+12}{-5}$	-2
$6[-4 + 3(2 - 5)]$	6 ([(–)] 4 + 3 (2 – 5)) [enter]	6(-4+3(2-5))	-78

POWERS AND ROOTS

You can use your calculator to simplify and find roots and their decimal equivalents. You can also evaluate expressions containing exponents.

Examples:	Press:	The display reads:	
Simplify $\sqrt{48}$.	[2nd] $\sqrt{\ }$ 48 [enter]	$\sqrt{48}$	$4\sqrt{3}$
Find the decimal value of $\sqrt{48}$.	[2nd] $\sqrt{\ }$ 48 [enter] [◄►]	$\sqrt{48}$ $4\sqrt{3}$ ◄►	$4\sqrt{3}$ 6.92820323
Evaluate $\sqrt[3]{-64}$.	3 [2nd] $\sqrt[x]{\ }$ [(–)] 64 [enter]	$\sqrt[3]{-64}$	-4
15^2	15 [x^2] [enter]	15^2	225
$(-5)^4$	([(–)] 5) ^ 4 [enter]	$(-5)^4$	625
$4^5 - 3^7$	4 ^ 5 ► – 3 ^ 7 [enter]	$4^5 - 3^7$	-1163

BASIC FORMULAS

Perimeter (P)	**Formula**	**Definition**
Rectangle	$P = 2l + 2w$	l = length, w = width
Polygon with n sides	$P = s_1 + s_2 + ... + s_n$	s_1, etc. = each side
Circle	$C = \pi d$ or $C = 2\pi r$	C = Circumference, d = diameter, r = radius

Area (A)	**Formula**	**Definition**
Rectangle	$A = lw$ or $A = bh$	l = length, w = width, b = base, h = height
Square	$A = s^2$	s = side
Parallelogram	$A = bh$	b = base, h = height
Triangle	$A = \frac{1}{2}bh$	b = base, h = height
Trapezoid	$A = \frac{1}{2}h(b_1 + b_2)$	b_1 and b_2 = bases, h = height
Circle	$A = \pi r^2$	r = radius

Volume (V)	**Formula**	**Definition**
Rectangular/right prism (includes cube)	$V = Bh$	B = area of base, h = height
Cylinder	$V = \pi r^2 h$	r = radius, h = height
Pyramid	$V = \frac{1}{3}Bh$	B = area of base, h = height
Cone	$V = \frac{1}{3}\pi r^2 h$	r = radius, h = height
Sphere	$V = \frac{4}{3}\pi r^3$	r = radius

OTHER FORMULAS

Surface Area (*SA*)	**Formula**	**Definition**
Rectangular/right prism (includes cube)	$SA = ph + 2B$	p = perimeter of base, B = area of base, h = height
Cylinder	$SA = 2\pi rh + 2\pi r^2$	r = radius, h = height
Pyramid	$SA = \frac{1}{2}ps + B$	p = perimeter of base, s = slant height, B = area of base
Cone	$SA = \pi rs + \pi r^2$	r = radius, s = slant height
Sphere	$SA = 4\pi r^2$	r = radius

Other Useful Formulas	**Formula**	**Definition**
Simple interest (I)	$I = prt$	p = principal, r = rate, t = time
Distance (d)	$d = rt$	r = rate, t = time
Cost (c)	$c = nr$	n = number of items, r = rate per item
Slope of a line (m)	$m = \frac{y_2 - y_1}{x_2 - x_1}$	where (x_1, y_1) and (x_2, y_2) are points on the line
Slope-intercept form of the equation of a line	$y = mx + b$	m = slope, b = y-intercept
Point-slope form of the equation of a line	$y - y_1 = m(x - x_1)$	m = slope, (x_1, y_1) = a point on the line
Pythagorean theorem	$a^2 + b^2 = c^2$	a and b = legs of a right triangle, c = hypotenuse